UNDERSTANDING OUR WORLD

UNDERSTANDING

by *FRANKLIN B. CARROLL*

Head, Science Department, Frankford High School, Phila.

Keystone View Co.

OUR WORLD

THE JOHN C. WINSTON COMPANY • Philadelphia

Chicago   Pasadena   Atlanta   Dallas   Toronto

INTERPRETING SCIENCE SERIES

UNDERSTANDING OUR ENVIRONMENT

UNDERSTANDING OUR WORLD

UNDERSTANDING THE UNIVERSE

Preface

The aim of this series of textbooks is the introduction of the pupil to intelligent participation in a world dominated by science. The pupil's participation is immediate, not at some future date. Attention is directed to the present surroundings, and the science is developed from the experience of the pupil. Sometimes the experience that starts an investigation has been common to all the pupils, but often the common experience is provided by experiment. The experience of other observers is drawn upon to supplement the present observation. The horizon of pupils' interest is far away, and this series alternately leads and follows, showing the same laws of science operating in the ultimate distances and in the intimate world about us.

The material content of the series is that body of knowledge usually accepted by formal courses of study and by tacit agreement. No attempt is made to divide the field among the sciences. A topic or problem is followed after the manner of modern scientific studies across the uncertain boundaries that divide the domains of special sciences.

No wide agreement exists in the division of topics among the several grades, but such agreement is of no great consequence. In the present series of texts each volume has sufficient breadth of field to allow the selection of topics to fit the local need. Omission or sketchy use need not destroy the unity or breadth of scientific interpretation of pupils' environment.

Attainment of the pupil's point of view is an aim of modern teaching and modern text. Who knows the pupil's point of view? The observant teacher accumulates a knowledge of pupils' mistakes and pupils' questions, where questions are encouraged. Such knowledge may smooth the rough way through a prescribed course of study, but how far a teacher may draw deductions from this evidence as to the pupil's point of view toward the objects and phenomena of his environment is problematic. Certain illuminating studies have attempted to learn the subject of native pupil interest, but, as teachers know full well, "native" interests may be aroused by skilled teaching. "Motivation" is standard practice in overcoming teaching resistance. This series attempts to use as points of departure the interest displayed in actual classroom experience as well as out of school.

The method of science is kept constantly before the pupil's attention. Establishment of facts through observation is presented in experimental

studies as well as through text and narrative. The organization of facts
into a body of knowledge, their interpretation in a generalization at the
pupil's level, the use of such generalization in the interpretation of facts
in a new situation, the framing and testing of hypotheses, receive attention
at strategic positions. Solution of problems by scientists illustrates the
method in use, and guidance in solution of problems provides opportunity
for its exercise.

Recurrence of facts throughout the series and within the book provides
opportunity for amendment and expansion of concepts, an essential char-
acter of scientific thought. Knowledge grows. Unlike the laws of the Medes
and the Persians, the laws of science change as the partial nature of earlier
statements becomes evident. The discovery of nature's processes must be
gradual with addition of fact to fact. Our statements describing these processes, the laws of science, must also change. The man-made laws of science
are always subject to amendment and repeal on sufficient evidence. That
attitude is fostered throughout this series.

The establishment of basal facts through observation is brought repeatedly to the attention of the pupil through experimental procedure and
text account. Accuracy of observation is required in suggested experiments. The danger of inaccuracy is told by illustration in the story of the
text. The necessity of "an explanation" through natural causes is developed
through instances.

Procedure and terminology in these books is reduced to simple terms.
Experiments and observation are kept within the grasp of pupils of the
grade. Experiments require as little laboratory apparatus as possible, and
techniques that divert attention from the question of the experiment are
avoided. A scientific term is introduced when a concept has developed to
the stage where a definite term is needed.

Ample provision is made for more extensive work by capable pupils.
At the end of each chapter are suggestions for further study and activities.
Spontaneous suggestions by the pupil, however, often serve far better than
any printed directions to investigation where interest dictates.

The aim of the present volume is to bring the pupil into more intelligent
contact with selected factors of the world about him. He has made the
contact previously, but often it has been meaningless. This text calls freely
to the mind the common experiences and creates the opportunity for others.
The pupil is led to seek a meaning in terms of science and of influence
upon human life. Mud has been mud. Now the pupil is led to see erosion
and soil-making with their important consequences to man and other living
things.

Contents

Unit One: How Living Things Fit into the Earth

Unit Two: Astronomy

Unit Three: Weather and Climate

Unit Four: Water

Unit Five: Some Plants and Animals of the House and Garden

Unit Six: Health

Unit Seven: Energy Around Us

Unit Eight: Heat in the World

Unit Nine: Magnetism and Electrical Energy

Unit Ten: Making Work Easier

Unit Eleven: The Changing Earth

Unit One

How Living Things Fit into the Earth

You probably think in a vague sort of way that every living thing has a home of some sort. One can tell the kind of animals to look for in the meadow and the brier patch, in the deep woods and the thicket, and even in the city. The plants and their animal associates seem to fit together.

Do you know why animals sometimes leave home and go abroad? Do you know how they select a new home? How can our ponds and streams again become the homes of fish, ducks, and geese as they were when they supported the Indians? Why did buffalo live on the plains and moose in the deep woods? Why did wolves live in both places? Why does the robin live in the dooryard and the grouse in the thicket? Why do many birds not go south in winter? Why are the owl, cat, fox, and raccoon asleep by day and abroad at night? Why do animals live on and in your pet dog?

What use are dead things in the world? How does Nature use them?

Man upsets and rebuilds. Is it always for his benefit? Must man die of diseases in the city he has built? Can he control his surroundings on earth?

(1) J. C. Allen, (2) Harold M. Lambert, Phila.;
(3) (4) Black Star, N. Y., (facing page) Catalina News Service

Chapter One

A Place to Live

Hunting new homes. Did you ever finish an autumn hike with your stockings covered with burs and "stickers"? Nature was just using you to do some work for the plants. If you ate peaches or cherries and dropped the stones as you walked along, or tossed an apple core in a fence corner, you were also doing Nature's work. The cherry trees that grow along the fence or at the edge of the woods grow from seeds that were dropped by birds or other animals. Nature pays for some of this service. She paid you and the birds with the juicy fruit for scattering the seeds around. Cherry stones

An acorn found this spot between field and road a good place to grow

Harold M. Lambert, Phila.

and apple seeds are not garbage to Nature; they are the beginning of new trees. But Nature slipped a trick over on you when she stuck the stickers on your stockings. Many of them were knocked off as you walked along, and the rest you scraped off and dropped along a fence where the new plants could grow up with some protection. Nature also uses wind and water to scatter seeds about.

Why they must find new homes. If new cherry trees all started to grow just beneath the parent tree, there would be a jungle of new trees. Each young tree sends roots to search the ground for water and mineral food, and each sends its branches upward and outward for sunlight. The young trees would soon struggle against one another, and none would get enough to eat, just as, when there are too many cows in a pasture, none gets enough to eat.

If you gathered all the apples from one tree and counted the seeds produced by the tree, what a mass of seeds you would find. The number of seeds on a certain mullein weed were estimated to be over 900,000. Each plant usually produces a vast number of seeds. Similarly animals produce large numbers of young. A pair of robins will have eight or ten young robins each year. A pair of squirrels will have six to ten young squirrels each year. A pair of foxes may have eight or nine young; white-footed mice may have twenty young a year. A queen bee lays two thousand eggs a day.

If all the robins that were hatched in one nest tried to get food in the same yard all summer, some or all would go hungry. If all the squirrels that were born in one nest tried to remain in the home tree, there soon would not be enough food. If all the foxes remained in the same den, some would starve to death.

But Nature sends the young ones out when they are old enough to find new places in the world. When the young robins of early summer are able to care for themselves, the old birds lead them away to a woods where they may become independent. The old birds return to their nesting ground and raise a second brood. Young squirrels are continually exploring new trees and new holes, and so wander away to look out for themselves. When young foxes have grown up, they are driven off by the old foxes to find a new hunting ground and make their own way in the world.

So there is a search each year for new hunting and feeding grounds and new homes. Where there are too many mouths to be fed, life is hard. Therefore, as the animal population increases, the animals spread into new land if they can find suitable land not already occupied. Sometimes a catastrophe removes animals from a land. It may be a forest fire;

Section of a dandelion. What would happen if all seeds grew?

it may be an unusually severe winter; it may be disease; often in our country it is the clearing of land by the ax or the destruction of animals by the guns of hunters.

Wild animals will spread into unoccupied land if they can. If there is shelter from the cold and enemies, if there is food, if there are places for homes for their helpless young—and if the gunners have left any animals or birds to raise young—the land will be populated again. As young are raised they will occupy the unoccupied land where there is food and shelter. Deer, pheasants, rabbits, and other creatures multiply, if given a chance. In many protected areas deer have become too plentiful. There is not enough food, and they starve in winter. Rabbits have in some places become a nuisance.

3

Ducks have large families, but they need protection from hunters and adequate marshland for feeding purposes to save them from total destruction

Pheasants have become so plentiful that they damage the farmers' corn.

Suitable homes for wild creatures. Near a certain large city in the eastern part of the country, there was a patch of woods where birds sang in spring and early summer, where they built their nests and raised their young. Catbirds lived near the edge; farther back in the woods were wood pewees, scarlet tanagers, thrushes. In winter chickadees, creepers, and downy woodpeckers could always be found searching the branches and trunks for insect eggs and cocoons. On the ground and about the roots and bushes were wrens. White-footed deer mice made their homes about stumps, and tracks of the little wild mice could be found in the snow. Squirrels scolded and scampered in the trees, and rabbits squatted in snug little lairs to dash away sometimes when you came too close.

One morning a gang of workmen came to the woods with axes and brush cutters. The land had changed owners, and the new owner was "clearing up." For several days the workmen cut bushes and young trees and piled them to dry and burn. When they left not a plant could be seen under six inches in diameter. The following spring no catbirds sang in the edge of the woods, no thrushes sang in the open trees, no wrens called from along the little brook. Shelter, food, and safety for their young were gone. The birds sought other homes. Cutting brush and trees has driven away grouse, squirrels, thrushes. Cutting brushes and brier tangles has driven away our native sparrows and juncos. Draining of marshes and ponds has driven away ducks. To keep birds and wild animals about, we must spare their food plants and their shelter.

Saving the wild life. More important in the loss of wild life than the axes and fire are the guns of hunters. Less than fifty years ago ducks

Ewing Galloway, N. Y.

In Yellowstone Park buffalo herds are protected. They multiply and, if some were not removed, they would soon over-run the park. Many would starve

and geese in spring and fall covered the ponds and bays inland and along the coast. Now geese are unknown where formerly they were important food. Many kinds of wild ducks are on the very verge of extermination. Once gone, they can never return. Fifty kinds of birds have been exterminated, totally wiped off the earth, since the days of the colonial settlers of eastern America. One thing may save those that remain. Stop shooting until the breeding grounds are again filled. It has been stated that a closed season of two years on all ducks would largely restore the breeding flocks of many kinds of ducks. When quail are protected in farming country, they rapidly become plentiful and tame. When deer are protected, they rapidly fill the woods. Buffalo, protected in the Yellowstone and in Canada, have multiplied until they have become too numerous for their range. It is to be hoped that similar protection may save the ducks.

The United States Government and many of the States have established refuges where ducks and other wild things may not be destroyed. In the refuges wild conditions furnish shelter and food for wild creatures. Hunting is not permitted. Many refuges and sanctuaries also have been established by private organizations and by individuals. In these places wild animals have only their wild enemies to struggle against. The refuges are a great help in preserving our vanishing wild life, but there are not enough refuges to preserve what life remains.

A name for all the surroundings. Saving the lives of wild creatures and of domestic animals, as well as wild and cultivated plants, requires us to find or to create suitable surroundings. There is a convenient word for all the surroundings of a living thing. The idea includes not only the ground on which the plant or animal lives, but the air and

5

water, the temperature and light, the food and enemies, all living things and all nonliving things—in fact, everything that is there to influence the life of the plant or animal. The word that is used to convey this big idea is *environment*. To understand how living things live, to protect them and raise them, we must understand their environment. The study of our environment is the purpose of your course in science. We have started the work this year by studying the living environment. We shall continue this study of living environment in the next few chapters, and then we shall study the nonliving environment.

Environments vary. The environment of a codfish is not the same as the environment of the red squirrel. The environment of the orange is not that of the cranberry. The environment of hard winter wheat is not that of sea-island cotton. To protect our wild creatures and to grow our crops and raise domestic animals we must understand the environment that each requires. The nonliving environment of soil, water, temperature, air, and light must be studied, as well as the living environment. All sorts of living things cannot live together. It is evident that you could not raise foxes and chickens in the same pen, but it took the world a long, long time to find that it is hard to raise babies and flies in the same house. It cost millions of lives from yellow fever and malaria to learn that certain kinds of mosquitoes and people could not live together because mosquitoes carried the germs of those diseases.

Necessities in all environments. Though the environments vary, there are certain things that must be found in all environments. These necessary factors, or parts of the environments, are common to all environments if plants or animals are to live in them. Among these necessary factors of environment are heat, light, air or oxygen, water, food materials. In our studies we shall examine all these factors and see something about how they influence us and to what use we put them.

How to Learn about a Place to Live In

I. Read the chapter through to get the general idea of the subject and how it is studied in the field.

II. Study environment.

1. Go out into the fields and woods and make a collection of the various fruits and seeds that are scattered about at this season. Mount representatives of the various kinds on large cards for display to the class. Group them according to their method of traveling.

If you cannot go out into the fields at this time, perhaps you can illustrate seeds and fruits by drawings or by pictures cut from newspapers and old magazines.

Black Star, N. Y.

What factors of environment necessary to support life are present in all three scenes on the opposite page? Which are insufficient in each for some kind of life?

2. From field study and inquiry or by consulting books in the library learn how many young common animals have in a year: chickadees, ducks, dogs, cats, white mice, aquarium fishes, and others. Make a suitable report of your findings in your notebook. You might report under the following headings: (1) Subject of report: How many young do cats have in a year? (2) Date of investigation: (3) Source of information: Observation where? Inquiry from whom? How your informant learned? Books consulted with author, title, and page.

3. Estimate how many seeds a plant produces. Select a weed. Count the number of seed capsules. Count the number of seeds in a few capsules. Decide what is the average number. Estimate the number of seeds on the plant. Estimate the number of square feet or square inches of ground the plant occupies, and calculate how much ground the offspring would need next year if all lived. Write a report as in No. 2. (1) Subject of report: ....; (2) Kind of plant: ....; (3) How many capsules: ....; (4) How many seeds in an average capsule: ....; (5) How many seeds on the plant: ....; (6) How much ground the plants occupy: ....; (7) How much ground the new plants would need next year if they all grew: ....; (8) Means of dispersal: ....

4. In the country, the parks, or in the city what possible places do you find that animals might occupy as their home region? Write a report describing the place, its location, size, plant covering, what animals it is suitable for, any evidence that it has been visited by animals, the probability that they could make a living if they were placed there.

5. How could your home grounds be made suitable home grounds for birds, butterflies, bees, fishes, and other animals? Set up suitable conditions for some of these. You can easily make suitable conditions for fishes, snails, and other aquarium animals. Try to establish an aquarium that maintains itself with very little daily care by you, a home maintained by its inhabitants.

6. Set up a terrarium where land animals may live as natural a life as possible. Supply food and water and clean out refuse. Otherwise keep everything as "natural" as possible. In the terrarium you might keep lizards, grasshoppers, beetles, other insects, small snakes, and other small animals. Observe the kind of place in which you find the creatures, the plants and animals among which they live, and try to provide a new home for them which is as nearly as possible like their natural home.

7. You might care to build bird nesting boxes and bird-baths, also feeding boxes that will be used on the home grounds for birds.

8. Locate sections where there are many birds and try to learn why the birds gather there. Look for food, shelter, possibilities of enemies and disturbers, water, and other conditions. Learn whether most of the birds are feeding on seeds, fruits, insects, or other things. Find out why the food is there. Learn what kinds of seeds, fruits, and so forth are present. Can these bushes, young trees, wild fruits, weeds, and other plants be used in your home grounds or parks to make them more suitable for birds? If you live near a waterfront or harbor, do gulls and other water birds come at certain seasons and times? What brings them?

9. If you can visit a wild-life refuge or bird sanctuary, what type of animals or birds is it provided for? What is the land, water, rock, and soil environment? What is the plant environment? What provision is made for food, shelter from weather, home for young, protection from enemies? What animals and birds did you find? What insects in abundance? What weeds, grasses, bushes, and trees with seeds and fruits? What provision was made for visits by people?

III. Test yourself and then look up the facts for those questions that you cannot answer.

1. By what means are plants spread abroad?

2. How is any kind of plant benefited by the wide scattering of its seeds?

3. Why do animals leave home?

4. Why does the animal population change with the plant population?

5. What conditions must be established to secure a woodland with a large variety of birds and animals?

6. Why are wild ducks fast growing scarce in many sections? What two measures may bring them back?

7. What has happened to deer, buffalo, and many other wild creatures when all hunting has been stopped?

8. What is environment? Name several different types of environment and show why their inhabitants differ.

9. Name some factors of environment that must be present in the environments of all living things.

IV. Test yourself on these chief concepts, or "big ideas":

1. Why do plants and animals move into new areas?

2. What will probably happen to the animal population of an area if the vegetation changes? Why?

3. What must be known before a successful sanctuary, refuge, or preserve for wild life may be established?

4. What is the term used to indicate the total surroundings of a living thing?

5. What factors must be part of all such surroundings?

V. Think out answers to the following:

1. What factors determine the number of any kind of animal in a region? There are several factors that you may be able to determine.

2. Should all gunning be stopped? Do not consider the loss of sport. Consider only the effect of stopping all gunning.

3. A kind-hearted lady near New York City urged a boy to open the cage of his canary bird and allow the bird to fly away. From what you know about environments, would you say that this act would have been a kindness to the bird? State your reasons.

4. Would it be a kindness to a dog that is shut up in a city apartment to take him out to the country and let him go free to take care of himself? Be sure of your reasons.

5. A large number of American monarch butterflies were seen one summer in England, but they all disappeared, leaving none next year. Can you suggest any reason for their disappearance?

6. What stops animals from wandering to the uttermost parts of the earth?

VI. Vocabulary. You must have names for things and you must have words for ideas. Otherwise, you would be little better off than "dumb" animals. An educated man or woman has a good vocabulary (collection of words) at command. You will meet new words in science, some of them for ideas that you have had or for new ideas, and some of them common English words that occur in books and newspapers. Keep a word list in your notebook. Write down every new word and its meaning. Then drill yourself on those words. A few suggestions will be given you from time to time, but you alone can tell what words you do not know. Use your dictionary when necessary.

environment   refuge
catastrophe   factors
          extermination

Chapter Two

Each in Its Own Place

Adapted to their home. A clam cannot live long on dry land and a kitten cannot live long under the water. We say that the clam is adapted or fitted to life under the water and mud, and a wildcat is adapted to life in the woods. A Pekinese is adapted to live in the house, after a fashion, but not adapted to live wild in the woods. The shells of a clam are structures that protect the clam. We say that they are adaptations for protection. The wildcat's legs and claws are adaptations to catch its prey. The fox's legs are adaptations that enable it to run fast, and its jaws and teeth are adaptations that enable it to catch and tear its prey. The poor little Pekinese has neither legs adapted for running after a rabbit or running away from a wildcat, nor jaws and teeth adapted for providing food or fighting battles in the wildwood. The clam, the wildcat, and the fox can take care of themselves; the Pekinese must be taken care of.

To live in its natural home, a creature must be adapted to it by its structures and habits. The woodpecker is well adapted to its home and its food by its wings which enable it to fly to the tree, its toes and claws which enable it to cling to tree bark, and its sharp beak which enables it to chisel its insect food from under the bark. A duck is adapted to reach its feeding pond by its wings and to escape from the pond when an enemy comes. The duck's webbed feet are adaptations that enable it to swim on the surface or underwater. Its broad, flat beak is adapted to feeding in the soft muddy bottom.

An animal's habits, too, must be adapted to his home and method of feeding and to its body structure. Mice are small creatures that cannot fight off a dog or a cat. They creep into small places where a cat or dog cannot go, and spend the day in sleep and hiding. At night they venture out. You may have learned that fact about your own home. Wood mice and field mice, too, hide by day and are abroad at night in search of food and new homes. You may see their footprints in the snow.

The fox and the cat that feed on mice must be on the hunt at night. You no doubt know how cats prowl at night. You probably have seen them leaving the farm houses in the evening and making their way into the fields, or you have heard them quarreling at night through the back yards and over the fences. Notice the pupils of the cat's eyes as daylight fades. In the daytime the pupil is a narrow slit, but it widens at night

The owl hunts at night. How is he adapted for catching the mice that scurry about at night?

to a big round hole which enables more of the faint light to enter. The cat's ears are keen. You perhaps have scratched the floor very lightly to see a kitten prick up its ears. The fox and the night-prowling dog not only have keen ears but exceptionally keen noses which serve them well in the dark. So the fox, the dog, and the cat prowl at night and can spend the day at rest.

You can think of many other night prowlers. In order to hide from their enemies or to find their night-loving prey, they have adapted their working hours to their necessities. Opossums, raccoons, owls, and many insects are nocturnal (abroad at night).

Other creatures are equally adapted to the daylight. Bees tend their flowers when the sun shines. Then the flowers are open and easily found. Squirrels find their food most easily by daylight. Most birds, whether they search for seeds, fruits, insects, or for smaller birds, can find their food most easily when there is plenty of light. Birds sitting on their eggs or caring for their young can leave them more safely in the warmth of day than during the chill of night. Most birds are daytime workers.

Adapting themselves to the season. You know what most songbirds do when winter comes. They migrate south. There is much debate as to why they migrate and how they first learned to migrate, but it is certain that it is an adaptation to the cold and food scarcity of the winter

11

season. In the spring they again come north. Why is a fascinating question. We are not sure why. But we feel sure that the migration is an adaptation to the warm, bright season.

Many other animals migrate. Caribou in northern Canada migrate southward, and with them many rabbits, birds, foxes, and wolves. In the old buffalo days, the herds also migrated with the season. Fish also migrate. Fisherman along the coast meet the returning fish off the Georgia and Carolina coast and move northward with the fish. Many kinds of fish migrate up the rivers to spawn (to lay their eggs) in the springtime.

Still other animals do not migrate, but prepare otherwise to spend the winter. Squirrels gather and hide nuts and seeds for the winter and build themselves snug nests in hollow trees and in secure branches high above the ground. When the storms rage, they lie snug. When the good weather comes again, they dig into stores of food laid by for the winter.

Other animals just find a good hiding place and curl up. They fall into a kind of sleep or stupor in which they breathe with extreme slowness and the heart beats very slowly. This kind of sleep is called *hibernation*. Ground hogs, bears, ground squirrels, and chipmunks, as

(1) *Nat. Assoc. of Audubon Socs.*,
(3) *Black Star, N. Y.*

Each of these animals is adapted in its

well as frogs and toads and turtles and snakes, spend the winter in hibernation. This is an adaptation of habit to the seasonal environment.

Fur-bearing animals grow heavier coats in autumn. By the time the cold weather arrives the sheep have heavy wool coats that can defy the winter. Perhaps you have noticed how long and shaggy the coats of farm horses and cows become in winter. Furs for the market are taken in the winter season, for only then are they in good condition. When spring comes with its long, warm days, the long fur gradually comes out of the sides of the furry animals. Perhaps you have noticed your pets shedding.

Adapting habits to change. Certain wasps hunt spiders to store away in their nest as food for the young wasps when they hatch from the eggs. Suppose that spiders were scarce for some reason, but caterpillars plentiful. Would the wasps take the caterpillars? They would not, and if they took caterpillars, the young wasps would starve to death without tasting them. Other kinds of wasps hunt a particular type of caterpillar, and if this kind of caterpillar were not to be found, their young would not take a spider though spiders were everywhere. These wasps cannot change their habits. Many insects eat only one kind of plant and will starve in the midst of other kinds of plants.

own special way to its environment

Black Star, N. Y.   *Ewing Galloway*

Man has successfully adapted himself to many, varied conditions

These creatures cannot adapt their habits to new surroundings.

If a fox cannot find a hole amid the rocks to make its den, it will dig a hole in the woods, or it will take a hollow log, or adapt itself in other ways. If a dog is not fed, he will hunt rabbits, mice, or birds. If he is unfed in the city, he will hunt garbage pails. Dogs will fit into the surroundings when taken to the seashore or to the mountain top. They are on the arctic shores and in the tropics although the dog of the far north does not seem to be healthy and happy in the warm countries. Horses, too, will fit themselves to a variety of regions, but their foods cannot be so varied.

Of all living creatures man is the most adaptable. He lives on the edge of the eternal ice, in the "heat-rotted jungle hollows," in the dry, sun-scorched desert sands, and crowded into smoky, high-walled cities. He spends his life either in the wind and sun of the open plains and the briny sea or in the stuffy stores or the stifling factories. The same individual

14

But even man must find certain basic conditions to produce the necessities for sustaining life

man may pass from one such place to another. He may not enjoy them all, but he can live in them all one after another. Few wild animals could make such changes and survive.

Depending upon environment. Yet there are limits even to man's adaptability. There must be light for him and for the green plants which produce his food. There must be suitable temperatures, for there are both upper limits and lower limits, although he is very adaptable to temperatures if he has proper supplies. There must be water in sufficient abundance. There must be air. There must be the right food.

Man can alter the supplies to a very considerable extent. He can change foul water into pure water. He can purify air for breathing and make it dry or moist. He can warm or cool his buildings and make clothing to fit a variety of climates and weathers. He can use a great variety of foods and change them in a multitude of ways.

Yet man, too, has his limitations. Although his food is various, there is a very small number of chemical substances that must be present in his food or he will sicken and die. He must find water, and in the civilization of today he must find vast quantities of water. He must find the substances to burn or the power with which to make heat. He must find the substances with which to build houses, machinery, and utensils. He must find the material for clothing. He can alter his environment, but he is still dependent upon it.

How to Learn How a Plant or an Animal Fits into Its Place

I. Study adaptation by observation.

1. Study your dog or cat or other pet. If you have no pet, any animal will do. Even pictures will serve.

Look first at the dog's legs and paws. They are arranged quite differently from yours. For what purposes are the dog's legs suited or adapted? How is the dog adapted to use them? Then look at the dog's teeth. If you are gentle, you can examine them all. For what purpose are the front teeth adapted? Look at the long teeth just at the sides of the front teeth. For what are they adapted? If you have been bitten by a dog when he was really in earnest, you know which teeth he uses. Have you seen a dog catch and shake a rat? Which teeth does he use? When the dog bites meat off a bone, which teeth does he use?

Now think of the wild ancestors of the dog. What kind of place did they live in? What was their food? How did they get it? How were the wild dogs adapted to find their food? How does the modern dog find its food? How is the dog fitted to endure the winter cold?

2. Similarly study animals that get their food in very different ways. Select a rabbit, or a white rat; a horse or a cow; a fish; a frog; or any other different type of animal.

3. Study the habits of an animal to see if they are adapted to securing its natural food and escaping its natural enemies. You may select any animal, but we will use the cat to show how the study may be made.

Is the cat more active in the morning, during the day, or in the evening? Does it usually prowl about more by day or by night? Examine the cat's eyes by day and by night. How do they differ? What is the cat's natural food? When is that food most easily secured?

4. On your hikes, study the habits of birds, squirrels, and other animals in the autumn. What are they doing? Do you see them preparing for winter? How? Do they show any evidence of providing winter homes or winter food? Do they band together or stay alone? Do they show any evidence of moving to a different climate?

If you cannot go afield immediately, you may gather evidence in the library. Look up summer and winter homes and habits of birds, of caribou, fishes, other animals. Look up the subject of migration, the lives of birds, of animals, of fishes, of hibernation.

Draw your conclusions in answer to the following questions: What animals adapt their habits to the season? What animals apparently make very little change in their habits?

5. Examine the coats of your pets and of domestic animals. Do they show any difference between summer and winter?

6. How is your body better adapted than your dog's to live in your house; in your city; to live your civilized life?

(1) Consider feet and paws.

(2) Hands and paws.

(3) Posture.

(4) Brain size compared to size of head and body?

7. How are the habits of other animals unsuited to civilized life without man's care?

(1) What acts must you perform that your dog could not perform?

(2) What acts necessary for civilized life can your dog perform as well as you?

II. Read the chapter through once.

III. Test yourself with the following questions and look up the answers to those on which you have failed.

1. What is the word which is used to indicate that a structure is suited to a certain use?

2. Mention several examples.

3. Show how each of the following animals is adapted to live its natural life in the wild: a wildcat, a fox, a deer, a hawk, a clam, a fish.

4. Show that the habits of the following animals are adapted to their needs of life: a squirrel, a sparrow, a deer, and a duck.

5. How do the habits of the following show adaptation to the changing seasons? Bear, ground hog, squirrel, most birds.

6. What wild animals seem to show no adaptations of habits to the winter season?

7. Do farm animals show any adaptations to winter or do they depend entirely upon man?

8. In spite of his adaptability, how is man dependent upon his environment?

IV. Think out the answers to these questions:

1. Think of all the domestic animals. Which of them is best adapted to live in the artificial life that man has forced upon it? Do you know any wild animal that man has attempted to tame but has failed in his efforts because the animal could not adapt its ways to man's conditions?

Of all the domestic animals, which do you think could go wild and live throughout the year without man's care?

2. Why is it that the housefly is such a nuisance and the bee with its painful sting is not a nuisance?

3. What birds have adapted their habits to man's environment? Do you know some birds which have not adapted their ways to man's ways?

4. Which domestic animal could best make its living in the city if not taken care of? Which wild animals have adapted their habits to the city and live in spite of man's opposition?

5. Of all wild animals, which has a body most nearly adapted to carrying on man's activities?

6. How has man changed his habits to live in a city environment?

7. Is man better or less well adapted to live in the wilds without help of civilization than wild animals?

V. Think out the big ideas, or chief concepts, of this chapter. The first one is written out; two more are hinted.

(1) An animal's and a plant's body must be adapted by structure to its environment.

(2) An animal's . . . . must also be adapted to its environment.

(3) Of all living things, man shows . . . .

VI. Vocabulary.

adapt   hibernation
adaptation   migration
      prey

Chapter Three

Changing the Place for Better or for Worse

When a herd of cattle has grazed in a field, you can tell they have been there from the condition of the vegetation. When a flock of chickens has been fenced into a large lot, you can recognize the former chicken yard by the damage to the vegetation. The plainsman in buffalo days knew when the buffalo had passed over the prairie. The hunter knows when deer are in the woods. Deer make certain changes in the woods as they feed and travel. Bushes and smaller plants are cropped; paths are worn; ferns and grass are crushed where they lie down. The beaver meadow is easily recognized. Animals change the place in which they live.

Even lowly animals like insects change their surroundings. When a large population of young Japanese beetles took up residence in a certain lawn, feeding upon the grass roots, the dead grass told the tale. When a flock of blackbirds and starlings spent several hours on several successive days digging young beetles out of this lawn, again the lawn changed in appearance. When bumblebees visit a field of red clover, there is an abundant crop of seed. Where there are no bumblebees, the crop eventually dies out without seed. A visitation of gypsy moths may produce a leafless and unsightly forest.

Gulls are effective scavengers. They are nature's beach cleaners

How the change depends upon the population. Of course, the greater the number of animals, the greater is the change they produce. A herd of buffalo may devastate a region. When a herd of wild elephants wanders into the little fields of the African natives, there is little left as food for the natives. Even a flock of birds may bring a great change to the surroundings. On a Maryland farm, the tree sparrows fed one winter on weed seeds, and the next year there was no smartweed growing on the farm. Gulls gather around the fish wharves and feed on the entrails and heads of fish that are thrown out. The fisherman would change the place to a foul, smelly garbage heap. The gulls change it back when the fisherman finish throwing the fish refuse about. On the other hand, if the number of animals is few, they may not change the surroundings sufficiently for any one but a hunter or naturalist to know that they are present. A bobcat might live in the woods without making itself known to anyone who was not trained to look for and recognize signs. Otters are occasionally trapped in the streams of settled regions when no one but the trapper knew they were around. Many foxes live near cities.

Both the number of animals and their method of living influence the change. Few animals that hunt other animals for food live in any region, for many would so change the region by destroying the prey that all

If unchecked, this colony of tent caterpillars will change their environment by eating all the leaves of this wild cherry tree

would starve. Animals that feed on plants (herbivorous animals) may be much more abundant. The number of hawks along a creek valley will be small, but the number of seed-eating and insect-eating birds may be very large. The number of grazing animals in the great game region of Africa far exceeds the number of lions. The number of buffalo on our Great Plains was far greater than the number of wolves, which fed upon buffalo calves and injured animals.

We notice more quickly the great change in the surroundings produced by grazing animals than by beasts of prey. We probably notice first the destruction of grass and other vegetation. We might not see so quickly the destruction of a great number of birds or mice. However, we should notice after a little while the bad effects of destruction of the birds. Insects, weeds, and field mice might multiply until they became bad pests. This has happened again and again when birds have been killed off. Plagues of mice have followed the killing of hawks and owls. When the mice increase in vast numbers, growing crops may be destroyed, as has happened in our West and in Europe.

How plants change their environment. When the first weed seeds fall on the bare ground left by the bulldozer, they find a barren soil. This soil dries out rapidly when the sunlight falls on it and the wind blows over it. It probably packs so hard that delicate young roots often fail to make their way into the ground. As a weed seed here and there sending out its delicate root finds a crack in the dry soil, the hardy weeds spring up. Many weeds send roots, or underground stems, sidewise on which grow up more plants. Gradually the ground is shaded somewhat and does not dry out so thoroughly. Insects may lay their eggs and the young insects dig into the ground, thus loosening it. As the ground becomes soft and moist, grasses may start. They may soon cover all bare ground. Their penetrating roots and their shade further loosen the soil. Earthworms and more insects, field mice and perhaps moles dig into the soil. After a while the weeds may be crowded out by a solid turf of grass.

When hardy trees like scrub oaks and scrub pines or poplars start, the ground may be wholly shaded. Dead tree leaves cover the ground and the grass may be killed. Wood plants replace the grass. Thus successive stages of plants change the ground from a bare spot, to a weed patch,

What stage in the changing of the bare earth does this woodland scene indicate? Note the absence of grass on the forest floor

U. S. Forest Service

then to a grassland, and finally to a forest. And with each change of environment comes a change in the animal population, as was mentioned in the first chapter.

Intentional and unintentional change. Of course, plants and most animals that have been mentioned have no intention of changing the surroundings. Each is looking out for itself, and then what happens to the surroundings does not worry it. Certain animals, however, seem to show intelligent purpose in their alteration of surroundings.

Ants of some kinds build elaborate nests by digging passages and chambers below ground and piling up the soil above ground. The agricultural ants of Texas clear away vegetation for several feet. They carry in seeds of a grass. The seeds grow to be mature plants. When new seeds are ripe, they are harvested, carried into the nest, and stored in chambers that have been prepared. Other kinds of ants carry pieces of green leaves into the nest and on them plant fungi which they use as food. These animals and certain others change their surroundings as if they intended to.

Most animals make less elaborate changes in their surroundings, and they seem to care nothing about the resulting change. If it is good, they profit. If it is bad, they move on to another place. Few try to undo the damage that they do.

How men improve and damage their environment. Men make changes in their surroundings either intentionally or with indifference. Some of the changes benefit man, and some bring destruction of his property, starvation, sickness, and death. When forests are destroyed on the hills, the rain and melted snow run quickly away, carrying downhill soil, gravel, and even

Man has ruined this land by his abuse of the soil

Soil Conservation Service

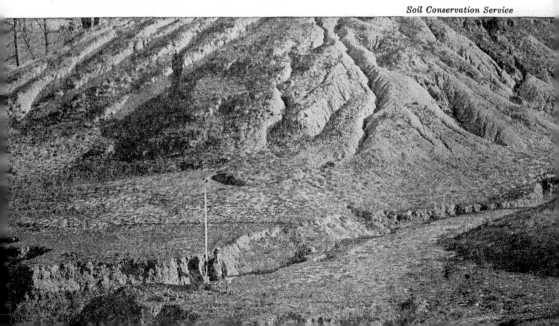

large stones. Hillside farms may lose all their fertile soil. Mud, gravel, and stones may be spread upon the farms in the valley, destroying good fields. Stream beds may be choked, and floods spread destruction among farms, villages, and cities. And when the rains are over and the season of drought has come, the water that might have been stored in the damp forest soil has been lost. If the forest and its soil had been left on the hills, the water would have oozed out slowly to feed the springs and streams during the dry season. Changing the hillside forests may bring many changes not intended.

Turning great herds of cattle and sheep into the national forests and on the open ranges brought unexpected changes. The hoofs of cattle and sheep trampled the young trees and destroyed the future forest. On the grasslands, overgrazing brought destruction of the grass and its replacement by weeds. If overgrazing is too severe, the plant cover is destroyed, and rains wash away the fertile soil. Then the land that might have supported cattle and sheep is destroyed because too many cattle were turned in to graze. Changing the environment has brought loss.

Scientists are now studying the changes due to overgrazing, forest cutting, and farming. Scientists of the United States Government study the plants of the ranges. When certain kinds of weeds appear on the range, it indicates that enough cattle have been turned in. If more cattle are then turned in, the range will be damaged by overgrazing.

In the forest also, the scientists are studying the kinds of trees that grow together or that succeed one another, the kind of trees that should be planted on bare, rocky land to prepare the soil for better trees and the kind that should be planted on barren sand. Thus, on the rocky lands of northern United States, the poor jack pine is planted because few trees besides the jack pine will grow on such land. After the jack pine has grown and improved the soil, more valuable trees may be planted.

The agricultural experiment stations of the United States, of the State governments, and of universities are studying many problems for improving the farm lands: the best crops for the kind of soil; the effect of various crops on various soils; the crops to grow in dry climates and those to grow in rainy climates; the kinds of crops that will improve soils that are dry; the kinds of crops that should follow one another on different soils; and other problems involving the effects of plants on their home soils.

While the plant and animal world of the open country is being brought under the control of the farmer, the stockman, and the forester, the city environment also is being brought under the control of the engineer and the public health officer. It was not a very long time ago in our history

Man *can* better his environment. Note the difference between the government housing in this picture and the same scene below when it was slum area

when the gutters of our cities were little more than open sewers. Flies swarmed around open markets and manure heaps of miserable stables. Little wonder that babies died by the hundreds in fly season, and the cities were pest holes of typhoid fever and other diseases. But now many of our cities have torn down insanitary tenement houses and little houses in alleys without running water and sunlight. In their places have been built light, airy apartment houses with space outdoors for rest

and play. Environment is being brought under control, but there is still need for scientific study.

Where science is needed. Although many diseases, such as diphtheria, typhoid fever, smallpox, and malaria, have been brought under control, others are still deadly. Among these unconquered diseases are infantile paralysis, pneumonia, and cancer. Scientists of public health departments, those in the hospital, the universities, and medical foundations like the Rockefeller

By strip-farming and other modern methods the wise farmer conserves his land. Science teaches him how

Foundation, are constantly studying, both in this country and abroad, the nature of these diseases and possible measures of control. In time the problems of these diseases and other causes of ill health will be solved.

Great has been the success of the engineer in bringing comfortable and healthful life to the dwellers in city and country. Electric power, good lighting, heat, comfort, entertainment by radio, and quick transportation to town have been brought within the means of the country people. Good schools and good medical service are increasing.

The work is not yet done. There are still valleys where the doctor's car never goes and the school bus never stops. In the cities there are still houses unfit for human occupation, people underfed and without suitable clothing. Science has solved many problems in bringing health, comfort, and education. Our country has abundant supplies of food. It can make enough warm clothes for all who need them. It has the material for apartments and houses that may be healthful and comfortable. Our country has the money to provide the health and comfort. Yet the poor, the unhealthy, and uneducated are still about us. The scientists have provided the means. You will learn in your social studies about programs to provide for all.

In this course, we shall continue the study of our environment and our own bodies and methods of bringing them under control.

Laws of nature and laws of science. Living things as well as nonliving things act in definite ways. We know if we carry an iron weight up to the top of a building or to the top of a cliff and let it go, it will fall toward the earth. We can calculate how fast it will be moving at any particular height on the way down, and how long it will take to reach the earth. We can make the calculations because we have learned at what rate bodies fall and have described the fall in a "law of science."

Through study we have learned much about living things. Although they are much more uncertain in their actions than nonliving things, we can predict some of their actions. We make statements describing these actions in "laws of science."

For example, scientists have discovered how certain characteristics are inherited or passed from parents to offspring. The knowledge of these laws of inheritance has enabled scientists to make new kinds of plants and animals, for our purposes vastly improving upon nature. Nature's wild cow produced enough milk to raise one calf. Modern cows produce enough milk to raise ten calves in a year. The wild jungle fowl lays twenty or thirty eggs a year. Modern prize hens lay over three hundred eggs a year. Knowledge of the laws of growth and of inheritance has enabled man to produce kinds of wheat that will grow a thousand miles farther north than nature's wheat. Man has produced juicier and sweeter apples, peaches, and oranges, and other fruits than nature produces. We are learning rapidly to control nature by using the laws of her household.

To Learn How Living Things Change Their Environments for Better or for Worse

I. Study changes of environment by observation and experiment.

1. Locate an area where animals have been, as shown by the condition of the vegetation and other features of the environment. Determine how they have changed the area.

2. EXPERIMENT No. 1. Set up three aquaria. In one, place plants and animals such as fish, snails, water insects, salamanders. In the second, place the plants without animals. In the third, place animals without plants. Watch them from day to day. Note down changes that you observe in each. Write a brief report.

Question of experiment: How do plants and animals change their environment in an aquarium?

Materials: (Tell the things used in the experiment.)

Procedure: (Tell how the three aquaria were set up.)

Observations: (Tell what you saw happen.)

Conclusions: (In this experiment think out general statements.) How do the plants change the environment? How do animals change the environment in the aquaria?

3. Observe an area on a farm that is not under cultivation and a similar cultivated area. How does the farmer change the environment for the benefit of his plants? With a camera, take a picture before and after cultivation.

4. If you live about the edge of a town where a factory has been built, make a study of the change in the environment due to the building of the factory and then the change due to the operation of the factory.

5. Study any other change made by an activity of town or city dwellers.

6. What changes in environment have careless picnic parties made along the roadways or in the parks?

7. Study the change made by weeds or by trees in their environments.

8. Can you find an instance in which an animal, perhaps your pet, has made an intentional change in its environment for its own benefit?

9. Locate and describe an area in city or village that is a poor environment for people.

10. Locate an area in which the environment has been improved.

11. Learn what your city is doing to improve the environment of its citizens.

12. List conditions in your neighborhood that indicate a poor environment and the changes that are needed.

II. Read the chapter through once.

III. Test yourself with these questions and study those which you cannot answer satisfactorily.

1. Tell how several different kinds of animals change their environments.

2. Mention some changes made by animals that are harmful to men.

3. Tell some changes made by animals (including birds and insects) that are helpful to men.

4. Do beasts and birds of prey make any changes helpful to us?

5. What changes made by plants are beneficial to us?

6. Mention some changes made intentionally by animals.

7. What changes made by man in his environment have brought him harm?

8. Mention some instances in which science can determine what changes should be made in environment.

9. What changes in city and in country environment of man should still be made?

10. What is a law of science? Who makes the laws of science?

IV. Think out these questions:

1. Is a law of science subject to change? Can you mention a law of science that has been changed?

2. Name some discoveries in science that have improved your environment.

3. Now you will need to do some clear thinking in answering the following trick question: Has the environment improved in your locality since the Indians lived there?

4. Does draining swamps always improve the environment?

5. If you are not getting along well at a school, it may be due to your lack of adaptation or poor environment. If you are not doing well in some respect, try to think out the reason. If you are doing well, try to think out a case in which adaptation is the reason and one in which environment is the reason.

V. What are the big ideas, or chief concepts, of this chapter?

1. Do plants and animals change their environments?

2. Is the change always beneficial?

3. Do animals and plants intentionally change their environments?

4. When man changes his environment, are the changes always beneficial?

5. What studies can aid man in improving his environment?

6. What is a law of science?

VI. Vocabulary. Did you find any words for your list? What about indifference, paralysis, predict, offspring?

Chapter Four

Living Together

A rabbit cannot live on the bare ground. Plants must grow to furnish its food. A fox cannot live where the only other living things are plants. The fox must find rabbits, mice, birds, or other animals for food. Although the fox will eat a great variety of animals from grasshoppers to chickens, it cannot live on plant food alone. Similarly, birds cannot live without other living things. Some birds eat seeds chiefly, but even the seed-eating birds catch insects to feed their young. Some birds, like the swallow, feed entirely on insects; and others, like the hawks, feed upon other birds, mice, and even grasshoppers. Plainly animals cannot live alone. There must be other animals and plants for them to eat. In the end, all animals must depend upon plants for their food. The fox may eat mice, but mice eat plants. So animals cannot live on bare ground: there must be plants.

Parasites. We are quite accustomed to the idea that many animals eat other animals, and when we study plants with a little care, we find that many plants eat other plants. Have you seen on tree trunks mushroom-like growths or woody growths like shelves? Under the bark of the tree you will find white threads to which the growths are connected. The mushrooms and shelf brackets are the fruits of the white threads. The threads and their fruits are a curious group of plants that cannot make their living in the soil as green plants do. They take their food from other plants or from animals. Plants of this group are called *fungi*.

Some fungi live on dead things. Mushrooms, very common fungi, live on dead material in the soil. When they are grown for market, they are raised on manure mixed with soil. You often see mushrooms growing in the woods on the dead material that has fallen to the ground, dead branches and leaves, dead plants and dead animals, and the droppings, or manure, of animals. The molds that you see growing sometimes on old shoes that have

Some shelf fungi are true parasites. These are feeding on a living tree

been left in a damp barn or cellar are other fungi. The molds are living on the dead skin of a cow, which is the leather of the shoes. You will find molds, too, on moist bread that has been forgotten in the box or in a paper bag that you brought home from the picnic.

Some kinds of fungi also grow on living plants, or even on living animals. Perhaps you have seen an ear of corn in the field with a great mass of black stuff bulging through the husk. The black stuff is a mass of

fruit of the smut fungus that lives on and destroys the corn. Other smuts and fungi called *rusts* live on wheat and other grains. These fungi sometimes destroy millions of dollars worth of wheat in a single year. Many other plants are destroyed by fungi that live on them. The chestnut blight that destroyed our chestnuts was a fungus that lived under the bark of the tree.

You have heard of the mistletoe and perhaps you have gathered it. This plant does not grow on the ground, but in the living wood of trees. Perhaps you have seen weeds, blackberry bushes, and other plants tangled together with brown stems of something that looks like rusty

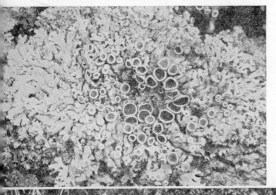

Hugh Spencer, Chester, Conn.

(1) Lichens are really two plants living together

(2) Mushrooms live on dead matter. They are saprophytes

Wm. Thompson, Mt. Vernon, N. Y.

wire. Along the "wire," if you look carefully, you may see little bunches of tiny flowers. The "wire" is a plant called the *dodder*. It lives by taking its food from other plants. Such plants that live by eating other plants are called *parasites*.

There are animal parasites also, animals that live on other animals. Did your pet dog ever have fleas? Most birds have lice. You may see birds taking dust baths to rid themselves of lice by smothering them. These insects are parasites feeding upon the larger animals. Some parasites live inside their hosts. Tapeworms live inside cows, pigs, and sometimes human beings. People get tapeworms sometimes by eating meat without cooking it thoroughly. The young tapeworms are inside the muscle of the cow or pig, coiled up in a little sac. When the muscle is eaten as meat by a man, if the worm has not been killed, it attaches itself to the wall of the intestine of the man and lives and grows there. Several other kinds of worms and several kinds of insects live inside other animals, including man, as internal parasites. Disease germs also are parasites, living in or upon plants,

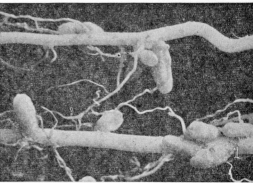

Hugh Spencer, Chester, Conn.

(1) Bacteria living in nodules on clover roots supply nitrogen to the clover

(2) Penicillin is a mould. It has proven invaluable in fighting infections in the human body

Philip D. Gendreau, N. Y.

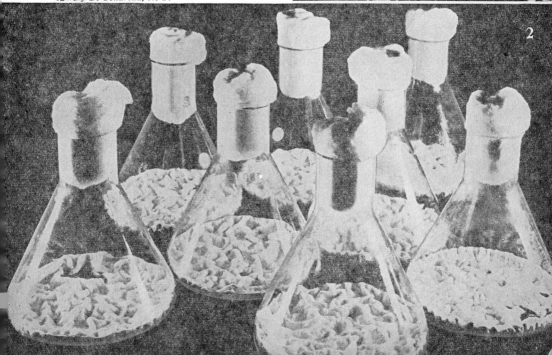

animals, and human beings. Now let us make sure of two scientific words. A *parasite* is a plant or animal that lives on or in another plant or animal and at the expense of the second plant or animal. The animal or plant that supports a parasite is called its *host.* [A plant, like most mushrooms, that lives on dead stuff is not a parasite but a *saprophyte.*]

Good neighbors. In addition to plants and animals that live together as parasite and host, the parasite living at the expense of the host, there are plants and animals that live together like good neighbors, helping one another. If you gently pull up a clover plant or an alfalfa plant, you may find on its roots little swellings called *nodules.* In these nodules live bacteria. These bacteria are very valuable to the clover and therefore to the farmer. The farmer knows that they make the soil rich. When alfalfa is planted on new soil on which it has never been grown, sometimes it does not grow well or will not produce a crop at all. If the bacteria then are mixed in large quantities of water and sown upon the field, the alfalfa will grow luxuriantly. Farmers may buy these bacteria from seedsmen to use on fields on which they want to grow alfalfa or clover. The bacteria grow in the roots of the clover, and the clover benefits by the fertilizer that the bacteria manufacture, while the bacteria get part of their food from the clover.

You have seen on your hikes little crusty or tough, leathery plants growing on the bare rocks or on dry tree trunks. These plants are called *lichens* (lī'kĕns). When the lichen is torn to pieces and examined under the microscope, it is found to be composed of two plants. One plant is one of the fungi and the other is a tiny green plant, a cousin of the seaweeds and green scummy plants that grow in fresh water, called *algae.* Thus the lichen is an alliance of two very different kinds of plants that help each other by living closely together.

Certain kinds of animals also live together and help one another. If you watch ants when you see them running up the stem of a plant, you may find them tending their "ant cows." Perhaps on the underside of the leaf you will see little "plant lice," or aphids. Each little aphid stands with its beak driven down into the leaf, sucking the sap. They suck so much sap that a sweet juice comes out of two little openings at the rear of their bodies. When there are many aphids on a shade tree, you may find the sticky juice dropping on the sidewalk below. The ants like this juice. You can sometimes watch an ant approach an aphid and tickle it on the back with its feelers, or antennae. Then the aphid gives out a little drop of sweet fluid which the ant promptly sucks up. When bad weather comes, some kinds of ants take the aphids down into their nests and place them on the roots of plants underground where they suck the sap and live until the weather clears. Thus the ants

This manure-spreader is used to enrich the soil. Manure becomes good plant food

and aphids each are benefited by their living together in their relation of brotherhood or alliance. [This alliance is called *symbiosis,* which means "living together."]

Mother Nature's housekeeping. In a larger sense all plants are helping animals and animals are helping plants. Animals could not live unless there were green plants living in the soil to feed them. The bodies and wastes of animals also feed the plants. You know that the farmer carries out the manure from the barn and spreads it upon the fields to make plant food. In the woods all the dead trees, dead leaves, and smaller plants make a kind of manure. Gardeners often go out to the woods and gather this dead leaf mold from the floor of the forest and bring it back to mix in the garden soil. It contains plant food. Did you ever stop to ask what becomes of all the dead animals in the world? Insects and worms eat them, and per-

haps you say they *decay.* When they are gone, all the material that was in their bodies has gone somewhere. Most of it has gone back to the soil and serves again as plant food. Thus the dead bodies and wastes of animals feed plants.

Nature thus has a use for all dead stuff and waste stuff. They make good fertilizers. When living plants or animals no longer have use for wastes or for their own dead bodies, other living things feed upon them. Dead stuff is food for living things. That which is waste to one plant or animal is food for another. No material is wasted in nature.

Men live with animals and plants. Have you read the story of Robinson Crusoe, the man whose ship was wrecked on an "uninhabited" island? The island was uninhabited by other men, but many other living things were there. To protect himself from the sun Crusoe made clothing and an umbrella

The cutworm is a garden pest and eats the tender shoots

from the skins of goats that lived there. Birds and other creatures also lived on this "uninhabited" island. And to support the animal population, there was a great population of plants. Animals can never live alone

Attended by workers, the queen bee (in the circle) is going about her task of laying eggs in empty cells

with no other living thing to aid them, for they cannot, like green plants, live on soil, water, and air. Man cannot live alone, with no other living things, for he cannot live on soil, water, and air. Green plants must support him, directly or indirectly.

From the study of foods and nutrition, it would seem probable that man could not live indefinitely without animals as well as plants to furnish food. Plant food seems not to contain all the necessary food substances in sufficient quantity to keep children healthy and growing. Some animal food is necessary. We shall study later what these food substances are.

Because we must live with plants and animals, we must learn how they live together. It is evident that we cannot raise crops in the vast quantity needed in modern civilization unless we know how crops grow. Of course, we must know how to feed our farm animals and our pets. We must know, also, about the vast population of other animals that feed on our crops without asking our permission. Vast hordes of insects eat the crops we plant. A billion and a half dollars worth of crops each year are eaten by insects in the United States. If we raise more crops, we shall raise more insects. To control this vast population of insects, we must learn how they arise, increase, and die. We must know their enemies. Birds, toads, frogs, garter snakes, and many other crea-

Among beavers the dam and the "beaver house" that looks like a pile of sticks and mud are the work of the community, each animal doing his job

tures feed on insects. These animals are good neighbors to us, whether they intend to be so or not. It is to our interest to do everything we can to help these good neighbors live and multiply.

There are tiny animals that are not good neighbors to us but live with us as a matter of their natural rights without asking our permission. We must learn the lives of the parasites that destroy our crops and our animals. Millions of people and vast numbers of domestic animals and crops and plants die each year from diseases caused by parasites.

For family and nation. Did you ever fight a nest of bumblebees or yellow jackets? The little insects fight valiantly to protect their homes and their "people." It is because of their fighting qualities that digging out a bumblebee's nest has been a favorite sport of small country boys. But this sport, like other killing of wild animals, is bad for the farmer. Without bumblebees, red clover produces no seed, for bumblebees carry the pollen from flower to

flower. It is not the service of bees to mankind, however, that we wish to study just now, but their service to one another. Honeybees also have a society in which the labor and duties are divided among the members. The queen lays eggs. The young workers take care of the young. The older workers gather food, repair the nest, and clean it. The workers also are very efficient defenders of the colony. Some kinds of ants have an even more elaborate society. Soldiers with jaws so large that they cannot feed themselves are fed by the workers. But these great jaws are deadly weapons when the soldiers rush out to meet the enemy.

In none of the larger wild animals do we find a "nation" as well organized as among the ants, wasps, and bees. In a colony of beavers, all hands work to build the dams, dig canals, and bring in food. When a flock of crows is feeding in a field, one old crow may be seen perched on a high tree from which he may watch for an approaching enemy and give the alarm. One mountain

33

goat or one old baboon will similarly stand sentinel while the rest feed. Often in the herd or flock there is one leader. The herd or the flock makes it safer for the individual, even though the group runs instead of fighting. Many eyes, ears, and noses among a herd of antelopes or zebras are much more likely to spy the lion stealing up than is one animal grazing alone. The sentinel on the high perch is an added safeguard.

Not until we reach man do we find a "nation" or community as well developed as among the "social" insects. There are men who wander off in the wilderness and live lonely lives, but most men enjoy the society of others. Their organization into societies enables them to control their environment, both living and nonliving, which they could not do if each worked alone. By working together the native tribes of hunters can gather more food, skins, and other supplies so that all live better. In the days when the Indians hunted the buffalo on the plains, the tribes were well organized into scouts to locate the buffalo, the main body of hunters, who did most of the killing, and the women who came quickly up to skin the animals, cut up the meat, and carry home meat and skins. Then back in the village the work went on. Drying the meat for winter, preparing the skins, and making clothes and lodges was the work of the women. The young men scouted for more game and for enemies. Al-

ways the men must be on guard. At no moment day or night was it safe to rest without the sentinels patrolling the country. Enemies might swoop down at any moment to kill and plunder. At the signal of the scouts, the men of the village must be ready to run out immediately to the fight or the hunt.

Where the tribe has cattle, sheep, and other domestic animals, as among the wandering peoples of Central Asia and the natives of South Africa, the herds must be constantly guarded from beasts of prey and from raiding tribes. Organization is needed to arrange guards, herders, and war parties. Where agriculture has developed, organization is needed for planting, harvest, and guarding, as well as for building the irrigation works such as those whose ruins we find scattered over the dry lands of Asia.

Organization built our cities and our nations. Think of the great steamships, taking a year or two to build. Think of the great number of different kinds of experts needed to complete the work. There must be financiers and statesmen to raise the money and protect it. There are architects to design and plan, steel workers and miners to furnish materials, carpenters, electricians, painters, glassworkers, and a great host of other specialists as well as the unskilled workers who do the great mass of general work. Working with all the "workers" are the officials of the government, ash collectors, police, doctors, soldiers, clerks, legislators, judges, and government executives, and serving too in the great work of civilization are teachers and their students.

This great development of organization by which each person helps every other person is possible only with the development of science. When the savage tried one piece of stone after another until he found that he could chip flint into the best arrowhead, science had begun. When he learned the ways of beast and bird; when he learned that he must not sleep in the marshes under penalty of sickness and death, the science of living things had begun. The scientist in the costly laboratory with delicate instruments is carrying on the work of studying nature which began so long ago. The "laws of science" are the general statements made by scientists to tell what has been discovered about the ways in which nature acts.

How to Learn about Living Together

I. Read the chapter to get the general idea of what is to be studied, and how it may be studied in the field, in the laboratory, at home, and in the library.

II. Study through observation and experiment how plants and animals live together.

1. Try to locate a piece of bare ground. It might be around an old quarry, a railroad bank or a road cutting, a gravel bar along a creek or a bare sea beach. Is there any evidence of animal life? Search carefully for insects, worms, and other small animals. What do the animals do on this piece of bare ground? Do they make their homes there or visit there? What food can they find? Are permanent residents invading the ground? Are plants invading any part of it? Do the plants attract any animal life? What do the animals find about the plants?

Write a short report telling the location of the piece of ground and how it was laid bare, the date of your study, and the answers to the questions above and similar observations. If you have a camera, add photographs of the ground and the first invaders.

Think of the organization necessary to plan, build, and supply this great city

Black Star, N. Y.

2. Search in the woods and fields for parasitic fungi and fungi that feed on dead materials. Trace the white threads of the fungi to find where the parasite gets its food. Collect mushrooms and "toadstools" of different kinds. You can learn from library books the names and which are poisonous. Do not take a chance in eating an unknown mushroom. Some mushrooms contain some of the most deadly poisons known. Make a "spore print" by setting the head of a mushroom bottom down on a piece of white paper and letting it stand until the next day. Then gently raise the head. The dark lines that you see are masses of spores, the tiny bodies that start new mushrooms as seeds start new plants. You might be interested in growing mushrooms. Mix up rich soil with well-rotted manure. Seed it with mushroom spawn that may be purchased from seedsmen. You may also seed it with mushroom spores from the field, but if you intend to eat the mushrooms be sure that you have the right mushrooms from the field.

3. Moisten a piece of bread. Let it lie out for an hour or two. Do not have it wet, just moist. Then set it away where it will not dry out. Examine it every day to note the development of the bread mold. Examine the mold with lens and microscope, if you have one.

4. Search for dodder and mistletoe. Carefully cut away the stem of the host plant to see how the parasite taps the host for food.

5. If your dog or cat has fleas, catch one and examine it with a lens to see what the parasite really looks like. How does it get on the dog? What will kill the parasite without hurting the dog on which it lives?

6. Dig up carefully the roots of a clover plant or alfalfa plant or any wild plant of the bean family. Carefully wash away the dirt under a faucet or in a brook. Look for the nodules in which bacteria live.

7. Gather lichens of several different kinds. If you have a microscope, wet the lichen and carefully tear it to pieces with two needles. Examine it under the microscope to look for the two kinds of plants that are living together.

8. Search for ants tending "ant cows." Watch the ants that are running up the stems of plants. Capture some ants and aphids and take them to school in a bottle. Look at them with a lens.

9. Set up an ant's nest in your laboratory or at home. Dig out a nest until you find one with pupae, the white bodies that look like eggs but are as big as the ants. Sweep up ants and pupae into a jar with a lid. A feather is a good instrument to sweep with, or a soft camel's hair brush may be used. Your fingers are too big and clumsy to handle ants. Dump them out in a large jar at home or put them in an artificial ants' nest made by building a box with a wooden base about a foot long and two or two and one-half inches wide, with wooden ends of the same width about nine or ten inches high. For the sides of the box use pieces of window glass attached to the ends and base with narrow molding. Fill the box two thirds full of sand or fine earth, put in the ants, and cover the top with a piece of glass or a cloth to prevent the ants' escape. The ants will arrange the nest to suit themselves. Then watch what they do. Learn by experiment what they should be fed. Do not forget that they get thirsty. Try them with some juicy fruit.

10. Collect some of the dark, rich soil in the woods and fields. Examine it carefully to see what it is made of. Spread it out on a piece of paper and examine it with a lens. As you dig, note any tiny living things in the soil.

11. Make a collection of insects that you find living on weeds and crops.

Learn their name from books in the library. Learn how the farmer and orchardist and florist protect plants from different insects.

12. You might be interested in making a collection of pictures of animals that live in herds or colonies and those that live singly. When you have grouped them, you will notice something about their food and how they secure it. If you mount your collection on large cards with proper labels, it will make a valuable display for class study.

13. To the collection in No. 12, you might add primitive people throughout the earth showing how various "group activities" develop.

III. Test yourself with the following questions and look up the answers that you do not know.

1. Can animals live without plants? Does a fox live without plants?

2. What is the name of plants or animals that live on or in others and feed at the expense of others? Name some such animals and plants.

3. Tell how the dead bodies of plants and animals enable other things in the world to live.

4. What is the name of the group of plants to which mushrooms belong? How is their method of obtaining food different from that of green plants?

5. Are such plants helpful to us or harmful, or do some help and others harm? Explain.

6. Name some common parasites of domestic animals and of man. How can they be avoided?

7. Tell some different kinds of plants that live helpfully together.

8. Tell some different kinds of animals that live helpfully together.

9. Explain how nothing dead is wasted in nature.

10. Why can man not live independently of other creatures?

11. Make two lists of very different kinds of plants and animals that live in our farms and gardens whose lives we must understand although we have no use for them. Head one list, *Our helpers,* and the other, *Our enemies.*

12. Tell how certain social insects are organized to help one another.

13. Tell how the work of certain primitive people is divided among the members of the community.

14. Show how the members of a modern nation divide the work to help everyone.

IV. What are the chief concepts, or big ideas?

1. Do living things live independent lives?

2. In what ways are living things damaged by other living things?

3. In what ways are living things helped by other living things?

4. Can man live independently of other living things?

5. Can a man live independently of other men?

V. Think out these questions or investigate:

1. Do weeds do any good in the world?

2. Do lions, wolves, and other beasts of prey do any good in the world?

3. Can man make any use of parasites and beasts and birds of prey?

4. Do women do more work for the good of society among primitive people or among modern "civilized" people?

5. How does the division of work between men and women compare with the division between male and female among wild animals, including insects?

VI. Vocabulary. Here are suggestions to add to your own selection:

parasite	social
society	fungi
alliance	nodule
host	

Chapter Five

Fitting into Our Human Environment

The problem of living together. If a person lives alone in the woods, he needs to think only of fitting himself into the woods and the weather. He needs to adapt his life to the wild animals, as a wildcat does, and once in a while perhaps to a hunter or an officer of the law. If one lives in a city, he faces a very different problem. In the city he must not only fit himself into the conditions of weather, of buildings, and streets with their traffic, but also he must adapt himself to many other people. Then a big series of problems arises that a wildcat never has to solve. A million people living together need food, water, clothing, shelter, medicines, light, heat, and transportation. They can do nothing in the city to produce the raw materials with which their wants are supplied. They cannot find what they need in the city, and in that way they are much worse off than the wildcat in the woods. In addition, the vast amount of waste materials, including sewage, garbage, and rubbish, must be quickly and safely destroyed.

What lives in a city? Then there are many other things living with men, women, and children in the city. You see some of them. You see dogs and cats, and sometimes you still see horses. You may see English sparrows, starlings, and pigeons. In the city parks you will probably see other birds. You may see some pets—guinea pigs, white rats, and white mice. And you may be aware that there are mice and rats around that are not pets, although you seldom see them except in traps. You may also see—and feel—mosquitoes and flies. Your dog may feel some other kinds of insects. Shade trees along the street and in the parks may be sometimes attacked by plant lice and caterpillars. In addition to all these living things in the city, there are disease germs of many kinds, and sometimes in vast numbers. These disease germs have fitted their lives to their surroundings. The surroundings just suit them where people are crowded together with polluted air, and little or no sunshine, and often with poor food and clothing. People living in the city must adapt themselves to these germs. We shall see in this chapter how people have adapted themselves to some of these conditions, and in later chapters we shall see how they solve the problems of some others.

38

How our living together affects our control of rats and mice. Unless you have had mice about the house, you do not know what cunning and able little creatures they are. During the absence of the family, mice climbed up a lamp cord and ate a bundle of chocolate ornaments wrapped in tin. A mouse was seen to climb up the edge of a door and jump to a high shelf where crackers were stored. Mice eat anything man will eat, including castor oil. When they can find nothing else, they eat the binding of books. They are small enough to get under baseboards and doors. Their sharp teeth gnaw through most building materials, even mortar.

Mice have large families and have them often. A mouse may have her first young when she is six weeks old; she may have eight or nine litters of young in a year; and she may have seven, eight, or nine young ones in a litter. That rate will soon make a big population of mice. If there is plenty of food around and a pair of mice to start with, there will soon be a mouse city in the house. If there is not food enough indoors, they will go outdoors to hunt more and come back to rest and raise their families.

Rats are a little bigger and cannot squeeze into such small crevices, but they can make up for this difficulty by their stronger jaws and their greater jumping power. Like mice they eat anything that man eats and many things that man cannot enjoy. The garbage can with the loose lid is

Acme Photo

Open refuse and garbage are a menace to community health

the rat's dinner pail. Rats swarm around poorly kept market houses and food storage houses that are not made rat-proof. On the farm, the barn and the corncrib will probably be alive with rats if the farmer does not rat-proof his corncrib and feed bins.

Traps, cats, and owls destroy rats and mice, but the only effective way to control these great breeders is by starvation. Keep the rats and mice out of the food and out of the garbage. Cover the food in mouse-proof and rat-proof containers, and keep a tight lid on the garbage pail. Keep the rats out of the house. It can easily be done in modern houses. Concrete and wire screen will keep them outdoors.

Very often the food dealers and canners are careless about keeping food protected and garbage safe from rats. These people would rather lose some money by neglect than save by the expense of protection.

Carefully guarded is a city's water supply. Here we see purified water for New York City being aërated to restore its taste

Unfortunately it is not only they that lose, but many other people in the city lose by their feeding and harboring rats. Rats spread to other houses.

In addition to their destructiveness, rats are exceedingly dangerous. They spread the terrible disease, bubonic plague, that in earlier centuries killed hundreds of thousands of people. In 1665 when London had a population of 400,000, the plague killed 69,000 people. Fleas that live on rats carry the germs of the plague. The plague is kept in control now only by the watchfulness of the public health authorities.

They who feed rats have not learned to adapt themselves to other people who live in the city. To control selfish people, we must support the police department to aid the public health officials. The department of public health gives us expert advice which will enable us to fit into the conditions created by our human environment. Many people readily accept the aid of the public health department in solving the problem of fitting into the human environment, but some need the restraint or the stimulus of the strong arm of the police force.

Insects of our human environment. The carelessly kept market house furnishes food for flies. The carelessly kept stable furnishes them breeding places. The housefly's favorite home for her family is the manure pile. Houseflies mean filth. If the filth is not in your back yard, it is on someone's premises. If the fly's food and feeding and breeding places are cleaned up, there will be no flies.

The department of public health takes a very active part in keeping down flies. Flies mean sick babies. Sickness of babies increased regularly with the flies until the health

40

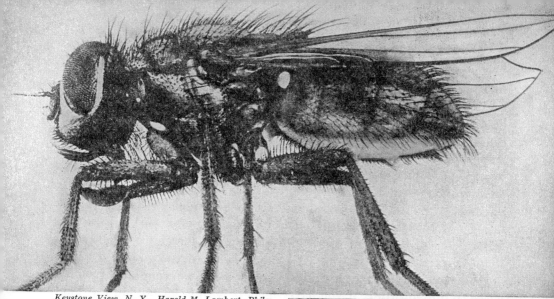

This is an enlarged view of public enemy No. 1, the common housefly

(*Right*) A modern store protects its food from flies, yet keeps it visible.

BUTTER   EGGS

SERVE YOURSELF

department showed why, and then enforced regulations to protect babies and the rest of us.

Flies walking in filthy gutters, manure heaps, and other filthy places gather great loads of disease germs on their feet. When they then walk on the baby's bottle and other food, it is small wonder that the baby gets sick. If you see them walk on your cake and pie, just think where they might have been walking a few minutes before. Since the health departments have taken a hand in the control of flies and foods, the health of babies has been vastly better. The flies breed in vast numbers because of our careless human environment. Since the human environment has been improved by education and the police, the flies have decreased.

Mosquitoes also bring disease. The germs of malaria and some other diseases get into the human body by the bite of mosquito. The mosquito must first get the malaria germ from a person who has malaria. Therefore, if we would live healthily and happily with one another it is necessary that patients suffering with malaria be kept away from mosquitoes—a simple matter with screens. Mosquitoes also may be prevented from breeding. They

41

breed in stagnant water. By draining swamps and upsetting tin cans that hold water, or better by burying the cans or destroying them, mosquitoes may be destroyed. It is necessary to control both the patient and the mosquito to get rid of the mosquito diseases. We must work together, fitting our lives with those of our fellow citizens, to rid our community of disease.

How to prevent giving diseases to one another. If you have a cold and sneeze into the air, you spray the air with fine drops of water loaded with disease germs. If your baby sister, or your mother, or your classmate breathes in those germs, there is a very good chance that there will be another case of cold or sore throat. Did you ever notice how quickly colds run through a schoolroom when they get started?

Government food inspectors are on the alert constantly to protect the community's health

Black Star, N. Y.

Now suppose the first person who got the cold had stayed at home for a few days until the cold was well. Then the epidemic of colds would not have run through the school and would not have been carried home to hundreds of little brothers and sisters and mothers, and to fathers who must go to work where they may spread the germs to others.

At home, if you go to bed with a cold or stay in your own room, it may be a little lonely, but it is kind to the rest of the family. It may help to save them. If you cover your mouth with your handkerchief when you feel a sneeze coming, you will prevent the entrance of many disease germs into the air that others must breathe. Use your own towel only and your own glass, and see that your dishes and handkerchiefs are sterilized (germs killed) by boiling. And remember it works the other way around when you are well and the other fellow has the cold. If the spirit of helping the other fellow is abroad, you will get fewer colds and other diseases.

The public health departments do little about colds, but if a case of smallpox develops in a community that is well educated in health matters, there is swift action and only one case. If the community is indifferent, there will be many cases and deaths. Smallpox can be stopped. It has been stopped in many States. It has not been stopped in States where people think every man has a right to have a case of infectious disease

(disease spread by germs) if he feels like it. Such people have not fitted their lives one to another, and many people therefore suffer sickness and death. There are other diseases as well as smallpox that spread from one person to another and that may be stopped when people help one another through the department of public health.

Food and water have been very often in the past the means of spreading disease from person to person. Such spread of disease has been stopped to a very considerable extent. But we have not stopped it entirely because some communities are not willing to take care of the food and water supply. We shall study later how food and water should be cared for so that they will not carry disease. This again is a matter of living together, of fitting our lives to the lives of others so that all shall be healthy. In some communities people have not learned to adapt themselves to their living human environment.

Fake medicines. Lack of education leads people to buy patent medicines. Do you believe what it says on the bottle of patent medicine? Most patent medicines are mostly water with a little something bitter to make you think you are getting medicine, a little sugar so that it will not be too bad, a little alcohol to give it a kick, and a little dye. The Pure Food and Drug Act has improved the control to the extent that the labels are not as bad lies as they formerly were.

Fraudulent claims of cures are prohibited on the labels of the bottles but not in newspaper advertising of the "medicine." Alcohol and certain drugs must be declared, but other drugs, some of which are dangerous, need not be declared. The law is very defective in protecting us from those who would make money by endangering our health. We need better laws to restrain those who have not learned to live helpfully with one another.

Civilization an adaptation to one another. Civilization involves the fitting of our lives to one another. By helping one another, the terrible plagues that destroyed hundreds of thousands of people on a single visitation have been conquered. Science discovered the nature of the disease and the methods of control. The agencies of government, of people helping one another, used the scientists to conquer the diseases. In many ways we, or most of us, have learned to help one another. We have learned that helping one another is the secret of fitting our lives together so that we may live healthily and happily. Yet we still have the criminal and the unscrupulous business man. There are as many deaths on our highways in one year as in some wars. The highway deaths and injuries are due to those who, in one respect at least, have not learned to live with others. They are unwilling to restrain themselves for the good of others, and sometimes they bring injury and death to themselves and to others.

How to Study the Way We Fit into Our Human Environment

I. Study by observation and thought your own human environment.

1. Write a list of things that you want to do and others want to do at the same time. Can everybody do what he wants to do without interfering with others?

2. Write down a list of things that you want to do but cannot do without the aid of others?

3. Write a list of things that you need in order to live, and decide who gets them for you? What do you do in your turn to help those who have helped you? If you live in the city, these two questions are not easy to answer. If you live in the country, you may also find some difficulty in answering although some of the supplies may be easily traced to their source.

4. Write down a list of some of the living things that you see or know of that are getting a living where you live. How does their living affect you? Do any of these living things harm you or others? Can you alone control the harmful kinds, or must you have the help of others? Are you doing anything to make the control of the harmful kinds more difficult?

5. Make a tour of your city or town, observing work that must be done with the help of others. What work do you see that is necessitated by the living together of many people? How do the people co-operate in getting the work done for the care of the city?

6. Who brings supplies of food and other materials to the city? Who takes care of ridding the city of wastes and protecting the citizens from disease and criminals? Are any of these services done by individuals or must they be done by organizations?

II. Read Chapter Five.

III. Test yourself:

1. Name some problems that arise from the living together of many people.

2. What problems must be solved by the individual acting alone?

3. What problems of city life can only be solved by people acting together?

4. What harmful living things live with people crowded together? Select some of these living things and show what the individual acting alone can do to control them and what can be done only by people acting together.

5. What makes up your human environment?

6. Name some things that you cannot do in your human environment that you might do in a wild environment.

IV. Think out these questions:

1. Are there more advantages in living alone than in living in human environment?

2. Do any wild animals have problems like those arising among human beings from living together?

3. Do any wild animals act together for their common advantage? Explain.

4. Suggest some modification of your immediate human environment that would be of advantage to all persons concerned.

V. Vocabulary. Did you find any new words for your list? Do you know *fraudulent? unscrupulous?*

Unit Two

Astronomy

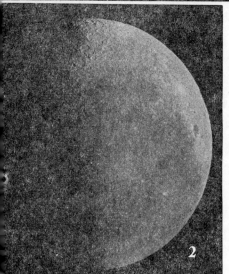

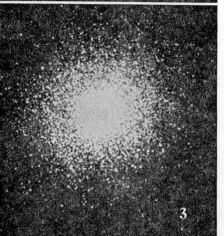

Once between midnight and morning in the uninhabited woods of the north, a canoeist was traveling an unfamiliar lake. He kept to the middle of the lake to avoid rocks along the dark shores and chose the two stars in the bend of the handle of the Big Dipper as his guides. Hour after hour he kept the bow of his canoe pointed to the stars. Finally, at the far end of the lake, the little campfire he sought gleamed from behind sheltering rocks.

Runaway slaves followed the North Star to gain their freedom. The ancient mariners used the stars. Mariners and aviators use them now. You can easily learn some stars that will serve as guides. It is great fun to explore the sky, and when you know some of the stars, you feel more at home in the mystery and beauty of a night far from the gleam of electric lights.

What are the stars? What are they made of? Where are they? How far away are they? How many are there?

In the sky are also: the sun and several moons; comets and meteors; faint mists called nebulae. What are they? What are day and night? Why do we have winter and summer? What is on the sun? How would you like to live on the moon?

(1) *Black Star, N. Y.,* (2) (3) *Harvard University,*
(4) *Ewing Galloway, N. Y.*

4

Chapter Six

Learning the Stars

Have you seen the stars? Have you ever been outdoors alone or with a companion on a clear night, far from electric lights? If you have, you have seen the stars; you could not help it. You have probably been awed by the wonder of the night sky and the beauty of it. If the stars could be seen only one night of the year, how the city dwellers would go by car and train and trolley, far from the glare of white lights, red lights, and blue lights to see the marvelous beauty of the night sky. Because the stars are there every night, most city people never see them. But if you have been camping and have gone out of the tent late at night and looked up at the sky, or if you have gone out from the country home away from the lights, you have seen the stars and you have felt the awe and the mystery of them as the savages and the ancient peoples did.

You will not wonder that the ancients and primitive peoples told myths or stories about them. When you have felt the wonder and awe of looking into the depths of space where the bright spots gleam, you will not wonder that the ancient worshippers sought to find that the stars had some influence upon us. They are so clear, so silent, and so mysterious. The astrologers tried to find in the position of the stars some prophecy of events on earth. During superstitious ages predictions of the astrologers were accepted by a great many persons who were among the educated people of their day. Even today some superstitious people still seek to know what will happen by reading coming events in the stars. As you study astronomy, the science of the stars and other heavenly bodies, you see how silly it is to expect that human events will be foretold by the magnificent bodies so far away that the astronomers' figures mean nothing to you.

Go exploring in the sky. All you need is a star map like those in this chapter, and a flashlight or candle to illuminate the map—and you need darkness. Get far away from

Studying the sky can be doubly fascinating if you use a telescope

Underwood and Underwood, N. Y.

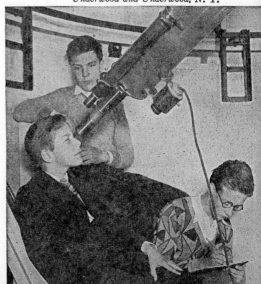

electric lights to see stars at their best. You may see some from the city back yard or roof, but the city glare hides many of them. From most big cities you rarely see the glory of the great Milky Way, the great Galaxy of which we are a part. Far from the glare, you are impressed with the great number of stars. Millions? Who can number the stars of a summer night? The astronomers have done so. On the clearest night you see with the naked eye only about two thousand, and if you are away from the glare of electric lights, you see the Milky Way composed of millions, so far away and so many that they blend into a milky cloud stretching across the sky. Locate the Milky Way; it will help you find your way in the sky.

The bears in the sky. You need to get your bearings for this exploring trip; you need to locate the north in the sky. Locate the North Star. The astronomers call it *Polaris,* the pole star. You can easily find it. Turn generally toward the north and you can easily see the Big Dipper. Look along the outer stars of the bowl of the dipper, the Pointers, and about five times their distance away, and there is the North Star. It is the end star in the handle of the Little Dipper. (See the map on page 46.)

These two groups of stars or *constellations* are parts of the larger groups which the ancients called the *Great Bear* and the *Little Bear.* The astronomers call them by their Latin names *Ursa Major* and *Ursa Minor,* which mean "great bear" and "little bear." The ancients told stories to account for the bears in the sky. Jupiter, the ruler of gods and men, was very fond of a certain beautiful woman. In fact, he fell in love with her. Naturally, his queen Juno was sorely displeased. Juno removed her rival by changing her into a bear. When Jupiter discovered how his love had been treated, he was moved with sorrow and placed the bear and her little son in the sky. There you may still see them—if your imagination is good.

The Indians also traced out the figures of bears in these two constellations and told a tale to account for them. Long ago the bears suffered from the winter cold. The Great Spirit pitied them and taught them to go into their dens when winter came and sleep until spring. To show them when it was time to go to bed for the winter, he placed two bears in the sky. When the sky bears are above the North Star, earth bears should be out and about the woods. When the sky bears are under the North Star the bears should be under the ground in their dens.

The sky clock. You can see the sky bears or dippers telling the season. At eight o'clock in the evening of the middle of February, you will see the bears as on page 49. Both are below the North Star. An hour later the bears have climbed up the eastern sky a certain distance. Turn the book around until the word *March* is at the bottom. That shows the position of the bears at ten o'clock on the February evening. The sky turns around as the night goes on. That is the way a savage might express it. You would say that the earth is turning around. You can learn the position of the bears at any hour if you watch closely every night. They turn around the North Star in the direction opposite to the hands of a clock.

The stars, however, do not keep sun time. They keep star time. The day as measured by the stars is about four minutes shorter than the day as measured by the clocks. The earth turns around in about twenty-three hours and fifty-six minutes as measured by the stars. Therefore, the bears are not in the same position every night at eight o'clock. The bears gain about four minutes on the clock every night. In a month they gain about two hours on the clock. So that on an evening in the middle of March the bears are in the position that you see if you turn the book until *March* in the picture below is at the bottom. If you turn the book until *June* is at the bottom, you will see that the bears are above the North Star. Thus, if you know the

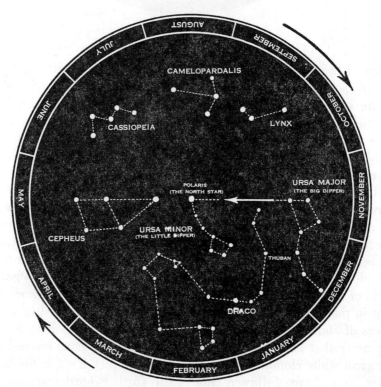

A sky calendar. The text tells how to use it

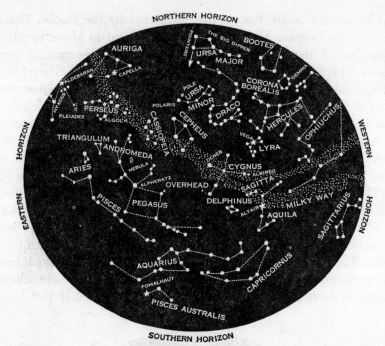

The October sky

position of the bears well, you can use them as a clock and a calendar.

Some other constellations in the autumn sky. If you started this science course in September, it is probably now October. Take your map and a light to illuminate it and go out under the open stars. Look up straight overhead. Almost overhead and stretching away to the northeast and toward the southwest is the beautiful Milky Way. To see it in its glory, you must be away from the light of the city. Just think as you look at it, that it is made up of vast numbers of stars, so numerous and so far away that their light blends into a great white cloud.

After you have followed the Milky Way, look again directly over-

head. There you see a bright star shining in the midst of the Milky Way. Tracing southwest in the Milky Way you can make out a group of stars in the form of a cross with the bright star at the head of the cross. This is the Northern Cross, or Cygnus. To the northwest of the bright star of the cross is another bright one, a bluish white star, lying in another smaller constellation (the constellation called *Lyra*). The name of this bluish white star is *Vega*. In the summer evening it is overhead and the brightest star in the heavens. Now in October you see it to the northwest. Once you have learned it, you can easily pick it out in the heavens. Still further northwest and down toward the horizon is a curve of stars,

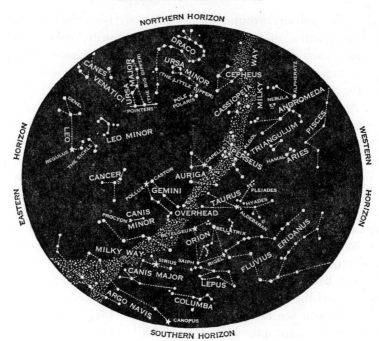

The February sky

the Northern Crown, or Corona Borealis. The crown is not a complete circle but is open on its northeast side. Perhaps you have seen it in summer, shining higher in the sky.

Now go back to the Northern Cross and follow the Milky Way to the northeast until you come to a group of stars lying in the Milky Way in the shape of a crude letter W. It is just about opposite the Big Dipper, on the opposite side of the North Star. The ancients traced out of the form a woman seated in a chair and told that she was put there because she boasted too much of her beauty. Her name is *Cassiopeia* (pronounced kăs′′ĭ-ô-pē′yȧ).

Go back to the bright star at the head of the cross. Move your eyes eastward and about halfway down toward the eastern horizon. In a little while you will make out a great square, so big that at first you may not recognize it. The square does not lie on its side, but stands up on one of its corners. This is the constellation of Pegasus, the winged horse. You may not be able to imagine the winged horse, but you can easily see and remember the great square of Pegasus.

The stars in February. If you make this study in February, you will see some of the October stars in a different position, and you will see others that you would not have seen in October unless you had watched the sky until the wee, small hours of the early morning. For the earth has traveled on its journey around the sun in these months, and the stars, rising earlier each night, bring new beauties to the evening sky.

Look for your old friends the bears, or dippers, and you will find them below the North Star, just as the Great Spirit planned. You will find the Northern Cross still in the Milky Way but now far over in the northwest in the evening, partly below the horizon. Cassiopeia is higher up, in the western sky and about halfway up the Milky Way toward the spot overhead.

Turn your back to the north. As you look toward the south, but well up in the sky, you see three bright stars in a row. They form the belt of Orion (ô-rī′ŏn), the mighty hunter of the sky. His upper right shoulder, the northeastern star of the constellation, is the great star Betelgeuse (bē′tl-jōoz). It is a giant. It is over 200,000,000 miles across. Our sun is only 866,000 miles in diameter. A bright star at the opposite corner of the constellation, the southwest corner, is Rigel. In August you would wait till long after midnight before Orion rose from the eastern horizon. In February it is high in the sky in early evening.

Eastward of Orion you come to the brightest star of the heavens, Sirius (sĭr′ĭ-ŭs) the Dog Star. Sirius is in the constellation of the Great Dog (in Latin, *Canis Major*). More to the north is Procyon (prō′sĭ-ŏn), a bright star in the Little Dog (*Canis Minor*).

Now look straight overhead and let your eyes move westward and northward a little and you will see a close cluster of stars. If your eyes are very good, you may see seven stars; if your sight is not so good, you will see six. They are the Pleiades (plē′yȧ-dēz). They form the shoulder of the Bull, Taurus (tô′-rŭs). The bright star halfway toward Betelgeuse in Orion is the Bull's Eye, the bright star Aldebaran (ăl-dĕb′ȧ-răn).

These are only a few of the constellations that you will be able to trace out in the sky with the aid of the star maps. If you make a journey through the skies one night a week at about the same hour, you will learn new stars and new constellations, and you will see many stars by which you can tell the time after you have learned how. You can tell the seasons, for the stars come back as regularly as birds in spring. They came back to ancient peoples when Egypt and Babylon were great, and they will come back when our great cities are desolate.

How to Study the Stars in the Sky

I. First read the chapter.
II. Study the stars under the open sky.

There is only one way to learn to recognize and name the stars. That way is to study them under the open sky. Even if you live in the city you can learn some of the stars. Select the darkest place you can find. Study them with a map as suggested in the chapter. Follow them week after week. Follow them night after night at the same hour. You will soon learn how to tell the time of night and the time of the year by the stars.

III. Test yourself with the following questions:

1. How can you tell the north in the sky?

2. Why do the stars seem to travel as the night wears on? Why does the North Star never set?

3. What stars can be seen in both winter and summer?

4. Name some stars that are seen only in summer; some seen only in winter.

5. Name some stars in the northern sky; some that appear farther south.

IV. Thought questions:

1. Why are star time and clock time not the same?

2. Is there any spot on earth where the North Star is directly overhead? Is there any spot on earth from which the North Star can never be seen?

3. Does man make any use of the stars?

4. Where is the earth?

V. Vocabulary. Suggestions: astronomy, constellations

In this time exposure, the stars seem to revolve around Polaris or the North Star. In reality, it is the earth which spins on its axis

Black Star, N. Y.

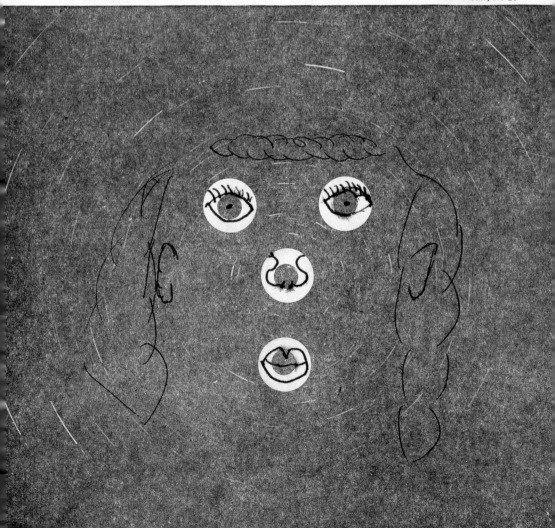

Chapter Seven

What Are the Stars?

How far away are the stars? The stars are far, far away. They are so far away that we cannot measure their distance in miles; it would take too many ciphers to write down their distances. A mile is too short. The astronomers have found another measure to use. The measure in the study of the stars is the light-year. A light-year is the distance that light travels in a year. That sounds strange until you know what it means, and get used to it.

To grasp what we mean by light taking time to travel, let us first talk about sound, for sound travels more slowly. When someone slams

Light which this observer sees through the telescope left the star years before it reaches his eyes

a book on a desk on the other side of the room, you seem to hear it the instant that the book strikes the desk. It seems to take no time for the sound to travel to you. But if the sound is made a long way off you can easily measure the time, for sound travels rather slowly. Perhaps you have seen a man chopping a tree at a distance and have heard the sound of a blow as he raised his axe for the next blow. Or perhaps you have seen a pile driver drop on a pile and heard the sound after the weight was raised for the next drop. Or perhaps you have heard the factory whistle still blowing after you saw the steam from the whistle stop. Or you have noticed that the sound of a flying airplane seems to come from some distance behind the airplane, as if the airplane ran away from the sound. All these instances show that it takes time for sound to travel. Sound travels only 1100 feet, about one fifth of a mile, in a second.

If someone flashed a light on the other side of the room, or a mile away, the light would get to you so quickly that the time could not be measured. Light travels much faster than sound, 186,000 miles a second. Light travels 5,880,000,000,000 miles in a year. This distance is called a *light-year*.

Light takes eight minutes to come from the sun to the earth. It takes four years to come from the nearest star. The star is four light-years away. Sirius, the Dog Star, is nine light-years away. There are some stars that are millions of light-years away.

Where are the stars? That is a difficult question to answer. You may say they are in the sky, but where and what is the sky? You may say that the sky is that which is above you out-of-doors. Now which direction is above? That question sounds silly, but wait a minute. In the daytime you are looking in one direction when you look up, but a man on the other side of the earth is in night, and when he looks up, he is looking in the opposite direction from you.

Well, then "up" means away from the earth. Suppose now that it were possible to travel away from the earth a distance of a dozen light-years. You would not see the earth, from that distance. Which way is "up"? There is no up or down. There is just distance stretching away in every direction. That "distance" that stretches away is called *space*. Space is just a sort of great emptiness where stars and other heavenly bodies are. Look up into the sky on a clear night. You are looking out into space. You see many things in space on a clear night. Most of the things are stars. In the daytime you look through space toward the sun. Space then seems light. That is

Man contacts moon by Radar! Radio waves traveling from the antenna at the speed of light struck the moon and rebounded to earth in 2.4 seconds. How long would they take to return from the Sun, 93,000,000 miles away? from Sirius, the Dog Star?

merely because you are dazzled by the sun. The air scatters the sunlight and makes the sky seem bright. If you were to go up to great heights in a balloon where there is less air above you, you would find the sky getting darker and darker. There is not so much air about you to scatter the sun's light. If you could continue far enough, the sky would be black with the round bright ball of the sun glaring through it. At night time you are looking away from the sun and the sky is black. You are looking through space. Space is dark, black, without light.

Space is cold. As you go up in the air, it gets cold. It is cold on high mountains. Aviators must protect themselves against cold. If you could get out into space away from the earth, it would be intensely cold, colder than anything experienced on earth.

The stars, then, are located at vast distances in this cold, dark, emptiness called *space*.

Why the stars shine. The stars shine out in the blackness of space because they are hot. If you heat a piece of iron hot enough, it shines. It becomes red hot. If you heat it to still higher temperature, it becomes white hot. Some stars are red. Some are yellow, hotter than the red. Some stars are even hotter; they are blue stars. The big star Betelgeuse is a red star. Sirius, the Dog Star, is a blue star.

Some stars give out very little light. There may be cold, dark stars, but we know little about them. We know stars chiefly by the light that comes to us.

How big are the stars? Many stars are about the size of our sun. They look smaller because they are far away, so far away that they are only points of light. Some stars are smaller than our sun, only about the size of the earth, 8000 miles in diameter. Among these stars are the white dwarfs, small stars that are not very bright. Many stars are far larger than the sun. The star Ras Algethi in the constellation of Hercules is 800 times the diameter of the sun. The great star Betelgeuse that you can easily find in the northeast corner of Orion is 400 times as large in diameter as the sun. It is so large

that if the sun were placed in its center, the earth would have room to travel around its orbit inside the star. Another star, Antares, is 300 times as large in diameter as the sun.

How many stars are there? On a clear evening, without a telescope, you might see 2000. From all around the earth, northern and southern hemispheres, 5000 stars are visible, but they cannot all be seen at the same time and place. A small telescope shows many more. The great telescope on Mt. Wilson, California, 100 inches in diameter, shows about fifteen hundred million stars. And now a greater telescope, 200 inches in diameter, is mounted on Palomar Mountain, California. Many of the stars revealed by these giant telescopes may not be seen with the eye even through the telescopes. They are photographed. Astronomers estimate that there are over thirty thousand million stars in the part of the sky that we call ours.

The Milky Way. The Milky Way appears milky because it is formed of vast numbers of stars far, far away. They are so numerous and so far away that they seem only a band of light to the naked eye. The great telescopes see many, many stars making up the cloud-like band. Astronomers call this great mass of stars the *Galaxy*. When you look away from the Milky Way, you see

The Milky Way (1) is seen as a person looks out through our own galaxy the longest way. The spiral nebulae (2), (3) are also galaxies seen on edge and flattened. How do these pictures help you explain the Milky Way?

(1) Globe Photo, N. Y., (2) (3) *Mount Wilson Observatory*

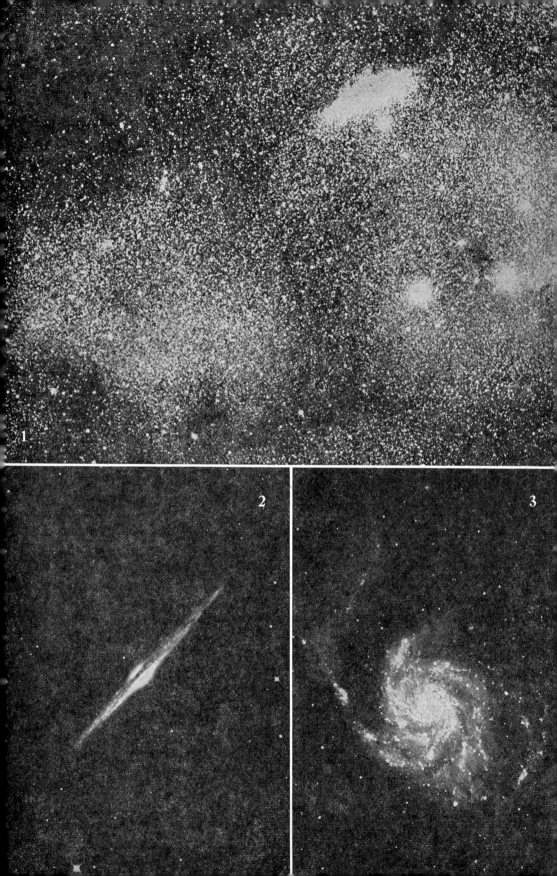

fewer stars. All the stars that you see lie in the Galaxy. We, too, our earth, and our sun belong to this Galaxy. We see the Milky Way when we look through the Galaxy the longest way. We see fewer stars when we look out the shortest way. The whole Galaxy is 100,000 light-years across. Light, traveling at the speed of 186,-000 miles a second, takes 100,000 years to cross it.

Island Universes. The great telescopes show galaxies far out in space beyond our own Milky Way. They are made up of many millions of stars as ours is. These distant systems of stars are sometimes called *island universes.* One of the island universes which can be seen faintly with the naked eye is one million light-years away. Most of them lie much farther away, but there is little use in saying how far. The figures are so big that they mean little to us. The distant galaxies appear as mists or faint, hazy clouds. They are, therefore, called *nebulae*, which means "mists." The astronomers find many patches of mist in the heavens. They may be gas or dust, sometimes shining, sometimes dark. All such mists are called *nebulae.*

How to Learn about the Stars

I. Read the chapter.

II. Observe and calculate sizes and distances.

1. Watch for opportunities that show that sound takes time to travel. Count the seconds between the stopping of the steam from a whistle and the stopping of the sound. Practice counting seconds with a watch having a second hand. Step off the distance to the whistle, first finding how many of your steps make a mile. (There are 5280 feet in a mile.)

2. Get a paper, ruler, and pencil. Draw a line one inch long to represent a light-year. Draw other lines to represent the distances to Sirius, to other stars, to the sun.

3. Draw diagrams to represent the sizes of some stars.

III. Test yourself with these questions:

1. How can you show that sound takes time to travel? How fast does it travel?

2. How fast does light travel? What is a light-year?

3. What is space? What is it like?

4. Why do the stars shine?

5. How big are some of the stars?

6. How many stars have been seen? How many can you see with your naked eye on a summer evening?

7. Why is the Milky Way milky?

8. What are nebulae and "island universes"?

IV. Think out the answers to these questions:

1. Why can you not see the stars by day?

2. How do you know that stars do not rule your fate?

3. Why is space black and cold?

4. What are the stars?

5. Where is space?

6. Where is the earth?

V. Vocabulary. Suggestions for your list:

light-year	nebula
galaxy	diameter
space	nebulae

Chapter Eight

The Sun and What It Sends Us

The sun is a star. If one could look at the sun from a position somewhere away off in space, it would look like other stars. It looks big to us because it is so much closer to us than are the other stars. It is only about 93,000,000 miles away, while the next nearest star is 24,000,000,-000,000 miles away. Fifteen stars only out of the millions seen by the astronomers are within 72,000,000,-000,000 miles of the earth, and the distances to most stars are many million times that figure. The sun is so close that light comes to us in eight minutes while from the next nearest star it takes four years.

How big is the sun? The sun is over a million times the size of the earth; that is, a million earths could be packed into a hollow sphere the size of the sun. Three earths could be packed into the sun-spot in the picture on page 61. Yet the sun is only a moderate-sized star. Its diameter is 866,000 miles. The big star Betelgeuse is 260,000,000 miles in diameter, and the diameter of the bigger star Antares (ăn-târ'ēz) is 350,000,000 miles. Smaller stars also are known. Some are smaller than the earth, which is 8000 miles in diameter. Compared to the earth the sun is a very much larger body.

What the sun is made of. By a study of the sunlight, the astronomers have learned what the sun is made of. Have you seen the colors of the rainbow produced when the sun shines through an irregular piece of glass? If the sunlight falls on a triangular glass prism, the rainbow colors are spread out in regular order. The order is always the same —violet, indigo, blue, green, yellow, orange, and red. This colored band of lights is called the *spectrum.*

When substances are heated hot enough, they glow, and light coming from them may be passed through a prism and their spectra seen. If you shake some common salt into the blue flame of the Bunsen burner or the gas stove, you see a bright yellow light. The spectrum of the element sodium, which is in common salt, has only yellow light. Each element has its own spectrum or scheme of colored lights. Thus, by obtaining the spectrum of an element, the scientist can name the element that produces the light. By studying the sun's spectrum, the scientist can tell the elements that make up the sun's mass.

The sun is made up of the same elements as the earth. About two thirds of the elements of the earth have been recognized on the sun. Iron, silver, nickel, platinum, hydrogen, helium, and many others have been found. Astronomers still study

To form a spectrum, sunlight is separated into its rays by means of a prism

the spectrum of the sun to add to the knowledge of what it is made.

How hot is the sun? The sun is very, very hot. When the temperature on the surface of the earth rises to 100° F. in the shade, we think it is hot. On the surface of the sun the temperature is over 10,000° F., and there is no shade. The interior of the sun is 36,000,000° F. or higher.

The sun is so hot that the iron, silver, nickel, platinum, and other elements are all gases. You know that if you warm a piece of solid ice, it melts to form liquid water. If you heat the liquid water, it boils to form vapor or gas that we call *steam*. Iron acts the same way. Iron melts at

2786° F. and boils at 4442° F. You can see that iron on the sun, where the temperature is from 10,000° to 36,000,000° F., must be a gas. The whole sun is a ball of hot gases.

The surface of the sun looks calm and peaceful when you see it as a big round, red ball at sunset or if you look at it through a heavily smoked glass at other times of the day. Through the instruments of the astronomer, however, the sun is a boiling, seething, churning, whirling mass, not boiling like the soup in the pot but violently shooting out jets and spurts of fiery gas. Great tongues and clouds of hot gases like gigantic flames shoot out at the rate of 250 miles a second, fifty or sixty times as fast as a fast airplane. These great *prominences,* as they are called, shoot upwards to heights of three or four hundred thousand miles above the surface of the sun. Remember that the earth is only eight thousand miles in diameter, so that the earth would be swallowed up in one of these great hot, shooting sun-clouds like a dead leaf in a gust of dusty wind. Were the earth to be swept into one of these fiery gas clouds, and sucked into the sun, all life would be burned to gases instantly, and the oceans and even the solid rocks would be turned to vapor.

Sunspots. There are storms on the sun. Perhaps you live in a part of the country where occasionally a

This is a spectrum of the sun. By comparing it with the spectra of elements known on earth the scientist can tell which exist also in the sun

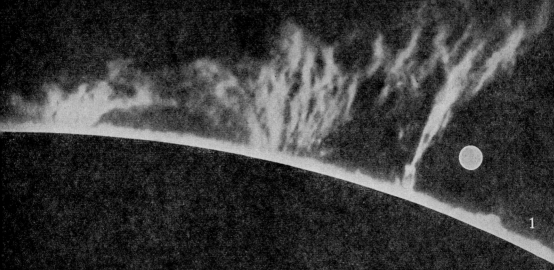

1

(1) (2) *Mt. Wilson Observatory,* (3) *Black Star*

Solar prominences (1) shoot out thousands of miles from the sun. The white circle shows the earth's size for comparison. Prominences are hot, swirling masses of gas. The sun's corona (2), extending several million miles, can only be seen during eclipses. Sun spots (3) are storms erupting on the sun's surface and create magnetic disturbances on earth

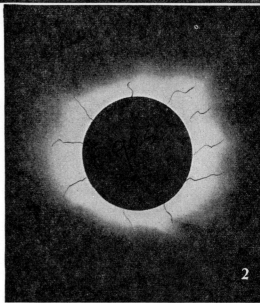

2

tornado or "cyclone" rips through the land and tears to pieces every building in its path and whirls the materials away. The worst tornado on earth would be a mild affair on the sun. The size and intensity of sun storms are in proportion to the size and fierce activity of the sun and its fiery atmosphere. As on the earth, there are stormy times and calmer times on the sun, but the sun's calm times would be violent commotion on earth and its storms beyond our imagination.

If you smoke a piece of glass *very* heavily, until it is a dense black, you can look through it at the sun without injuring your eyes, but do not do so unless the glass is heavily smoked,

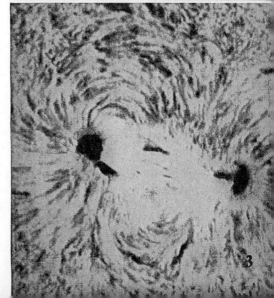

3

for a few minutes' staring at the sun without proper protection for the eyes may injure them for life. With smoked glass you may often see spots on the sun. They do not look very exciting to the eye behind the plain smoked glass, but through the telescope and other instruments they are fascinating objects to the astronomer. They are sunspots, and their study has taught the astronomer many secrets of the sun.

Some of the big sunspots may be 150,000 miles across. The earth would drop into such a spot like a ball into a tub. The astronomers now think the sunspots may be areas of whirling or spreading gases. They are, perhaps, gigantic whirlpools of gases. They are cooler than the surrounding areas. Although they seem like dark spots, they are brighter than anything on earth. Our brightest electric lamps would be dark against the black spots of the sun. Although they are cooler than the surrounding gases, they are vastly hotter than any gas on earth. On the opposite page are shown some sunspots. The one near the top of the sun would easily hold three of our earths.

In the sun's stormy times, the number of sunspots is greater and in its calmer times the number is reduced. They increase for a number of years and then fall off for a number of years. The periods of greatest number come every eleven years. (This period is called the *sunspot maximum*, meaning greatest number, while the time of least number is *sunspot minimum*.)

What the sun storms do to us. We do not know all that the sun storms do to us, but we know that they affect the earth. When the sunspots are numerous, there are times when our magnetic compasses are affected. Telegraph messages sometimes cannot go through, and long distance radio is blocked. Apparently magnetic storms are sweeping out from the sun and magnetic storms are sweeping over the earth.

There seems also to be some connection between sunspot activity and long periods of weather disturbance on earth, but we do not yet understand exactly how they are related. Scientists study the sunspot activity and the variation in the light from the sun to learn what connection exists between the sun and our weather. It is possible that some day they will be able to predict the weather for months and years in advance at least in its larger trends. We do not yet have enough information about the sun, however, to be able to make such predictions.

The value of the sun. The sun is our heat and light. Even the electric light that turns the night time into the gay white way is due to the sun. The heat that comes up from our cellar fires is sun heat. You know

(1) *Missouri Pacific R. R.*, (2) *Ewing Galloway*, (3) *Gendreau*, (4) *Black Star*, (*center*) *Globe Photo*
Can you tell how the energy radiating out from the sun (*center*) is used by man in each of the scenes on the opposite page?

that coal is the remains of plants that lived many million years ago. You know that plants cannot grow without heat and light. The sunlight falling on the coal forests many million years ago enabled the trees to grow and build their leaves, branches, and trunks that fell and made our coal. Without the sun-energy the trees would not have grown. The coal is the stored sun-energy that we bring forth again in our furnaces to warm us millions of years after it fell upon the earth. Even if we use the force of falling water to turn our dynamos and generate our electricity, we are but using sun-energy, for the water that falls in our streams was raised to the clouds by the energy of the sun. Our food and the food of our animals also is the product of sun energy, for plants that produce the food grow with the light and heat of the sun. Were the sun to be extinguished, all life on earth would promptly freeze, and the earth would journey around the sun a cold, dead, dark ball of rock.

How to Learn about the Sun and What It Sends Us

I. Read the chapter.

II. Study the sun by observation and experiment.

1. Take the largest globe in your school to represent the sun. Make a clay model of the earth in the proper relative size, or select some common round object the proper size to represent the earth.

2. With the aid of the star maps locate in the sky some of the stars larger than our sun.

3. EXPERIMENT No. 2. What color is sunlight? Hold a prism in a beam of sunlight so that the rainbow colors are spread out on a card or on the wall. If the room is darkened and the beam of sunlight admitted through a small opening, the spectrum is clearer. Write a report of the experiment as in Experiment No. 1.

4. EXPERIMENT No. 3. What determines the color of a light? Light the blue flame of a Bunsen burner or use the gas stove or an alcohol lamp. Shake some table salt into the flame. Write the report of the experiment in the same form as in preceding experiments.

5. Smoke a piece of glass heavily by holding it in the flame of a candle or oil lamp or the yellow flame of a Bunsen burner. When it is well smoked, look through the smoked glass at the sun. What do you see on its surface?

III. Test yourself with the following questions:

1. What is the sun?

2. How does the sun resemble stars? How does it differ from the earth?

3. What is the sun made of? In what condition are the elements on the sun? Why?

4. Of what advantage to us is the heat of the sun?

IV. Think out the answers to these questions:

1. Suppose that the sun cooled to the present temperature of the earth. What would happen to the gases of the sun? How would the cooling affect the earth?

2. Will the sun retain its present temperature throughout all eternity?

3. Does the earth receive much or little of the total energy radiated from the sun?

V. Vocabulary. Suggestions:

spectrum   sunspot

prominence

Chapter Nine

The Sun's Family

Wandering "stars." If you live where you see the stars, you have no doubt noticed that at times there is a very brilliant "evening star," Venus. At other times, you see no such evening star. You will notice a very few other "stars" that do not stay in one place, but move slowly, appearing each night farther along a course among the fixed stars. These wandering "stars" were called *planets* (meaning "wanderers") by the ancients. They are not suns like the fixed stars. They are earths going around the sun. The earth also is a planet. If you could move away from the earth some millions of miles, the earth would seem to wander like the other planets. The planets shine by sunlight; that is, they reflect the sunlight. They do not give out light of their own like the sun and the stars we see at night.

Where the planets are going. The planets are all going around the sun. Their paths around the sun are called *orbits*. The orbits are almost circular but not quite. They are really ellipses. The sun lies a little out of center toward an end of the orbits. The planets with their moons belong to the solar system (sun system).

The table shows the planets in order from the sun outward:

Planets	Diameter in Miles	Distance from Sun in Miles	Length of Day in Hours
Mercury	3,030	36,200,000	2,112
Venus	7,700	67,200,000	5,400
Earth	7,917	92,900,000	24
Mars	4,230	141,500,000	$24\frac{1}{2}$
Jupiter	86,500	483,300,000	10
Saturn	73,000	886,000,000	$10\frac{1}{4}$
Uranus	31,900	1,781,900,000	11
Neptune	39,800	2,791,600,000	?
Pluto	4,000	3,677,700,000	?

In this model, the nine planets are represented for comparison of size, but not for distance from the sun, which would be impossible to show. Why?

Life Magazine

PLUTO   NEPTUNE   URANUS   SATURN   JUPITER   SUN   MARS   EARTH   VENUS   MERCURY

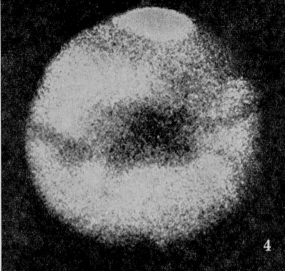

3

4

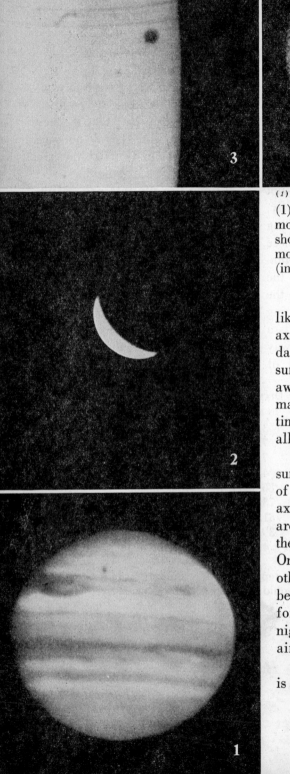

2

1

(1) (2) (6) (7) Yerkes Observatory, (3) (8) Mt. Wilson

(1) Jupiter photographed in ultra-
moon. Here it is a crescent. (3) Tiny
showing polar ice cap. (5) Saturn and
moons. (7) Neptune and its moon. (8)
(indicated by arrow)

Each of these planets spins around
like a top; that is, it turns on its
axis, or *rotates*. This turning gives
daylight to the surface toward the
sun and nighttime to the surface
away from the sun. They do not all
make one complete turn in the same
time. Their days are therefore not
all of the same length.

Mercury. The planet nearest the
sun has less than half the diameter
of the earth. It turns around on its
axis once as it makes its journey
around the sun. It therefore keeps
the same face always toward the sun.
On that side it is always day, on the
other side always night. It would
be much too hot for a person to live,
for Mercury is close to the sun. Its
night side would be frozen. It is an
airless, waterless ball of rock.

Venus. The next planet, Venus,
is about the size of the earth. Astron-

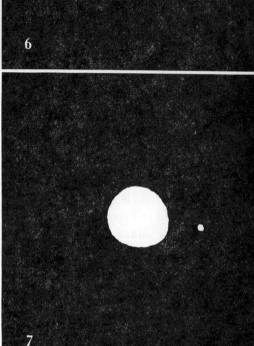

Observatory, (4) Ewing Galloway, (5) Globe Photo

violet light. (2) Venus changes like our
Mercury "eclipses" the sun. (4) Mars,
its rings. (6) Uranus and two of its
Pluto, the farthest planet from earth

omers have never seen the land surface of Venus for it is always covered with dense clouds. Once in a
while the clouds seem to thin out a
little, and a few hazy shadows seem
to show that there is land below the
clouds. There is little or no water on
Venus and scarcely a trace of oxygen, but there is carbon dioxide.
There is nothing alive. The land surface must be bare as a desert.

The third planet. The next
planet outward is the earth. You
know something about it and will
learn more. Conditions on it are just
right for life. There is warmth, light,
water, oxygen, and mineral substances to sustain plant and animal
life. Around the earth goes the life-
less rock ball, the moon.

Mars. Beyond the earth is a
planet a little more than half the
earth's diameter. This interesting

planet is Mars. Dr. Percival Lowell thought there were living things on Mars. The "canals" of Mars he thought were so regular that they must have been built by engineers. A white cap at the north pole of Mars disappears as if it were melting ice when this pole turns toward the sun and summer comes. The dark lines of the "canals" appear as if vegetation were springing into leaf. At the same time a white cap grows at the south pole where it would be winter. It is interesting, but present-day astronomers, or some of them, will grant only that there may be plants of some kind on Mars. Mars has a thin air, too thin for us to breathe.

There is a little water there. Most of the surface is red desert like that of some of our southwestern deserts. Therefore Mars looks red to the naked eye as well as through the telescope. Mars has two moons circling around it. The inner one is only 4000 miles from Mars. This moon is only ten miles in diameter. The other moon is smaller and farther away so that it would look from Mars somewhat as Venus looks to us.

The asteroids. Next outward from the sun are a whole group of over 1300 little planets. The largest, only 480 miles in diameter, is little more than the distance from New York to Buffalo. The smallest are mere bits of rock. Perhaps these little planets circling around the sun are the remains of larger planets which exploded. They are called the *asteroids* or *planetoids*.

The biggest planet. Outward is Jupiter, the giant planet big enough to include all the other planets with room to spare. It has a diameter eleven times that of the earth. It takes twelve of our years to go around the sun, but its days and nights go very fast for it makes one turn on its axis in ten hours. Jupiter is always covered by clouds. If it has a rock surface, astronomers have never seen it. It has eleven moons, four of them larger than our moon, two of them larger than the planet Mars. One might expect glorious moonlight nights, but the moons always would be hidden by dense clouds and the temperature is 220° F. below zero. No one could live there.

Saturn. Next outward is the most beautiful object in the heavens, Saturn with its rings. These rings are made up of tiny bodies like tiny moons circling around the planet. The nearest edge of the rings is 4000 miles away from the planet. In addition Saturn has nine or possibly ten moons. There is no one on Saturn to enjoy the glorious moonlight. It is so far from the sun, about 900,-000,000 miles, that the sun's heat is 100 times less than the sun's heat on the earth. Although it is a big planet, almost ten times the diameter of the earth, it is very light. There cannot be much rock there although there may be some ice. Most of Saturn, like Jupiter, is made up of the light gas, hydrogen.

The outer planets. Next comes Uranus (ū′rȧ-nŭs), nearly two billion miles from the sun. It is four times the diameter of the earth. It turns on its axis in the direction opposite to that of the earth so that the sun rises in the west and sets in the east, but there is no one there to see. It has five moons.

Neptune, about the same size, is nearly three billion miles from the sun. It takes 165 of our years to travel around the sun. It has one moon bigger than the planet Mars.

The outermost planet that we know is Pluto, from three to four billion miles from the sun. From Pluto the sun would look as Venus does to us, like a great bright star. Pluto's frozen surface has a temperature 380° F. below zero. Our air at that temperature would be frozen solid.

Shooting Stars. If you have watched the stars on a clear night, you have probably seen a shooting star streak brightly across the sky and disappear. Something rushing through the air took fire and burned up as you watched it. "Space is filled with debris—chunks of rock and metal," says Professor Donald H. Menzel of Harvard University. Most of these pieces are very small, no bigger than small pebbles. If they meet the earth and rush through the air, they get so hot that they take fire and usually burn up completely. Many of them flash at a height of seventy miles above the surface of the ground. Occasionally a big one crashes to earth. One—or perhaps a group of them—fell in Siberia in 1908 where it completely destroyed a thousand square miles of forest and a large herd of reindeer. The meteor was not big enough to cover a thousand square miles, but the heat of the meteor and the impact when it struck the ground probably produced an explosion that did the damage. In the center of the area several large pits mark where fragments probably buried themselves in the ground. It is estimated that 10,000,000 meteors enter the atmosphere each day. Very few, however, strike the ground. Those that have fallen have usually been stone or iron and nickel. A fallen meteor is called a *meteorite*. Meteorites add

Meteor Crater in Arizona is a mile wide. Perhaps the giant meteor exploded when it struck the earth

Ewing Galloway, N. Y.

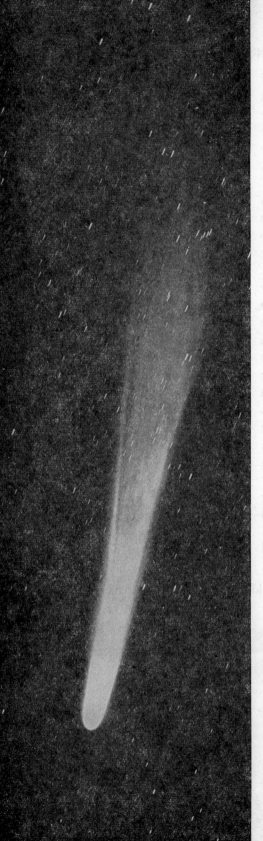

about one inch to the earth in a billion years.

Many groups of meteors travel around in orbits. In November the earth is met by such a group and again in August by another group. Some meteors seem to wander in from the depths of space far beyond the solar system. Some meteors may be parts of planets "spoiled in the making." Certain groups seem to be associated with comets. Perhaps they are comets that no longer glow.

Comets. Comets are very common objects to the astronomer. Few of them, however, are bright enough to be seen with the naked eye. Occasionally one is a very striking object, so striking that superstitious persons are filled with dread. Comets travel arounds orbits. Many are known and named, and their return is predicted. Halley's Comet last was seen in 1910 and will return in 1986.

Newspaper writers sometimes raise the question of what would happen if we hit a comet. Nothing would happen. Most comets that we know are many times the size of the earth, many of them are 80,000 miles in diameter, about the size of Jupiter. But they are chiefly very thin gas, much thinner than our atmosphere. Some of them have swarms of meteors in their heads, and if we struck them, we might see a brilliant display of shooting stars. Some of them contain poisonous gases, but so thin that they would

Halley's Comet, last visible in 1910

not poison us if we ran through them. It is hardly worth while worrying about being hit by a comet or a meteor.

How to Learn about the Sun's Family

I. Read the chapter.

II. Study the size of the planets.

1. On the blackboard draw a series of circles to show the relative sizes of the planets. Calculate the sizes from the table on page 65. Let a circle one inch in diameter represent the size of Mercury.

2. You might try making clay models to represent the planets and the sun. You had better start with Mercury $\frac{1}{16}$ inch in diameter. Make your calculations before you begin. You may be surprised.

3. Go out in the schoolyard and set down the clay models in their relative distances from the sun. Calculate where you must locate the nearest star.

III. Test yourself with these questions:

1. How do planets differ from stars?

2. Name the planets in order, beginning with the planet nearest the sun.

3. Which planet is most like the earth? Why can there be no life upon it such as we know? Tell why it would be impossible for you to live upon any one of the other planets, if you could get there. What conditions on earth, lacking on other planets, make it suitable for life?

4. What are shooting stars? Why do they "shoot"?

5. What are comets?

6. Why do certain comets and certain swarms of shooting stars return at regular intervals?

IV. Think out the answers to these:

1. Some persons have suggested that life might have reached the earth on a meteor. Why is this very unlikely?

2. Suppose you were on Venus. What would the earth look like?

3. Suppose the earth's temperature were to increase to that of the sun. What would happen to the earth? to the moon?

4. Go back to Chapter Six, Thought Question 4. Does your answer now agree with the trial answers you first made?

V. Vocabulary. Suggestions:

planet   ellipse

orbit   rotate   axis

This meteorite fell to earth near Willamette, Washington

Philip D. Gendreau, N. Y.

Chapter Ten

Why the Planets Keep on Their Courses

Why the planets do not wander away. Why do the planets keep going around and around the sun? Why, as they are constantly moving, do they not move away in a straight line and get lost from us in the depths of space? Why does the earth not wander off in cold, dark space where all life would promptly freeze? Something seems to be holding them in their orbits.

Did you ever tie a string to a ball and swing it around and around your head? The string kept the ball from flying away. The ball, if the string broke, would promptly fly away in a straight line, or nearly a straight line. The string pulled it constantly in and held it in its or-

bit, or path around your head. What pulls the earth in toward the sun and holds it in its orbit? What pulls the moon in toward the earth and holds it in its orbit?

You know that objects tend to move toward the earth. If you let go of your books, they move to the earth. Perhaps you say they *fall*. Probably you never asked why they fall. You learned when you first reached over the side of your crib or over your mother's lap, that things fall. You have become used to the idea. It is quite a common occurrence. Science continually asks questions about such common occurrences as why things fall to the earth.

Why does the moon not fly away from the earth like the ball on the right?
Gravitation. Why does the moon not stop revolving? *Inertia.* (See text)

Philip D. Gendreau, N. Y.

Why does the bowling ball roll until it hits the pins? *Inertia.* (See text)

Sir Isaac Newton (1642–1727), the great English scientist and one of the greatest scientists of all time, found the answer to the problem, "What holds the planets in their courses?" He found it, it is said, when an apple fell to the ground in his garden. The great scientist found a great law of science in a common occurrence. The apple tends to move toward the ground. The moon tends to move toward the earth. The earth and the other planets tend to move toward the sun. Every body tends to move toward every other body in the universe. This is the universal *law of gravitation.*

This law tells us that because of the attraction of gravitation the planets do not wander away from the sun, and the moon does not wander away from the earth, and the stone does not fly up from the earth and sail away into space.

Why the planets keep going. But there is another question to ask. Why does the moon keep going around and around? Why does it not come sailing straight into the earth? Why does the earth not sail straight into the sun?

When you swing a ball on a string around your head, do you ask why the ball does not come straight in to your head? You realize that a force keeps pulling it out. A similar force keeps pulling the moon out from the earth and the earth out from the sun. If the string breaks, that force makes the ball sail away in a straight line.

The orbit of the ball around your head is due to two forces acting together, one force pulls it in toward your head, the other pulls it in a straight line. If the forces balance, the ball goes around in its orbit.

So it is with the moon. One force tends to send it in a straight line away from the earth, and one force tends to send it straight in to the earth. The two forces balance, and the moon goes around and around. So it is with the planets and the sun.

[That force which tends to make a body fly away from a center around which it is traveling is called *centrifugal force.* That force which tends to pull the body toward the center is called *centripetal force.* The path taken by the body is the result of the two forces.]

What is the force that keeps the moon and the earth going? Let us try to find the answer in common occurrences. It is a common experience to see an automobile bump into something. Even if the driver

73

takes his foot off the gas and jams on the brake, the automobile may keep on going until it crashes. Things tend to keep on going when they are going.

A speeding car is harder to stop than a slow car. That is what makes the smash when the car hits the pole. A swift ball is harder to stop than a slow ball. Once going, a thing tends to keep on going at the same speed.

Things once going tend also to keep going in the same direction. That is why the car tends to shoot off the road at the curve. That is why the ball on the end of the string sails away when you let go the string.

Similarly, when things are at rest, they tend to remain at rest. A book lying on the table will stay there unless someone moves it. It takes more force to start an automobile, a bicycle, a baby carriage, or a rolling barrel, than to keep it going. The tendency of a moving body to keep moving and a resting body to keep resting, is called *inertia*.

When the scientist finds something common to all occurrences of a certain kind, he writes what he finds as a law of science. The law describing what is common to all the occurrences we have just studied may be expressed thus: every body continues at rest, or in motion in the same direction and at the same speed, unless something outside changes it. [This is called the *law*

of inertia. It is Newton's First Law of Motion.]

The answers. The answer to the question, "What makes the moon, the earth, and the planets keep moving?" is inertia. Why do they not fly away? They are held by the attraction of gravitation. Why do they move around their orbits? Because the orbit is the result of two forces acting in different directions, one force, due to inertia, would keep them going in a straight line, the other, gravitation, would move them in to the center of the orbit.

Finding new planets with paper and pencil. If you saw a boy running across a field in a curve and watched for a while, you would look over at the far side of the field and see where he was going. In that way the astronomer finds where a planet is going. He watches it for a while, not necessarily continuously, but at intervals, and draws its path, or as we usually say, he calculates its orbit.

The ancients knew the planets out to and including Saturn. The outer planets cannot be seen without a telescope, and a telescope was not used until about A.D. 1600. It was not until 1781 that the English astronomer, Sir William Herschel, searching the skies with his telescope, found the planet Uranus. You will notice that was at the time of the American Revolution.

After Uranus was discovered, its orbit was calculated and tables showing its position in succeeding years

How is the banked curve shown here similar to the string attached to the ball on page 72? How does it help the bicycle racers?

were published. But Uranus did not occupy the positions calculated. Two astronomers, Adams in England and Leverrier in France, calculated that if another planet were in a certain position in an orbit outside Uranus, the force of gravitation would pull Uranus out of the calculated position to the position that it actually occupied. No such planet was known. In 1846 Leverrier sent to the German astronomer, Galle, and told him to turn his telescope to a certain point in the sky to find the new planet. Galle did so and found the new planet never before known. This planet was called Neptune.

But still Uranus failed to follow the new orbit calculated. Another planet still further outside was suspected. Percival Lowell at the Flagstaff, Arizona, observatory calculated where the next planet must be. It was not till 1930, after Lowell's death, that the new planet was found and named Pluto.

How to Learn Why the Planets Keep on Their Courses

I. Study by observation and experiment why a ball moves and stops, and then think of the moon's motion.

1. Experiment No. 4. A. Tie a hollow rubber ball, or a small bundle of paper, to the end of a string. Swing the ball

around your head. Describe the path of the ball.

B. As you swing the ball, let go the string. Describe the path of the ball after you let go.

Why did the ball go around the path in A? Why did it not immediately fly away as in B? Why did it fly away in B? In A what force was pulling it toward your head? Why did the ball not go into your head? What force was keeping it away from your head? The path the ball took around your head is its orbit. It follows this orbit because two forces are acting upon it at the same time. What two forces?

2. Compare the ball in its orbit around your head to the moon in its orbit around the earth Why does the moon keep going around its orbit? Why does it not fly away as the ball did in Experiment No. 4 B? What force holds the moon? Lay the ball on the table. Why does it not fly away from the earth? What force holds the ball? The same force holds the moon. Why does the moon keep on going? Roll the ball down the table. Why did it not stop rolling the moment it left your hand? The moon keeps going for the same reason that the ball kept going. Now you may think there is a difference in that the ball eventually stops but the moon does not. Why did the ball stop? Something got in its way, perhaps only the table. Nothing gets in the way of the moon.

II. Now read the chapter.

III. Test yourself by answering these questions:

1. What force holds the planets around the sun and the moons around the planets?

2. What law of science is illustrated in Experiment No. 4?

3. Mention another illustration of this law.

4. What is the law of science that tells why an automobile hits the telegraph pole even after the driver has put on the brake?

5. How does this law help us to understand the movement of the planets and the moons?

6. Using the two laws just mentioned, tell why the planets keep going around the sun.

7. How did an understanding of these laws enable astronomers to find new planets that no man had ever seen before?

IV. Think out the answers to these questions:

1. Why does not a rocket shot upward keep on going instead of returning to the earth? What would be the chief force to overcome in shooting a rocket to the moon? If such a rocket could be invented, would it move to the moon in a straight line or in a curved line?

2. If a small body, say a ball of rock, should be traveling in an orbit that crossed the orbit of the earth, what might happen to it? Did you ever hear of such an object?

3. If the stars are attracting the earth, why does the earth not fall into a star?

V. Vocabulary. Suggestions:

gravitation   inertia

Chapter Eleven

The Moon

Moonlight and earthlight. If you can get a good pair of field glasses, take them out and look at the moon next time you see it as a thin bright crescent with the big, round disk just faintly lighted. This condition has been called the old moon in the new moon's arms. Seen with a pair of field glasses, the moon then looks startlingly like a big, round world.

The bright crescent is the sunlight reflected from the moon to us. The darker disk is the earthlight reflected to the moon; that is, the sunlight has struck the earth and been reflected to the moon. If you were on the moon, you would see earthlight as we see moonlight. Earthlight would be much brighter than moonlight for the earth reflects more light. The moon has no light of its own, just as the earth and the other planets have no light of their own. The light is reflected sunlight. The planets and their moons (or satellites) all shine by reflected sunlight.

Why the moon lost its air. If you could travel the 240,000 miles to the moon, you could not live there, for there is no air to breathe. If the moon had an air at one time, it has lost it. If air were supplied to the moon, it could not stay there. The law of gravitation shows why. A bigger body, that is, a body with more substance, has a greater attraction than one with less substance. The moon has much less substance than the earth. The earth's diameter is about 8000 miles, and the moon's 2160 miles, about the distance from Washington, D.C., to El Paso, Texas. The earth, therefore, has a greater attraction for bodies than has the moon. If a man weighing 180 pounds on the earth were taken to the moon, he would weigh only 30 pounds there. He could jump 25 to 30 feet. That is because the moon has less pull or attraction of gravitation. The moon would have so little attraction for a light substance like air that the air would float away into space.

The desert plains and mountains of the moon. There is also no water on the moon. With no water and no air, there is nothing alive on the moon. It is just dead rock. With a telescope you can see mountains on the moon, great craters, and plains. It is a puzzle what made the craters. They look like volcanic craters but some are forty, fifty, or more miles across. We have no such volcanoes on the earth. Some astronomers have suggested that the craters were made by meteors striking the moon. We know that big meteors have made craters on the earth, but to account for the craters on the moon we should have to suppose that there were

77

Globe Photo

Craters, plains, and mountain peaks of the moon

swarms of tremendously big meteors and that they struck in some parts of the moon and missed other parts. We have not had similar experience on the earth, and we are not far away from the moon, only 240,000 miles, a very small distance in astronomy.

Catching up with the moon. When you look for the rising moon night after night, you find that it rises later each night. The moon revolves around the earth from west to east,

and the earth turns on its axis from west to east. By the time the earth has made one complete turn on its axis, the moon has moved some distance around its orbit so that the earth must turn further to catch up with it. It takes the earth fifty minutes further travel each night to catch up with the moon; that is, the moon rises fifty minutes later each night.

The changing face. As you watch the moon night after night, you

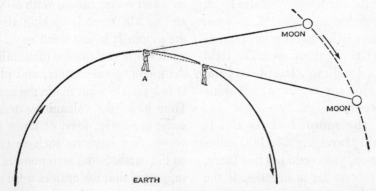

A man standing at A sees the moon in the position shown on the diagram. If he stood at the same place at the same hour a day later he could not see the moon because the curvature of the earth would come between him and the moon's position at that time. However, if he remained to watch, he would see the moon fifty minutes later, because the earth would in that time turn sufficiently to place him in line with the moon's new position

78

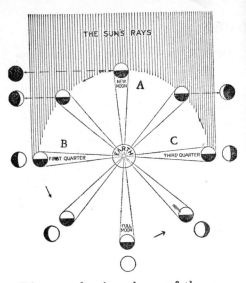

Diagram showing phases of the moon

notice also that its face changes. You may see it first in the western sky, just after sunset, as a thin crescent. It is called *new moon*. The crescent grows steadily larger night after night as the moon rises later and later. The moon at that time, in its journey around the earth, is getting farther away from the sun. In about a week you see a half moon. It is called *first quarter*. Then you see one quarter of the whole moon. In another week you see the full moon rising in the east as the sun sets in the west. After that the face grows smaller, until as the moon rises later each night, it again becomes half moon, but this time in the last quarter. Finally you may see it in the morning a thin crescent. These changing views of the moon are called its *phases*.

(1) (2) Harvard University, (3) Ewing Galloway
(1) First quarter moon, (2) full moon,
(3) last quarter moon

It is very easy to understand why the moon has these phases. Look at the diagram on page 79. The moon is revolving around the earth. When it lies between the earth and sun as at A, the dark side is toward us. We may see only a thin edge, a crescent, or nothing at all. This is the new moon. When the moon has gone one quarter way around its orbit, as at B, we see one quarter of it, a "half moon." When it gets on the side opposite to the sun, its whole lighted face is toward us, and it is full moon. As it moves on around its orbit, we see less and less of its lighted face. At C, we have the last quarter and as it approaches the new moon position, we see only a thin crescent.

What causes eclipses. If the moon gets directly on a line between the earth and the sun, the sun is shut off from us. This produces an eclipse of the sun. When the moon gets around to full moon position and directly on a line with the earth and sun, the earth shuts off the sunlight from the moon. This is an eclipse of the moon. When we get in the moon's shadow, the sun is eclipsed; when the moon gets in the earth's shadow, the moon is eclipsed. If the moon covers the entire face of the sun, there is a total eclipse of the sun. If the moon covers only a part of the sun, there is a partial eclipse. The occurrences of eclipses may be predicted by astronomers for centuries to come.

The moon makes tides. The earth attracts the moon and the moon attracts the earth. We have seen that according to the law of gravitation every body attracts every other body. The pull of the moon is not

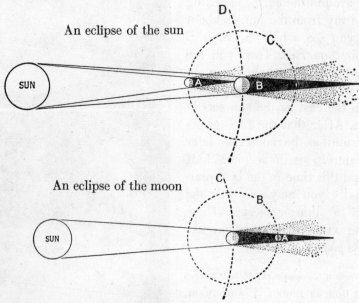

An eclipse of the sun

An eclipse of the moon

With the help of the letters, explain these diagrams

great enough to make the earth revolve around the moon, but it is great enough to pull the water up a short distance from the sea in a broad sort of wave or mound. As the earth rotates, this mound of water travels with the moon. The high water, therefore, moves across the ocean from east to west. As this high water comes up on our shores and into the bays and rivers, it makes high tide.

At the same time that the pull of the moon is making a high tide on the side of the earth next to the moon, there is another high tide on the side of the earth opposite to the moon. It is more difficult to see that this also is due to the pull of the moon. The moon is pulling the water away from nearer areas and pulling the solid earth away from the water that is heaped up on the opposite side of the earth. The further away an object, the less the force of gravitation. The water on the farther side of the earth from the moon is less attracted by the moon. The water nearer is more strongly pulled and so pulled

The same bit of coastline at high and low tide

Ewing Galloway, N. Y.

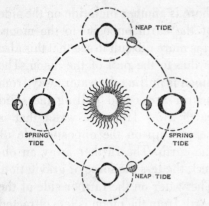

Diagram showing the difference between "spring tides" and "neap tides"

away from the water at the farthest part of the earth. The water, therefore, bulges out at the far point.

There are thus two high tides each day, separated by low tides. The high tides are about twelve hours apart. As the moon rises about fifty minutes later each day, the high tide under the moon rises about fifty minutes later. The tide on the opposite side of the earth also rises about fifty minutes later each day. Thus we expect a high tide in the open sea every 12 hours and 25 minutes. However, along shore there are many things to make the tides a little later still. Shallow water causes a drag, narrow bays cause more drag, and the current of rivers opposes the tide. The United States Government, therefore, works out tables for mariners showing times when high and low tide occur at different places along the coasts.

The pull of the sun also makes a tide. When the sun's tide and the moon's tide pull together, there is a

very high tide. When the sun pulls at right angles to the moon, the high tides are not so high. On this page is shown how the sun and moon sometimes help and sometimes hinder each other. The very high tides are called *spring tides,* but they have nothing to do with springtime. Indeed, they occur at every new moon and at every full moon. Thus there are two spring tides a month. The high tides that are not so high are called *neap tides.*

Why you never see the other side of the moon. Did you ever hear that the other side of the moon is made of green cheese? No man has ever seen it. That is because the moon makes one rotation on its axis in the same time that it makes one revolution around the earth, always keeping the same face toward the earth. Experiment 8 helps you to see why. The time of rotation and revolution is about $27\frac{1}{3}$* of our days. If you made a visit to the moon, you would get very tired of the daylight. You would get equally tired of the night. Its daylight is about fourteen of our days, and then its night about fourteen more. However, during some of the time you might enjoy very brilliant earthlight. (See the pictures of the phases of the moon on page 79.)

Moon temperatures. It is not likely that you would enjoy your visit to the moon. As you learned, you would have no air to breathe. You would have nothing to drink. During the day the sun would be vastly

* From new moon to new moon is about $29\frac{1}{2}$ days.

brighter and hotter than on earth. The earth's atmosphere reduces the sun's rays so that they are not so intense, and after sundown the atmosphere holds in the heat so that it cools off very slowly and does not lose all the heat it gained. On the moon, nothing would reduce the brilliance of the sun, and the temperature of the bare rocks would run up to above boiling water, 212° F., and at night it would drop about as far below zero. The moon is no place to live.

How to Learn about the Moon

I. Study the moon by observation and experiment.

1. Look at the surface of the moon with field glasses if you have them. Look at the dark areas and the light areas. Compare with photographs of the moon taken through telescopes to try to locate mountains and plains.

2. Watch for the rising moon. Record the time of rising night after night. What do you learn about its time of rising?

3. EXPERIMENT No. 5.

Question. Why does the moon not rise the same time each night?

Materials: A globe; a smaller ball.

Directions and observations: The globe represents the earth, and the ball represents the moon. Locate your city or town on the globe, as nearly as you can. The earth rotates, or turns around on its axis, from west to east. Rotate the globe in this direction one complete turn. That is twenty-four hours. Then carry the moon around the earth one complete journey. That is about $27\frac{1}{3}$ days gone by. Now that you have the direction clearly in mind, proceed with the experiment.

Locate your town on the globe. Have an assistant hold the moon as it would be at moonrise at your town. Now rotate the earth until your town is exactly where it was before. While the earth was making one complete rotation, the moon was moving one day's journey around the earth. Have the assistant carry the moon about a day's journey in its orbit. Is it now moonrise at your town? Rotate the globe until it is moonrise on the second night. Why did the earth need to turn a farther distance before moonrise? Does that additional distance mean that the moon rises at the same time, earlier, or later? About how much?

Conclusion: **1.** Answer the question of the experiment.

2. Does the moon rise earlier or later each night?

3. As you watch the moon from night to night, draw a picture of its face each night.

Write a report of the observations.

4. EXPERIMENT No. 6.

Question: Why does the moon's face change?

Materials: A large ball, a flashlight; a dark room.

Procedure: In the dark room the flashlight represents the sun, your head is the earth, and the ball is the moon. Set the flashlight on a support so that it illuminates the moon. Have an assistant carry the ball around you as the moon revolves around the earth. Have the moon held between you and the flashlight representing the sun. How much of the lighted face of the moon can you see? Draw a diagram on the board showing the position of sun, moon, and earth. Label this position "New Moon." Carry the moon (ball) slowly around the earth (your head) one quarter of its journey. Is the lighted part that you see increasing or decreasing in area? How much lighted area do you see at the quarter journey? Locate on the board diagram. Draw a picture of the lighted face as you see it from the earth. Label it "First Quarter." Carry the moon until it has gone half-way around its journey. Place on the board with a picture of its lighted face. Label it "Full Moon." Continue the journey of the moon to three quarters of its journey and indicate on the board "Last Quarter." Call the diagram "Phases of the Moon."

Conclusion: Answer the question of the experiment.

Write a report, including the drawing indicated.

5. EXPERIMENT No. 7.

Question: What causes eclipses?

Materials: Flashlight (the sun), a small globe or ball (the moon).

Procedure: Hold the moon on a line between the earth (your eyes) and the sun (the flashlight). The sun is eclipsed. How much of the sun can you see from the earth? Hold the moon in the shadow of your head. How much of the moon is lighted? This is an eclipse of the moon. Draw diagrams showing the positions.

Conclusion: Answer the question of the experiment.

Write a report with diagrams.

6. EXPERIMENT No. 8.

Question: Why is the same side of the moon always toward us?

Materials: A globe to represent the moon.

Directions and observations: Select a spot on the moon to watch. Have the moon carried around you so that the selected spot is always toward you. In one revolution how many times did the moon rotate? You may answer hastily that the moon did not rotate, but notice the selected spot faced north, west, south, and east.

Conclusion: Answer the question. Write a report.

II. Read the chapter.

III. Test yourself with these questions:

1. How does the light of the moon and planets differ from the light of the stars? Does earthlight resemble moonlight or starlight? Why?

2. Why has the moon no air?

3. Why has the moon less gravitation than the earth?

4. What is the moon's surface like?

5. Why does the moon rise later each night? Show it with a globe.

6. With a globe show why the moon's face changes.

7. How big is the moon and how far away is it?

8. What causes eclipses of sun and moon?

9. Explain how the moon causes tides.

10. Why do we not see the other side of the moon?

11. How do day and night upon the moon differ from those upon the earth?

IV. Questions to think out or investigate:

1. How do we know that the moon has no atmosphere?

2. If a man could be weighed on the moon, would he weigh more or less than on the earth?

3. If an airplane travels 200 miles an hour, how long would it take to reach the moon?

4. If an airplane could be placed on the moon, could it fly about to explore the surface? Your reasons.

5. The great plains on the moon were formerly called *seas.* How do we know that there can be no seas on the moon?

6. At what phase of the moon will an eclipse of the moon occur? At what phase will an eclipse of the sun occur?

V. Vocabulary. Suggestions:

gravitation eclipse
satellite   atmosphere
    crater

Chapter Twelve

Why Days and Seasons Come

What makes day and night? You probably know why we have day and night, but did you ever stop to think about day and night away out in space, say a hundred light-years away? Suppose you were away out there and not near any star, not within several light-years of a star. What kind of days and nights would you have? Cold, intensely cold, and pitch black all the time. You would have no light, not even as much as we have on a dark night, unless you were near enough to a star for its light to be your sunlight. For our sun is a star, and we live in its rays. Were it not for our location at just the right distance from our sun-star, we would not have our days and nights. If we were far away, we would have only night, the intense blackness of space.

Our time is divided into day and night, because the earth turns us around so that now we are looking toward the sun, now looking out into the blackness of empty space. We call it day when the sun's rays fall upon us, and night when we are hidden from the sun behind the earth. We have found it convenient to divide the turning around or rotation of the earth into twenty-four hours. The hours are the same length, but the number of hours of sunlight and of the blackness of space vary. Can you explain why? You may say that the length of day and night varies with the season, but can you explain just why daylight in winter is short and in summer long?

Why the seasons come. Because the earth is tilted, we have winter and summer. If it sat upright, we might have something like perpetual spring. How does the position of the earth make winter and summer?

At sunset the sun appears to dip beneath the horizon rapidly. However, the true movement is the earth's turning, imperceptible to us

Ewing Galloway, N. Y.

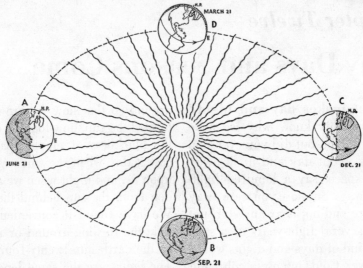

How the earth's revolution causes the seasons. Show this with a globe in a dark room, using a bright light for the sun

Look at the diagram. You notice that the earth's axis, and, therefore, the north pole, is inclined away from an upright position. It is inclined 23½ degrees. The north pole always points toward the North Star, Polaris. If the axis were not inclined but upright, the north pole would point to another part of the heavens. Notice now how the sun's rays strike the earth as the earth travels around the sun. At position A, the north pole is inclined toward the sun, and, of course, toward the North Star. A circle of sunlight covers the north pole and extends down 23½ degrees on the shady side of the earth. As the earth rotates on its axis, the part of the earth around the north pole is always in sunlight. There is no night then at the north pole. The edge of the sunlit circle 23½ degrees from the north pole is the Arctic Circle.

Inside a circle 23½ degrees from the south pole, the Antarctic Circle, it is always night at this season. The

The midnight sun, Alaska. The sun's picture was taken at intervals a minute apart and shows its course almost level with the horizon. The earth is tilted as in position A in the diagram above

Ewing Galloway, N. Y.

This diagram shows one reason why we receive less heat from the sun in winter than in summer

sun at noon is directly over a circle 23½ degrees north of the equator, the Tropic of Cancer. It is then summer in the northern hemisphere. The days are longer than the nights.

Now look at C. The north pole is still pointing toward the North Star, but the south pole is inclined toward the sun. It is sunlight for 24 hours a day inside the Antarctic Circle. The sun at noon is directly over the Tropic of Capricorn, and the southern hemisphere has longer days than nights. It is summer there and winter in the northern hemisphere.

Look now at B and at D. The north pole still points toward the North Star, but neither end of the earth's axis is inclined toward the sun. The noon sun is directly over the equator. Days and nights are equal over all the earth. The time is called the *equinox* (equal night). At B it is our autumn and at D our spring.

Why winter is colder. Long days give more time for the rocks, soil, sea, and air to heat. Short days mean less heating time. In addition, when the sun is not directly over-

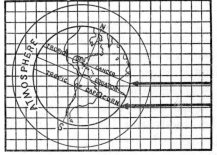

This diagram shows how the distance the sun's rays must go through the earth's atmosphere varies. The heavy arrows represent the sun's rays.

head, its beams come slanting into us. Those slanting beams are spread over more of the earth's surface than beams that strike directly and, therefore, give less heat to any one part of the earth. Also those slanting beams pass through more air. Passing through more air, they give up more energy and have less left to heat the surface of the earth when they finally strike it. Here are three good reasons why the sun's rays that strike the earth's surface more slantwise in winter give us less heat than those that strike us more nearly perpendicularly in summertime. It is not because we are nearer the sun in summer that we are hotter. Actually we in the northern hemisphere are farther away from the sun in summer than we are in winter.

What a tilt of the earth's axis does to living things. If you have discovered the fun of wandering in the fields and the woods, how you watch at the tail end of winter for the first bud of the maples, alders, and hazel bushes, and the first woodland flower on the sun-warmed ground. How you watch for the first migrant bird of spring and each succeeding kind as it comes up from its winter range.

For the warmth of the longer days and the more direct rays is felt in the woods and the fields, in the brooks and the ponds, and in the sea. The ducks go north as the ice goes out. The fish come into the shallows in the lake and the seas, and run up the streams to their spawning ground. The bumblebee queen, the big fat bumblebee you see in the early spring, searches for nectar in the first spring flowers and for a crevice under a stump or stone where she may build her nest and lay eggs for her first brood of workers. The brown mourning cloak butterfly with cream-edged wings flits about the warm, bare woods. Tiny flies and midges wing their airy dance in the sun.

As the ground warms up, a vast green carpet covers the winter brown of the woods and fields. The brown and gray trunks are gradually hung with rich green drapery of the forest, as the winter buds push apart the bud scales, spread out, and develop. The buds of bulbs push above ground to spread their flowers and leaves to the life-giving sunlight. The seeds send out their delicate roots to seek moisture, minerals, and a foothold in the earth, and send their delicate stems to expand the leaves in the sunlight.

Spring is the season of awakening life among plants, animals, and men. It is the season when most animals bring forth their young to develop and gain strength when the rich, tender food is abundant. Plants push out their tender seedling buds and stems when the sun is bright and mild, when the rains are frequent and gentle, and the soil has a bountiful supply of water and mineral solutions. Man follows the plan of nature and takes advantage of the seasons. The farmer sows and plants the seeds that cannot endure the rigors of the northern winter. Spring is the season of youth and growth. Living nature attunes itself to the motion of the earth on its inclined axis.

Summer follows, when the crops of nature's planting or of man's are sturdy and strong. The shade is dense

(1)(4) *Philip D. Gendreau, N. Y.*, (2)(3) *Ewing Galloway, N. Y.*

The seasons, (1) spring, (2) summer, (3) autumn, (4) winter, each have their changing characteristics as they merge one into another. Seasons are due to the tilt of the earth in its journey around the sun

and the sun is hot and the drought sucks the moisture from the soil. The downpouring deluge of the thunderstorm batters leaves and stems and washes away soil from the roots, and the rush of the thunder-gust strips leaves and branches and stalks from the plants. Hot suns, droughts, thunder-deluge and gust demand sturdy plants, birds, and animals. Summer is the season of abundance. The woods and fields and the waters are teeming with life. Living things are struggling against one another for a living place and food. Food is abundant, but it must be fought for. There are many mouths to be fed, mouths of mice and rabbits and squirrels, of birds, of frogs and toads and salamanders, of snakes and turtles, of beasts of prey, of worms, and most abundant of all, the thousands of different kinds of insects. The young must grow quickly, for hard times are ahead. They soon must be able to find their own food and shelter, or they must be fat and well-fed for their winter sleep. All this abundance of life and rush of growth is due to the tilt of the earth that brings the noon sun nearer the pole.

As the sun's rays retreat, the days shorten; autumn comes. Life again prepares to meet the seasons of hardship and scarcity. Man, the squirrels, and the bees finish gathering the autumn harvest and store it safely against weather, mold, and living plunderers. All living things prepare for the winter or they die. The trees withdraw the food from their leaves

and shed them. The bared branches coated with bark and tough skinlike covering can endure the winter winds. The tender buds formed on their twigs for the burst of growth the following spring are wrapped around with tough coats that shut out winter winds and cold rains. Weeds and grasses, bushes and forest trees are hung with fruits and seeds. Bulbs have been stored with food. Birds gather in flocks for their long journeys to friendlier climates. Some, like the swallows, have already gone in the latter days of summer. The failing daylight and the longer nights have told the creatures to prepare to meet adversity after the manner of their kind. Many caterpillars have spun their cocoons. Most insects become sluggish as the sun's light weakens and die at the first frost. Their eggs live over the winter to hatch the following spring. All these changes of living are brought about by the earth's revolving about the star that we call the sun, 93,000,000 miles away, and by the tilt of the pole toward the North Star, for that tilt sends the noon sun creeping away to the far side of the equator.

And now when the sun's perpendicular rays are at the ultimate end of their journey toward the opposite pole, midwinter is upon us. But we are prepared. The harvests are gathered and stored safely, and in the modern world there is enough for all, thanks to the conquests of science, although we do not always see that it reaches the needy in far distant lands or even in our own neighborhood. We learned the lesson from nature, but we are yet unwilling to share our hoards. We are yet like the squirrels that take care of themselves alone, or like the bees that take care of their own hive and allow their fellow creatures to do the same if they can. They who do not share in the labor do not share in the enjoyment of the products of that labor. But the problem of taking care of the needy or the loafer is not one for natural science, but one to be solved by students of social studies.

Winter is the season when nature has fitted itself to cope with the great enemies of life, cold and darkness. Many living things have solved the problem of life by laying up stores. Many have solved it by sleeping, like the woodchuck, the ground squirrel, and the bears. They, like the plants, suspend their activities. The larvae of many insects lie sleeping in warm cocoons, hidden in snug crevices. Many grasses and other green plants die away above ground, but keep alive their roots or bulbs or underground stems. Many plants die, leaving only their seeds to survive the winter. Seeds are well fitted to endure the cold. Each is wrapped around with tough coats that shut out the wet and the bacteria and molds. Dropping to the ground they are covered with dead leaves and then with snow and ice. They easily survive the cold of ordinary winter if protected by the soil and snow cover from the winter winds. The farmer who sows winter wheat in the autumn hopes for a covering of snow all winter to shut out the cold, fierce winds. The snow, the cold, and the winter sleep of the hibernating plants and animals, the storing of harvest by many insects, squirrels, and other animals are responses to the great source of warmth and power far off in the heavens. It is controlled by the two conditions that we have studied, the earth's revolution around the sun and the tilting of the earth's axis.

The busy gray squirrel prepares for winter when it is still far away

U. S. Department of the Interior

How to Learn Why the Seasons Come

I. Study the seasons by the following experiments.

1. EXPERIMENT No. 9.

Question: Why do the seasons change?

Material: A globe to represent the earth; an electric light to stand on the table or a candle to represent the sun; a darkened room.

Procedure: Set the light on the table. Mark your town on the globe. Place the globe on the table at the same level as the sun and several feet away. Now place the globe to the south of the light. Point the north pole of the earth to the north end of the room. If the light does not illuminate the north pole, move the earth farther away until the light extends over the north pole to the Arctic Circle. Rotate the earth and watch the spot which marks your town. A. Is the night or day longer at your town? Stretch a string straight from the light (the sun) to the globe (the earth) keeping the string level. The string represents the rays of the sun that strike the surface of the earth most directly. B. How close do these direct rays approach to your town? Draw a diagram illustrating the distribution of the sunlight and the position of the rays that strike the earth's surface most directly. C. What season of the year is this at your town? Entitle the drawing: . . . . season in the . . . . hemisphere.

Move the globe eastward in its orbit around the light until it has gone one quarter of its journey. D. Where are the most direct rays now? E. How far north and how far south does the sunlight extend on the earth? Rotate the globe. F. How many hours of daylight and how many hours of night does your town have at this season? Draw a diagram showing the distribution of the sun's rays and the position of the direct rays. Label the drawing . . . . season in the . . . . hemisphere.

Move the earth to the north of the sun. Keep the north pole pointed to the north end of the room. G. Where are the direct rays now? H. How far north does the sunlight extend? I. What is the condition of the light at the south pole? Rotate the globe. J. How does day compare with night in your town? Draw a diagram. Entitle it . . . . season in the . . . . hemisphere.

2. EXPERIMENT No. 10.

Question: Why is winter colder than summer?

Material: A flashlight; a cardboard tube to fit over the flashlight or a dark paper to make a tube around it; a darkened room; a sheet of paper; a ruler.

Procedure: (See page 87.) A. Lay the sheet of paper on the table. Turn on the flashlight and put it in the cardboard tube. Hold it directly above the sheet of paper on the table. Sketch the edge of the circle of light that falls on the paper.

B. Then hold the flashlight at an angle so that the beam of light slants to the surface of the paper. See that the flashlight is the same distance from the paper. Again sketch the lighted part of the paper.

How does the amount of surface covered in A compare with the amount in B?

C. Now you have finished the experiment in the dark. Take another sheet of paper. Draw a circle eight inches in diameter. Label it the earth. With the same center draw a circle outside the earth's surface, $8\frac{1}{2}$ inches in diameter. This circle represents the atmosphere around the earth. Very lightly shade in the atmosphere. With a ruler draw a straight line directly down to the earth's surface. Draw another straight line slanting in to the earth's surface. Measure with the ruler. Does the direct ray or the slanting rays go through more of the atmosphere? It warms the air as it goes through and has less heat to give to the

How to do Experiment No. 9

earth's surface. Which ray would have more heat to give the earth's surface?

D. Look back at your results in Experiment No. 9. Compare the length of day in summer with the length of day in winter.

Conclusion: State three reasons why winter is colder than summer.

II. Read the chapter.

III. Test yourself with the following questions:

1. Cover with slips of paper all the explanatory matter about the figure on page 86. For each position tell the following facts: A. Where do the rays of the sun strike the earth most directly? B. What hemisphere has longer days than nights? C. What is the distribution of sunlight? D. What part of the earth has spring? summer? autumn? winter?

2. What makes the change of season? (Make sure you state all the conditions.)

3. State three reasons why rays of the sun that slant to the earth's surface give less heat than rays that strike the surface more directly. Can you demonstrate each of these by experiment or drawing?

4. Why is winter colder than summer?

5. Write a list of the effects upon living things: A. when the most direct rays of the sun move north of the equator; B. when the most direct rays move south of the equator.

IV. Think out the answers to the following questions:

1. By demonstration similar to Experiment No. 9 show why we would have little or no change of seasons if the earth were upright instead of inclined $23\frac{1}{2}$ degrees.

2. Suppose the earth became tilted more than $23\frac{1}{2}$ degrees. How would the seasons be affected?

3. Do the other planets have seasons like the earth?

4. Are there seasons on the stars? (You may want to look back at the chapters on the stars although the questions are not directly answered there.)

5. Suppose the earth's atmosphere were much denser than it is. Possibly that was once so. What effect would it have on the seasons?

V. Vocabulary. Do not forget to collect words for your word list. Do you know just what the following mean?

perpendicular   ultimate

Chapter Thirteen

Finding Your Location and Time

Finding a ship at sea. A ship in distress at sea radios for help, and other ships arrive at its side. How did they find it? The distressed ship gave its position in degrees of latitude and longitude. These degrees located its position exactly.

Suppose you try to tell someone where a spot is on a perfectly smooth, plain, large ball. If you say it is on the side, which side? Where were you when you looked at the ball? How many sides has a ball? If you say it is on the top, suppose someone turns the ball over a little. To overcome the difficulty two sets of guide lines are drawn around the globe. Of course, they must be circles to go around. One circle goes around the earth halfway between the poles. This circle is the *equator.* It is zero degrees of latitude. Circles

drawn parallel to the equator are the parallels of latitude. Intersecting the parallels of latitude are the meridians of longitude. They are drawn from pole to pole and, therefore, cross the parallels of latitude at right angles. One meridian is selected as zero degrees. This is the meridian that goes through Greenwich, England. It is called the *prime* meridian.

One degree, indicated by 1°, is $\frac{1}{360}$ of a circle. A degree is divided into 60 minutes, indicated by 60'. A minute is divided into 60 seconds, indicated 60".

Finding where you are. How does a ship in the middle of the ocean know its latitude and longitude? How can it tell where it is? Let us first see how the latitude is determined. Suppose it is March 21. The sun is directly over the equator. The

Can you describe the position of the dot on the billiard ball? How do parallels and meridians enable you to locate a spot on the globe?

Ewing Galloway, N. Y.

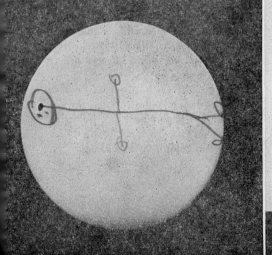

Without visible landmarks how does the cutter at sea meet its convoy at a specified spot? If the fliers on the raft were able to radio their position before they crashed, why are their chances of rescue better?

navigator on a ship at the equator at noon would see the sun directly over his head. If the ship were ten degrees north of the equator, the sun at noon would not be directly overhead but 10° south of the overhead point (called the *zenith*). If the navigator knows the number of degrees the sun is below the point overhead, he knows the latitude in which he sails. If the sun is 15° south of the point overhead, the latitude is 15° north.

It is a little difficult to measure the angle from the sun to the point overhead because you cannot be sure just exactly when you are looking at the point exactly overhead. Therefore, the navigator measures the angle of the sun above the horizon just at noon. The point overhead is 90° above the horizon. Then if the navigator sees the sun south of him at noon and finds that it is 80° above the horizon, he knows that he must be 90° − 80° = 10° North Latitude.

The sun is on the equator only on two dates each year, September 23 and March 21. At other times it is either north or south of the equator. Suppose that the sun is 20° north of the equator. And suppose at noon the navigator finds the altitude of the sun to be 80°. He knows that he is 10° + 20° = 30° North Latitude. The navigator must know the altitude of the noon sun and the sun's position, that is, its latitude. He finds the sun's altitude with his sextant. He learns the sun's latitude from the nautical almanac where its position is given for every day in the year.

Now the navigator must find his longitude. He must know how many degrees he is east or west of the meridian of Greenwich, which is 0° longitude. Suppose it is noon at Greenwich. The earth turns from west to east, and in 24 hours it is again noon at Greenwich. The earth turns 360° in 24 hours. In one hour it turns 360° ÷ 24 = 15°. Now it is noon at Greenwich, and the sun is on the meridian of Greenwich. The sun's longitude is 0°. An hour later it is one o'clock at Greenwich and the noon sun is over the meridian of

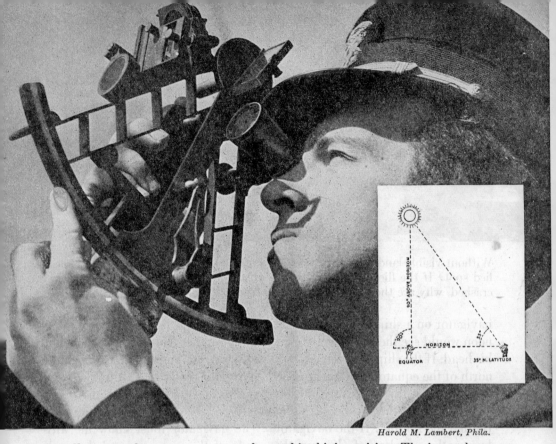

An officer uses the sextant at sea to locate his ship's position. The inset shows how the sextant is used

15° West Longitude. When it is two o'clock at Greenwich, the noon sun is on the meridian of 30° West Longitude. So if at noon on shipboard the navigator knows what time it is at Greenwich, he can tell his longitude. He allows 15° each hour between Greenwich time and his own time. The navigator tells with his sextant when it is noon for he finds when the sun is at its highest point. To tell Greenwich time he carries on his ship a very accurate clock, called a *chronometer*, which always keeps Greenwich time. He has then merely to find when it is noon on his ship, look at his chronometer, and he can tell his longitude. If at noon on his

ship his chronometer tells him Greenwich time is 2 P.M., he knows that he is 2 × 15° or 30° West Longitude. If at noon on his ship his chronometer tells him that it is 9 A.M. in Greenwich, he knows he is east of Greenwich, and that he is 3 × 15° or 45° East Longitude. If his chronometer tells him it is midnight at Greenwich, he is on the opposite side of the earth, 180° longitude. [He is at the International Date Line.] As the date changes at Greenwich, he changes his date, adding a day if he is sailing westward, and subtracting a day if sailing eastward.

Standard time. Suppose that you are in Philadelphia, 75° West

Longitude, at noon. It is long past noon at Greenwich; in fact, it is 5 P.M. (75° ÷ 15° = 5 hours). At St. Louis, 90° West Longitude, it is one hour earlier than in Philadelphia (90° − 75° = 15° = 1 hour) or 11 A.M. At Denver, 105° West Longitude, it is two hours earlier or 10 A.M. At Fresno, California, about 120° West Longitude, it is about 9 A.M. If you know the longitude, you can find the time, and if you know the time, you can find the longitude.

If it is noon in Philadelphia, it is not yet noon in a town 500 miles to the west, nor in a town 100 miles to the west, nor in a town 50 miles to the west. And it is afternoon at every town farther eastward. Suppose each town set its clock at 12 o'clock noon. Suppose you got on a train at Philadelphia (75° West Longitude) at noon and set your watch. Next day in St. Louis when it was noon, your watch would say 1 P.M. You would need to change your watch. If you went to a town 500 miles west of Philadelphia, your watch would not tell you the correct time. Nor at a town 60 miles west. If each town insisted you kept its time, would you not have a fine time keeping time when you traveled!

To avoid this difficulty every town in a belt 15° wide with the 75° meridian in its center keeps the same time. This is Eastern Standard Time. It is the true time of the 75th meridian. The Central Time belt keeps the time of the 90th meridian. Mountain Time uses the time of the 105th, and Pacific Time the 120th. Eastern Canada keeps Atlantic time, which is the time of the 60th meridian.

A world time map. The heavy lines and colored bands indicate actual times kept throughout the world. The plus or minus sign before numbers at the top shows hours to be added to or subtracted from Greenwich time

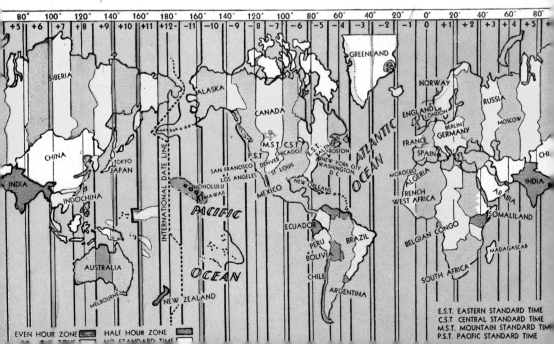

E.S.T. EASTERN STANDARD TIME
C.S.T. CENTRAL STANDARD TIME
M.S.T. MOUNTAIN STANDARD TIM
P.S.T. PACIFIC STANDARD TIME

EVEN HOUR ZONE   HALF HOUR ZONE

How to Learn about Finding Your Location and Time

I. Study latitude and longitude by observation and thought.

1. Get a smooth ball or plain globe without meridians and parallels shown. Put a pencil or chalk mark on the surface. Try to tell someone where you put that mark so that he can put a similar mark on his globe. Then let him turn your globe around, and without looking at it, again tell him where the mark is. Can you tell him?

Now work out two sets of lines so that you could tell the person where the mark is, as you would tell him that a house is at 42d Street and Washington Avenue.

Compare the set of lines that you worked out with the parallels and meridians of the globe. Where is zero degrees of latitude? Where is zero degrees longitude? What are the divisions of degrees?

2. Now turn to the Pacific Ocean and find Wake Island out about the middle of the ocean. Tell exactly where it is so that a ship could go there. Similarly find the latitude and longitude of your town.

3. Try to get the idea of how the navigator learns his latitude. Get a pair of dividers or compass with which to draw circles, and a protractor with which to measure angles. Let the light in the ceiling of your classroom or a spot on the ceiling represent the sun. Suppose it is March 21 and the sun is directly over the equator. Stand right under the sun. Open the dividers and, sighting with your eye at the hinge, point one leg of the dividers at the sun and keep the other leg horizontal as if it were pointed at the distant horizon. Then lay the dividers on the protractor and measure the angle. This angle is the altitude of the noon sun above the horizon.

Now set the dividers at ten degrees. Locate on the ceiling a spot ten degrees north of the "sun." Stand exactly under the spot. You are now standing at ten degrees north latitude on our imaginary ocean. You could not tell that on the ocean until you found it out from the sun. Let us see how you would find out. Again with the dividers measure the angle of the sun above the southern horizon. You will find it 80 degrees. You know then that your ship is $90° - 80°$ or $10°$ North Latitude.

II. Read the chapter.

III. Test yourself with these questions:

1. Why is it necessary to have latitude and longitude?

2. How does the navigator determine his latitude on March 21? To determine his latitude on any date what facts must he know? How does he find them out?

3. How does the navigator determine his longitude?

4. On September 23 if a navigator finds the altitude of the noon sun above the northern horizon is $40°$, what is his latitude? If his chronometer then says 2 P. M., what is his longitude? Look on a map to see where his ship is.

5. Why is Standard Time necessary? If Eastern Standard Time is 8 P. M., what is Pacific Standard Time? Look at the map of the time belts to figure this out, if necessary.

IV. Think out the answers to these questions:

1. In a certain village, if you asked the time, a villager would reply in this manner, "It is half-past nine sun time and nine o'clock standard." Was that village east or west of the meridian of the Standard Time belt?

2. If it is noon on the prime meridian, what time is it at the north pole?

3. How can the explorer tell when he is at the north pole?

V. Vocabulary. Have you remembered your word list? Suggestions:

latitude	prime
longitude	prime meridian
parallels	standard
meridians	Standard Time

Unit Three

Weather and Climate

Does east wind bring rain? Does west wind? Will the coming winter be bad because muskrats build their houses high or because fur is thicker on foxes and rabbits or because geese fly so and so? Have you heard an old man say it would rain because his rheumatism was bad? Have you heard that mare's-tail clouds make tall ships carry short sail? Rainbow in the morning sailor's warning, rainbow at night sailor's delight. There is reason to some of these things but not to others. We shall try to distinguish sense from nonsense by studying what storms are and how they come.

We shall study how the weatherman learns about the weather and how he makes his predictions. We shall study why it rains, hails, snows, and clears. We shall learn what produces fog and mists, dew and frosts. Does it seem queer that ice should fall from the clouds in the hottest part of the year? It does not after you understand what a thunderstorm is. You know that it is colder on the high mountain than in the valley; do you know why it regularly becomes colder in the valley than on the hill? You perhaps have had the experience of driving downhill on a summer evening and finding the valley filled with fog while the hill was clear. Why? We shall find the answers.

(1)(2) Philip D. Gendreau, N. Y., (3) Black Star, N. Y., (4) Ewing Galloway, N. Y.

Chapter Fourteen

Temperature and Weight of the Air

What is weather? By weather you mean warm or cold, cloudy or clear, windy or calm, and various degrees between the extremes. You mean the succession from day to day of these things. You have a general impression of the weather, but for a record of it there must be some ways of measuring the various factors that make it up. Let us see something of the science of measuring its various factors.

How a thermometer measures temperature. If you warm a piece of iron, you know that it expands, or grows bigger. You easily show such expansion in Experiment No. 11. If you warm water, it expands. Perhaps you have seen the full kettle run over when it was heated. You can show the expansion of water on heating by Experiment No. 12. When you heat air, it also expands. You can show it by Experiment No. 13.

By expansion of a metal, a liquid, or a gas, we might measure its rise in temperature. Water would be inconvenient out-of-doors in winter because it would freeze. Air also is inconvenient. Metals and liquids are largely used for measuring rise in temperature. You have seen a thermometer with a dial somewhat like a clock. (Such a thermometer is shown on the opposite page.) The

principle of this instrument is also shown in the pictures opposite. Two strips of different kinds of metal, such as brass and iron, are fastened tightly together. On heating, one metal expands more than the other, and the combined strip bends as indicated. The longer the bar, the more it bends. In the metallic thermometers the compound strip is coiled to allow a greater length without making the instrument too large. The bending is measured by an indicator moving over a scale on which the degrees of temperature are marked.

In most ordinary thermometers a liquid, usually mercury or colored alcohol, is used. The liquid is contained in a thin-bored glass tube with a bulb at the bottom as a reservoir. As the liquid expands, it rises in the tube. As it contracts, the liquid falls toward the bulb. In very cold climates mercury will not do because it freezes at 37° below zero, and temperatures of 40° below are not uncommon in northern United States. Alcohol thermometers may be used for the low temperature as alcohol does not freeze until 179° below zero is reached. Alcohol could not be used to test the temperature of boiling water because alcohol boils at about 173° while water boils at 212°. Mercury does not boil until 675° is reached.

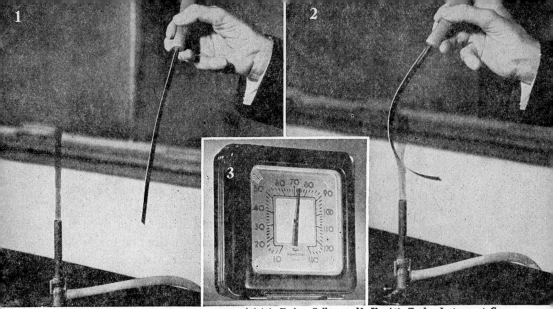

(1)(2) *Ewing Galloway, N. Y.*, (3) *Taylor Instrument Co.*

A straight bar, one side of which is brass and the other iron, bends when subjected to heat. Such is the principle of the thermometer shown(3)

Thermometer scales. We must have some way of measuring how much expansion takes place. We must have a scale. A scale is merely a series of graduations with certain figures to show the values of the graduations. Try to imagine yourself inventing a thermometer scale. Where is zero? How many degrees shall there be? How large shall a degree be? A German scientist, Gabriel D. Fahrenheit (1686–1736), selected the coldest condition that he could get in his laboratory, a mixture of equal parts of snow and ammonium chloride. By thrusting the bulb of the thermometer in such a mixture and marking on the tube the position of the mercury, the zero of the scale could be fixed. Then a high point was selected. Fahrenheit chose the temperature of boiling water and called this 212°. By dividing the tube between 0° and 212° into equal

parts a scale is made. This is the scale we use in our homes in the United States. It is also used by the United States Weather Bureau. When we say water freezes at 32°, we refer to the Fahrenheit scale.

In 1742 Anders Celsius (1701–1744), a scientist of the University of Uppsala, Sweden, made a simpler scale. Celsius chose the freezing point of water as zero and the boiling point of water as 100°. This is the centigrade scale used in all the world, except the United States and the British Empire, and by practically all scientific workers except those of our Weather Bureau.

Changing thermometer scale readings. At first it may seem a little strange if you use centigrade degrees, but they may be easily calculated from Fahrenheit. Look at the picture on the next page. Notice the freezing point of water and the

101

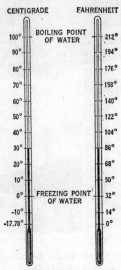

CENTIGRADE FAHRENHEIT

BOILING POINT
OF WATER

100° 212°
90° 194°
80° 176°
70° 158°
60° 140°
50° 122°
40° 104°
30° 86°
20° 68°
10° 50°
0° FREEZING POINT 32°
OF WATER
-10° 14°
-17.78° 0°

Comparison of centigrade and Fahrenheit scales

boiling point of water. The difference between the two points is 100° on the centigrade scale and 180° on the Fahrenheit scale (212 − 32 = 180°).

100 centigrade degrees = 180 Fahrenheit degrees

1 centigrade degree = 180 ÷ 100 or $\frac{9}{5}$ Fahrenheit degrees

180 Fahrenheit degrees = 100 centigrade degrees

1 Fahrenheit degree = 100 ÷ 180 or $\frac{5}{9}$ centigrade degree

Suppose the temperature is 30° C. What is it Fahrenheit? One centigrade degree = $\frac{9}{5}$ Fahrenheit degrees.

Thirty centigrade degrees = 30 × $\frac{9}{5}$ or 54 degrees Fahrenheit above the freezing point of water. (Look at the picture.) The freezing point of water is 32° F. Therefore, to find how many Fahrenheit degrees above

Fahrenheit zero we add 32°. (Look at the picture.) 54 + 32 = 86. Then 30° C. = 86° F.

Heated air rises. Make some observations. Hold a light ribbon of tissue paper or a smoking punk stick above a heated radiator. You will notice that the heated air is rising. If you hold it below an open window, you will notice that the cold air falls as it enters the room. Explore the room, floors, ceiling, and walls to locate the gentle air currents.

Why heated air rises. Cold air falls because it is heavier than warmer air. If you warm some of the air, it expands and becomes lighter. Colder air then floats it up as water poured into a basin floats up a cork. Therefore, heating the air in different parts of the room produces air currents as the colder air flows in under the warmer air. Similarly, when the sun heats one part of the earth more than another, currents of air or winds are produced. The region around the equator is heated most. Therefore, the air flows in toward the equator. When the land warms up in the daytime, the air moves in from the cooler sea. When the sun goes down and the air cools on the mountain, the cold air flows into the valley as a cool wind. You can often notice the cool air coming down from hills at dusk in summer.

Measuring the weight of the air. To understand the winds we need, therefore, some method of measuring the weight or downward pressure of the air. The Weather

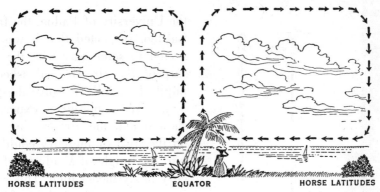

HORSE LATITUDES   EQUATOR   HORSE LATITUDES

How the trade winds blow

Bureau makes such measurements constantly. Aviators and mountain climbers make them. Scientists in their laboratories make them.

Air weighs something, as you know if you have picked up a hard automobile tire and a flat tire. The weight of all the air above the earth's surface is on the land and sea. We do not know how high up the air goes. Air was found at a height of fourteen miles—the highest point reached by man—by observers in the sealed gondola of a balloon. Perhaps the air reaches three or four hundred miles but it must be exceedingly thin at that height.

You can easily measure the pressure of the air. Get a glass tube closed at one end and about a yard long and less than a half inch in diameter. The diameter is not important. Fill the tube with mercury, cover it with the thumb, and invert it in a dish of mercury. The mercury in the tube will fall until it stands at just about thirty inches. This experiment was tried by Torricelli (pronounced tôr′rê-chĕl′lê), an Italian scientist who lived in the seventeenth century (1608–1647). Torricelli was trying to find why a pump could not suck up water more than thirty-three feet. His teacher at

Why does the smoke from chimneys rise? How does this picture help to explain the diagram above?

Philip D. Gendreau, N. Y.

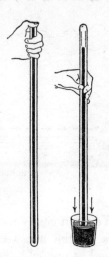

the University of Padua, the famed Galileo, suspected that it was connected in some way with the pressure of the air. He had asked his pupil, Torricelli, to solve the problem. The mercury experiment showed that the air pressing down on the dish of mercury could support the weight of a column of mercury thirty inches high. This weight is the same as the weight of a column of water thirty-four feet high. If the end area of the tube is one square inch, the weight of the liquid in it is about fifteen pounds; that is,

(1) A Torricellian barometer with its principle shown in the drawing
(2) An aneroid barometer. Through the opening may be seen the compressible metal box

(1) Philip D. Gendreau, (2) Ewing Galloway

1

2

the pressure of the air is fifteen pounds to the square inch.

The tube of mercury inverted in a dish of mercury is a *barometer* (from Greek meaning "weight measurer"). On page 104 (1) we see a form of mercury barometer often used in the laboratory. In another type of barometer the weight of the air is balanced against a metal box from which the air has been pumped. The sides of the box are dented in to a certain extent by the pressure of the air. A lever and an indicator measure the amount of pressure. This box is called an *aneroid barometer* (meaning "not liquid form"). The aneroid is more easily carried about than the mercurial barometer. It is the type used by aviators and mountain climbers. A pen may be attached to the arm of the aneroid, and a revolving drum carry a paper under the pen. This is then a recording barometer, called a *barograph* (meaning "weight writing"), pictured above, which keeps a record of changing air pressure.

Torricelli showed that the pressure of air is equal to the pressure of about thirty inches of mercury. For convenience we say that the air pressure is thirty inches. Pascal (päs"kål'), a French scientist (1623–1662), reasoned that on the

United Airlines

A portable barograph. Such instruments keep a record of air pressure

top of a mountain the pressure should be less and the mercury should stand lower in the tube. He had a mercurial barometer carried to the top of a mountain and showed that the mercury fell in the tube with the increased altitude.

By this series of experiments we learned the pressure of the atmosphere and how to measure it. We still use the mercurial barometer invented by Torricelli 300 years ago. We say that the atmospheric pressure is about thirty inches, as he found. We also say the pressure of the atmosphere is fifteen pounds to the square inch. The Weather Bureau reports the pressure in millibars and in inches. The average pressure at sea level is 1013 millibars or 29.9 inches.

How to Learn about the Temperature and Weight of Air

I. Study by experiment the measurement of air pressure and temperature.

1. EXPERIMENT No. 11. How does moderate heating affect a piece of iron? Arrange the apparatus as shown in the diagram on page 106. Have the iron weight just grazing but not touching the bottom of the stand. Start it swinging gently. Heat the wire. Write a report and make a diagram of the apparatus.

105

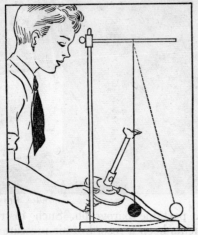

Apparatus for Experiment No. 11

2. Experiment No. 12. Does water expand when heated? Arrange as shown in the diagram. Heat the flask gently. Write the report in the required form. Draw the apparatus.

3. Experiment No. 13. Does air expand when heated? Heat the flask gently as shown. Then stop heating and watch the water in the tube as the flask cools. Write report. Draw the apparatus.

4. Experiment No. 14. How is the principle learned in the last three experiments used in the thermometer? Hold the bulb of a thermometer in the fist and watch the column of mercury. Then cool it by running water on the bulb. Watch the mercury. Write a report as required.

5. Experiment No. 15. What are the boiling and freezing points on a thermometer scale? Place a thermometer with a Fahrenheit scale and one with a centigrade scale in cracked ice. Read the thermometers. The melting point of ice and the freezing point of water are the same. Suspend the thermometers in boiling water as shown. Note the readings in your notebook. Make a report.

6. Experiment No. 16. Does warm air weigh the same as cold air? Place a piece of asbestos on the pan of a balance and on it place a large uncorked flask. Balance the flask with weights or sand. Remove the flask and make it very hot. Then return it to the balance. Write a report in the usual form. Unless the flask is large and the balance delicate, this experiment may fail.

7. Experiment No. 17. How is the pressure of the atmosphere measured? Take a glass tube closed at one end, one-half inch or less in diameter and thirty-two inches or more in length. The diameter is not important, but the length must be more than thirty inches. Fill the tube with mercury, close it with the thumb, and invert it in a bowl of mercury. Support the tube upright and measure the height of the column of mercury very accurately from the top of the mercury in the bowl. (See page 104.) Write a report as required. Draw the apparatus. This is a mercurial barometer. Keep a record of the readings of the height of the mercury every day for a week.

II. Read the chapter.

III. Test yourself with these questions: **1.** What effect of heat enables us to measure changes of temperature? Tell of two experiments by which you showed effects of heat in different substances.

Apparatus for Experiment No. 12

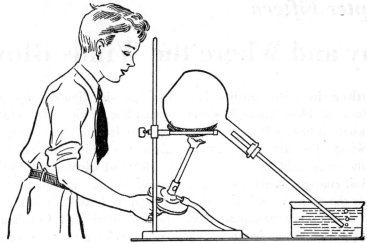

Apparatus for Experiment No. 13

2. What are the boiling and freezing points of water on the Fahrenheit and centigrade scales?

3. If the temperature is 60° centigrade, what is it Fahrenheit?

4. If the temperature is 50° Fahrenheit, what is it centigrade?

5. What happens to air, water, and iron when they are heated?

6. Suppose the air is heated in one part of a room and not in another. What happens to the air in the room? Why?

7. Does the air move as winds toward the equator or away from the equator? Why?

8. How can you show that air weighs something?

9. How is the pressure of the atmosphere measured?

10. What is meant by saying that the pressure is thirty inches? What is the pressure in pounds per square inch?

IV. Think out the answers to these questions:

1. Devise an experiment to answer the question: Does water get hotter with continued boiling?

2. Think of the action of the air in a room when it is heated or cooled and answer the following question: In winter when the air above a lake gets very cold, are there currents of water set up in the lake similar to the air currents set up in a room? Devise an experiment that will test the answer that you reasoned out.

V. Vocabulary. Suggestions:

barometer   aneroid

Fahrenheit   centigrade

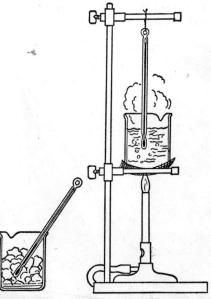

Apparatus for Experiment No. 15

Chapter Fifteen

Why and Where the Winds Blow

Whither the wind blows. The wind does not blow where it wants to but where it has to. It has to blow from where the air is heavy to where the air is light, as we learned in the last chapter. Wind, therefore, is simply the air moving. If the air is heavier in one place than in another, the heavier air moves in under the lighter air as water moves under a cork in a basin. There are certain places on the surface of the earth where it is light and certain places where it is heavy. We call the places where the air is heavy *high-pressure areas* because the barometer stands high. We call the areas where

The wind is a body of air in motion and has force behind it

the air is lighter, *low-pressure areas.* The air moves from high-pressure to low-pressure areas. If the air moves rapidly, we call it *wind*.

Belts of high and of low pressure. Around the equator the air is constantly heated. It is lighter than farther north or south. The cooler and heavier air moves in as wind toward the equator and lifts up the lighter air. The incoming air, of course, is also gradually heated. There is thus a constant flow of air toward the equator and a belt around the equator of lighter rising air, *the equatorial low.* The heated air rises until it cools at high altitudes. It reaches a height beyond which it cannot rise and then flows north and south.

This high cold air descends to the surface of the earth again. The belts where it comes down are belts of high pressure about 30 degrees north and south of the equator, *the subtropical highs.* From this belt of high pressure the wind blows again toward the equator. At the north and south poles are areas of intensely cold air and high pressure, *the polar highs.*

How the earth turns the winds. The wind cannot blow straight on the earth. It may seem to for a short distance but if the course of the wind is mapped through long distances, a thousand miles or so, the course is not straight. Let us see why. Suppose you are sitting in a car by the side of the road on a calm day when no wind is blowing. When the car starts along the road, the air seems to move past you from directly in front. You might say there is a wind from directly in front. Suppose again you are sitting in the car by the side of the road and there is a strong wind coming directly from the right. When the car starts and moves briskly along, the wind seems to come from a direction halfway between front and side, that is, obliquely from the right front.

If the earth were standing still, the wind moving in from the north and from the south toward the equator would seem to come directly from the north and directly from the south. But as the earth rotates from west to east, the winds are deflected. North of the equator the winds come from the northeast and south of the equator from the southeast. These two belts of winds are the *northeast*

Wind belts of the world

trades and the *southeast trades*. The belt of rising air at the equator, the equatorial low, is the belt of calms which the sailors called the *doldrums*. The belts where the colder heavier air descends, the subtropical highs, are also belts of calms called by the sailors the *horse latitudes*. It is said when sailing ships, carrying horses to Australia, were becalmed, the horses were thrown overboard because of lack of water.

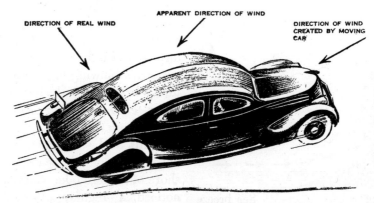

A side wind seems to come obliquely from the front when the car moves

Michigan Dept. of Conservation

The breeze blows off the water during the day because the land heats up rapidly

Evening   Land breeze

Morning   Sea breeze

Diagram showing land and sea breezes

In the parts of the earth between the horse latitudes and the poles, the wind is more variable than in the trade belts. From the subtropical highs the wind blows generally toward the poles. Because of the rotation of the earth, however, it is deflected and seems to come generally from a westerly direction. These westerly winds are often upset by storms so that the belts are called the *stormy westerlies*. Beyond the westerlies toward the poles are the *polar easterlies* blowing toward the equator. Where the westerlies meet the polar easterlies, our storms are stirred up.

Land and sea breezes. If you have lived along the sea or along the shore of a large lake, you may have noticed a regular alternation of breeze from the water and breeze

Ewing Galloway, N. Y.

When a hurricane strikes, winds do considerable damage

from the land. Except when they are upset by storms, sea breezes and land breezes are remarkably regular, as regular as the sun. They are caused by the sun shining on the land and on the sea. To understand the regularity we must study a little further what things do when they are heated.

If you put a pound block of iron and a pound of water side by side on the stove, the iron would heat to 100° before the water. If you used a pound of rock, a pound of sand, a pound of dust, and a pound of water, the water would take longest to reach 100°. It takes longer to raise the temperature of water than of any other substance known. Water must absorb more heat before its temperature will rise 100° or even 1°.

When the sun comes up and shines on the land and on the sea, the temperature of the land rises faster than the temperature of the water. The land is warm or hot while the sea is still cool. The sea and the land warm the air lying on them. The air resting on the land becomes warm while the air above the sea is still cool. The air over the land expands and becomes lighter. The air over the sea is cooler and, therefore, heavier. The sea air then moves in to the land as a sea breeze.

If you heated a pound of iron or rock or sand and a pound of water to 100° and moved them from the stove, the water would cool more slowly than the other substances. Water heats and cools more slowly.

When the sun goes down, the land and the sea give up their heat to the

111

A twister forms at sea

air. The land cools more quickly than the sea. Then in the evening the air is cooler and heavier over the land than over the sea. The air, therefore, moves out from the land to the sea as a land breeze.

How sea and land affect climate. Water must absorb more heat than land to rise in temperature one degree. At night and in winter the air becomes cool, and the water and the land give up heat to the air. The water has more heat to give up. Therefore, the air above the water is warmed for a longer time by the heat of the water. When the breeze comes in from the sea to the neighboring lands, it is warmer in winter. Land along the sea is warmed by this heat of the sea. The

climate of seacoasts does not have as low winter temperatures as the interior of large continents. This is also true along large lakes. A great fruit region lies along the Great Lakes where the temperature of the air is raised by the heat liberated from the lake water in fall and winter. In summer the land heats up more rapidly than the sea, and the sea takes from the air some of its heat. The sea in spring and summer, therefore, has a cooling effect upon the land near by. Thus the sea serves to modify the climate both winter and summer.

Whirlwinds. You have heard of the "twisters" or *tornadoes*. Perhaps you have seen them. In the hot season they sometimes tear through parts of our country, destroying trees, farms, and houses. Their paths are not wide, usually not much over a hundred yards, but within that path the wind may reach a velocity of two or three hundred miles an hour. In the eye of the storm the pressure is very low. Therefore, the wind around about rushes in with great, terrific violence. The wind is so violent that its speed has not been measured. Instruments would be smashed to pieces. It is estimated that it may reach five hundred miles an hour. An ordinary breeze may be five miles an hour. A fifty-mile wind uproots trees and an eighty-mile wind picks a man off his feet. The whirling winds of the tornado may level everything in its path.

112

The tornado is sometimes mistakenly called a *cyclone*, but it must not be confused with the true or cyclonic storm (the ordinary storm), which we shall study presently in Chapter Eighteen.

How to Learn Why and Where the Winds Blow

I. Experiment and apply your findings.

1. EXPERIMENT No. 18. Which warms and cools faster—iron, soil, or water? Place an iron plate on a retort stand. On the iron plate place the three cans containing a pound of water, a pound of iron, and a pound of soil. In each place a thermometer. Heat to 212° F. Record the time taken by each substance to reach the required temperature. Record also the time taken to cool again to the temperature of the room. Write a report in the required form.

2. With the results of the last experiment in mind, think out the answers to the following questions: When the sun rises in the morning, which warms faster, land or sea? What will happen to the air above each? What motion of air will take place between them? When the sun sets, which will cool more rapidly? What effect will the difference have upon the temperature of the air above them and upon the movement of the air?

II. Read the chapter and study the diagrams carefully.

III. Test yourself with the following questions:

1. What is meant by high-pressure and by low-pressure areas?

2. What relations have the pressure areas to the winds?

3. Where are the low-pressure and high-pressure belts of the earth? How do the winds blow between them? Quickly draw a diagram showing the belts and the winds.

4. Explain why the winds do not blow straight into the low areas but blow obliquely.

5. What kind of weather do they have at the low and high belts? in the trade winds? Why?

6. What are land and sea breezes? Why and when do they blow?

7. Why is climate along the coast milder than climate in the interior of continents?

IV. Think out the answers to these questions:

1. The greatest extension of the American continents is north and south. Suppose it were east and west, how would the climate be affected?

2. Why do east coasts usually have more severe climates than west coasts of continents?

3. In ages long, long past there were no high mountains along the west coasts of America. When the mountains arose, how was the climate changed?

V. Vocabulary. Did you make any additions?

tornado   cyclone

Chapter Sixteen

Water in the Air

Showing water in the air. You have seen an ice-water pitcher "sweat," and if you wear glasses, you have gone indoors on a cold winter day and found your glasses covered with a cloud. The "sweat" on the ice-water pitcher does not come from the water in the pitcher, but from the air of the room. The cloud on your eyeglasses also comes from the air of the room. If you set an empty pitcher in the refrigerator until it is thoroughly chilled and then bring it into the warm room, it will sweat, or cloud over.

You know that air holds water. If you put the kettle on the stove and forget it while you have a long chat over the telephone or dig in the garden, you may find the kettle boiled dry. The water all went into the air. The sun also is constantly warming the sea, the lakes, the streams, and the wet ground, and their water is passing into the air.

When you look across a room or across a field, you do not see the water in the air, yet with a cold glass you can show that water is there. The invisible water in the air is *water vapor*. The liquid has evap-orated. You make the water visible again with the cold-water pitcher or a cold glass. On the cold surface the water vapor *condenses* to liquid water again.

When the air contains all the water vapor that it can hold, it is said to be *saturated*. On damp days, wet clothes dry slowly on the line. The air is so nearly saturated that it takes up water vapor slowly.

You have probably gone into the kitchen when the air was filled with steam and found little streams of water running down the walls and windowpanes. When the air becomes saturated, no more water will pass into the air, and water will readily condense and come out of the air.

Heat and water vapor. If the sun falls on the wash on the clothes-line, it dries out more quickly than if it were in the shade. Water evapo-rates more quickly from a pan on the stove than from a pan on the window sill. Warming the water makes it evaporate more readily. Water takes up heat in becoming a vapor. When you fan your sweating face, it feels cool. That is because the evaporating water takes heat

(Top) *Philip D. Gendreau, N. Y.*, (Middle and Bottom) *Ewing Galloway, N. Y.*

(Top) Why are mountain peaks often surrounded by clouds? (Middle) A typi-cal cumulus cloud that forms on a summer day. (Bottom) Why does fog often appear in valleys when higher ground is clear?

114

Philip D. Gendreau, N. Y.   *Black Star, N. Y.*

The sun raises the temperature, and the moisture evaporates from the clothes into the warm air. The cold water lowers the temperature of the pitcher, and the moisture of the air in contact with it condenses into drops

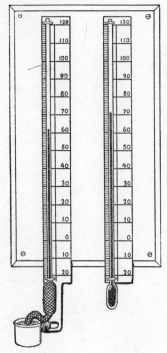

A hygrometer

from your face. The wet bathing suit or the wet shirt feels cool because the evaporating water takes heat from your body. Evaporation cools things.

Keep these two principles in mind as we proceed: First, water takes up heat when it evaporates. Second, when air cools, or loses heat, water vapor condenses.

Measuring the water in the air. The water vapor in the air is *humidity*. When the weatherman measures the humidity, he uses the principle we have just studied, that evaporation cools. He does not really measure the amount of moisture at all. He measures the temperature produced by evaporation. The instrument for showing the water vapor in the air, or humidity, is called a *hygrometer*. It has two ther-

116

TABLE SHOWING RELATIVE HUMIDITY

DIFFERENCE BETWEEN DRY- AND WET-BULB THERMOMETERS

DRY THERMOMETER. ° F.	1°	2°	3°	4°	5°	6°	7°	8°	9°	10°	11°	12°	13°	14°	15°
50	93	87	81	74	68	62	56	50	44	39	33	28	22	17	12
52	94	88	81	75	69	63	58	52	46	41	36	30	25	20	15
54	94	88	82	76	70	65	59	54	48	43	38	33	28	23	18
56	94	88	82	77	71	66	61	55	50	45	40	35	31	26	21
58	94	89	83	77	72	67	62	57	52	47	42	38	33	28	24
60	94	89	84	78	73	68	63	58	53	49	44	40	35	31	27
62	94	89	84	79	74	69	64	60	55	50	46	41	37	33	29
64	95	90	85	79	75	70	66	61	56	52	48	43	39	35	31
66	95	90	85	80	76	71	66	62	58	53	49	45	41	37	33
68	95	90	85	81	76	72	67	63	59	55	51	47	43	39	35
70	95	90	86	81	77	72	68	64	60	56	52	48	44	40	37
72	95	91	86	82	78	73	69	65	61	57	53	49	46	42	39
74	95	91	86	82	78	74	70	66	62	58	54	51	47	44	40
76	96	91	87	83	78	74	70	67	63	59	55	52	48	45	42
78	96	91	87	83	79	75	71	67	64	60	57	53	50	46	43
80	96	91	87	83	79	76	72	68	64	61	57	54	51	47	44
84	96	92	88	84	80	77	73	70	66	63	59	56	53	50	47
88	96	92	88	85	81	78	74	71	67	64	61	58	55	52	49
90	96	92	89	85	82	78	75	72	68	64	62	58	56	53	50

mometers, one of which is covered with a wick and is kept wet by the water in the bulb below it. Water constantly evaporates from the wick. This evaporation lowers the temperature, and the wet-bulb thermometer falls. The second thermometer shows the temperature of the air. If there is little moisture in the air, evaporation will be rapid, and the wet bulb will indicate a lower temperature than will the dry bulb. By looking at tables which have been worked out, the weatherman can find the humidity from the two temperature readings.

The humidity is reported as *relative humidity*. This does not tell us just how much water vapor is in the air but the per cent of saturation when the temperature was read. Thus when you see in the weather report in the paper that the humidity is 60, it means relative humidity. The air contained 60 per cent of the moisture necessary to saturate it at that temperature. At a lower temperature the air could not hold so much water vapor and at a higher temperature it could hold more.

The relative humidity at any time may be readily determined from the figures given in the table at the top of this page.

When water comes out of the air. If you have tramped through

Smoke and dust from factories fill the air with particles around which moisture can easily condense into tiny droplets to form fog

the grass on a summer evening, you have no doubt had your shoes wet with *dew*. When the sun goes down, the grass cools off rapidly. Then the air next to it is chilled, and the water vapor condenses on the grass as it does on the ice-water pitcher and the cold spectacles or the cold wind-shield of a car. If the temperature falls below freezing in the early spring or autumn, the vapor turns directly to ice and produces a *frost*.

When the wind blows over the mountain, it is cooled. It may be cooled so far that its moisture condenses into droplets. If the droplets are very fine, they may float as a *fog* or *cloud*. If they grow large, they may fall as rain. In mountainous countries you often see a cloud around the top of the mountain, or you may see the dark rain clouds on the mountain when the sun shines in the lowland. The air on the mountain has been chilled to the temperature where its vapor has condensed.

Anything that cools the air low enough may produce clouds, fog, or rain. When cold air along the coast meets warm air, the vapor of the warm air may be condensed as fog or rain. In summer when the air gets very warm and rises rapidly, it may go so high that its vapor is condensed into clouds. You can see such clouds on almost any summer afternoon. Perhaps you have had the experience of driving through a fog in an automobile when the sun went down. The air was cooled until its vapor condensed. Often you notice the fog in the valleys but not on the

118

hills. As the air cools after sunset, the cool air flows down from the hills into the valleys. The valley air may be cooled so far that its moisture condenses to form a fog while the warmer air in the hills is still clear.

If the droplets of water are very fine, they float in the air, but if they continually grow larger they become too heavy to float and fall as *rain*. If the temperature of the air is below freezing when condensation occurs, crystals of ice are formed. They may float in the air if they are very tiny crystals. Some of the very high bright clouds that you see on a summer day are clouds of ice crystals. If the crystals grow, they may become too heavy for the air to support and they fall as *snow*.

If raindrops freeze, they may fall as *sleet*. Hail also is frozen drops but formed in a more complicated way. If you cut through a hail ball, you will find that it shows layers of ice.

Hail usually falls in summertime and usually with a thunderstorm. You know that there may be very violent winds with a thunderstorm. There are also violent winds rushing straight upward from the earth. The violent uprush of the air may carry drops of water so high that they freeze. As they fall again, the water may collect on the pellets of ice, and the uprush of winds may again carry them up so high that the water freezes to form a new layer of ice. This may happen again and again so that many layers of ice make up the hailstone.

The condensation from water vapor to water in the air is called *precipitation*. Dust increases the ease of precipitation. Fogs are often heavy over the dusty cities, where smoke particles form centers around which water condenses.

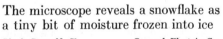

The microscope reveals a snowflake as a tiny bit of moisture frozen into ice

Black Star, N. Y.   *General Electric Co.*

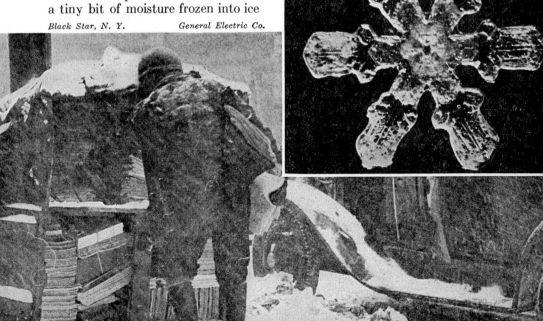

How to Learn about Water in the Air

I. Study by experiment the water vapor of the air.

1. EXPERIMENT No. 19. How can you show that there is water vapor in the air when you cannot see it? Place water and cracked ice in a glass. Observe what occurs on the outside of the glass. If you think that the watery mist came through the glass from the inside, devise an experiment to show that it did not. Call it EXPERIMENT No. 20. If you have a refrigerator, you can show it very quickly by chilling the glass in the refrigerator without using water. Write a report.

2. EXPERIMENT No. 21. How does evaporation affect temperature?

Directions and observations: Wrap cotton or cloth around the bulb of a thermometer and soak it with water. Swing the thermometer in the air until the cloth or cotton is almost or quite dry. Read this thermometer and one that has been standing in the room. Write a report.

3. EXPERIMENT No. 22. How to make a hygrometer to measure the humidity (water vapor) of the air. Study the hygrometer on page 115 and build one similar. Read the wet and the dry bulb and determine the humidity from the table on page 116. Determine the humidity in your classroom, in your living room, and out-of-doors. Keep a record of outdoor humidity for one month on your daily weather report.

4. EXPERIMENT No. 23. How does snow form? Put some "dry ice," solid carbon dioxide, in a beaker and allow to stand in the room. Note what forms on the outside of the glass. Write a report in the usual form. Caution: Do not touch the dry ice with the hands. It is so intensely cold that it will quickly freeze and destroy the flesh, causing a painful frostbite.

5. When it snows, examine snowflakes under a lens or microscope. You will need to take the microscope out-of-doors or catch a snowflake on an iron plate or cold plate that has been kept outdoors and quickly examine it indoors.

II. Read the chapter.

III. Test yourself by answering the following questions:

1. Can you see water vapor? How can you show that it is present in the air? What term do we use to indicate that the air contains all the water vapor it can hold? What determines how much water vapor may be present in the air at any time?

2. What effect has evaporation upon temperature? Why? How can this principle be used to indicate the humidity of the air?

3. Why does dew form? When does frost form?

4. Why may there be clouds on the mountaintop when the sun is shining in the valley? Why may there be fog in the valley when the sun shines on the hilltop?

5. What is the relative humidity when it rains?

6. What is snow? In what season of the year is hail most common? Why?

IV. Think out the answers to these questions:

1. Why do you feel warm on a humid day in summer? Why do you feel cold on a humid day in winter?

2. Why are rocks dry on a summer evening when the grass is covered with dew?

3. Why is it so often foggy on the Grand Banks off Newfoundland?

V. Vocabulary. The following are suggested:

vapor	evaporation
saturated	relative
condense	relative humidity
humidity	precipitation
	hygrometer

Chapter Seventeen

What Makes a Thunderstorm

The beauty of the storm. Nothing is more glorious in nature than the coming of a thunderstorm. Watch the thunderheads almost any summer afternoon. They are the great white rolls of clouds that pile up in the sky. The weatherman calls them *cumulus* clouds. They stand above the earth in the clear summer sky, broad at the base and narrowing upward in big loose pyramids of pure white wool rounded at the top where their gleaming white shines out against the bright blue sky. Usually thunderheads begin to form late in the morning and gather until midafternoon. Then they may slowly dissolve, leaving the purest blue in the late afternoon sky.

These beautiful clouds tell a tale to those who can read the signs of nature. When the sun warms the earth on a summer day, the air rises in gentle upward flowing surges. As the air reaches the upper, thinner heights, it spreads out and cools. As it cools, the water vapor that it brought up is condensed into droplets that float in the rising air. The droplets form the cloud that reflects the bright sunlight and looks like a great pure white mass of fluffy rolls. You will notice that the base is generally broad and flat, marking the level where the rising air spreads out. The stronger uprising currents rise higher, and the cloud grows with the day and the warming sun. In later afternoon as the sun sinks low, the land cools, the uprising of air slows, and the water droplets of the cloud evaporate and leave the sky clear.

Sometimes, however, the story is different in its ending. The uprush of the air is so great and the burden of water vapor is so heavy that the cloud grows larger, higher, and lower. It drifts toward us. We can see the dark underside where the sun cannot reach it, and above we see the shining bright reflection of the summer sun. Onward toward us the cloud comes. It drifts over us, and the sun is shut from our part of the sky. The great cloud of water drops is too dense for the sun to penetrate; the light fades, and it gets very dark about us. The summer day's gentle breeze suddenly stops. It is very still. The air seems hot and heavy. We expect something to happen. So do the birds. They stop singing and loiter near the trees and bushes. We make our way to shelter.

Then a great dust cloud comes tearing across the field and down the road. It strikes us and sweeps by, and a clear cold wind follows. Then the wind may slacken. An interval of calm and silence comes, and a few drops. A few minutes more and down comes the deluge. A moment in the

121

downpour would soak one's clothes. The branches bend low under the falling weight; the gutters and ditches rise in floods. Sudden brooks tumble down the banks, and floods of mud pour out from the plowed fields and across the roads. Delicious coolness wells around us. Meanwhile the gorgeous lightning flashes spring from cloud to cloud and occasionally to the ground by way of a tree. The thunder crashes and rolls in descending scale like the lower end of a vast piano scale but more grand and inspiring. Gradually the lightning passes on with its thunder and becomes faint in the distance. Only the downpour of the rain is near at hand. It, too, slackens after a short time, then stops. The drip of the rain from the trees and the rustle of the cool breeze furnish the final music for the great drama. The cloud moves on, and the sun brightens the earth again. A robin pours forth his joyous song. A gentle after-shower may come and quickly pass on; then all is clean, bright, and cool.

The science of the thunderstorm. Now let us add science to this fascinating drama of nature. On hot days the rocks and soil become very hot. The air above them, too, becomes heated. Its weight and pressure is lowered. The air from places not so hot flows in and raises the hot air. As the warm, moist air spreads out and cools, its vapor condenses into droplets of water. The upward movement of the air may become a violent upward rush, a great, strong wind blowing straight upward. The drops of rain that grew from the droplets of condensed vapor are carried higher and higher. So violent is the upward rush of the wind that the big drops cannot fall, or they fall only to be carried aloft again. They circle upward and downward through the cloud. They may be carried so high that ice forms, and rising and falling layer after layer of ice gathers around the hailstone.

The cause of lightning and thunder is a little difficult to understand. It was an English meteorologist

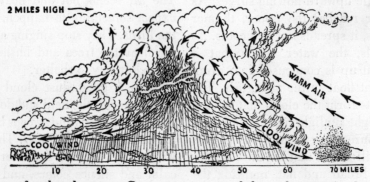

2 MILES HIGH

WARM AIR

COOL WIND   COOL WIND

10   20   30   40   50   60   70 MILES

Diagram of a thunderstorm. Can you see some of these elements in the picture on the opposite page?

Photo by Ewing Galloway, N. Y.

(weatherman) who, experimenting in the laboratory, discovered the secret. He discovered that when he turned a blast of air against drops of water and broke them to pieces, electricity was generated. The broken drops became positively charged with electricity while the damp air around them became negatively charged. In the thunderstorm the drops of rain are similarly broken by blasts of air, and electricity is generated. The violent upward rush of air separates the charges. Positive and negative charges accumulate in different parts of the great clouds. A highly charged cloud moving above the ground with its buildings and trees induces an opposite charge on the ground. When the difference becomes great enough, the electricity leaps across the gap, and we see a flash of lightning. Sometimes the discharge is between the cloud and the ground. The thunder is violent vibrations of air hurled aside as the charge darts through.

Hailstones did this damage

Black Star, N. Y.

The delicious, cool wind comes from the high places where the air is cool. The violence of the wind is due to the great differences of temperature that produce the thunderstorm.

Thunderstorms are local storms; that is, they occur over one locality. They do not, like our great two- or three-day storms, extend over a thousand miles or more. A thunderstorm may be ten to twenty-five miles broad and sometimes is so sharply limited that rain may fall on one side of the street but not on the other. The storm may be a hundred miles long, but often is only a few miles long. The thunderstorm may travel for a hundred miles or more or it may die out before it has gone so far, while other storms, our usual "cyclonic" storms, may travel thousands of miles. Thunderstorms may extend upward into the air five miles or they may be only a mile or two high. Thunderstorms often move across the country at rates of twenty to fifty miles an hour. Sometimes an automobile traveling along a straight road keeps just in front of the storm.

The danger of lightning. Lightning is much less dangerous than automobiles. Certainly the flash that you see will do you no harm. The electricity made its jump before you saw it. Lightning occasionally strikes a house or barn and may set it afire. It sometimes strikes a tree in the woods and starts a forest fire. A tree standing alone is a little more likely to be struck. It is just as well not to take refuge under the lone tree.

Ewing Galloway, N. Y.

Lightning rods may be helpful. It is thought that the projecting points prevent the accumulation of heavy charges of electricity that might discharge to the ground by way of the house. Should lightning strike, the rods insulated from the house might lead the charge into the moist ground. There is no agreement as to their actual value.

The land of the big thunderstorms. Thunderstorms are especially common in the great belt of hot calms around the equator. The great heat causes rising of the air which brings the heavy rains of this belt. The belt of calms at the horse latitudes, on the other hand, are belts of clear weather. There the air is descending toward the earth. It is warmed as it descends and then causes evaporation rather than condensation. The trade winds, blowing from horse latitudes into the warmer doldrums, are warmed as they go and so evaporate water. Where the trade winds rise over high moun-

Lightning is really a series of giant sparks

tains, however, they may be chilled and give abundant rain.

The whole system of trade winds, doldrums, and horse latitudes shifts north with the sun and south with the sun. This sends the rainy belt twice a year across the equator and produces two rainy seasons. Farther north and farther south, near the limit of the wanderings of the doldrums, there is one rainy season a year.

How to Learn What Makes a Thunderstorm

I. Read the chapter.

II. Observe thunderstorms.

1. In your next thunderstorm write down a list of the phenomena (happenings) that you see. How far do they agree with the description in this chapter? You may find a difference.

2. Look for thunderheads on clear days, both in summer and winter.

III. Test yourself with these questions:

1. In what season of the year are thunderstorms most common? Why?

2. In what time of day are they most common? Why?

3. What makes the thunder? What makes the dark cloud? Why is the blast of wind cold before the thunderstorm? Why is it so violent?

4. Why does hail frequently accompany a thunderstorm?

IV. Think out the answers to the following questions:

1. Why are thunderstorms rare in winter?

2. Why are thunderstorms rare before noon?

V. Vocabulary. Did you find any new words to add?

125

Chapter Eighteen

Foretelling the Weather

How the weatherman knows. Storms are not strange and mysterious acts of nature that we cannot hope to understand. They are governed by laws of nature that we are learning. The weatherman knows when to expect storms, and he follows them on weather maps across continents and over the seas. He foretells fair weather and storms. He knows the seasons of the terrific tropic hurricanes that bring thirty-foot seas over the land. When a hurricane develops, he locates it on the map, calculates its path, and warns

Balloons rising to great heights radio back weather information

General Electric Co.

people of the seacoast in ample time for them to seek safety inland or away from the storm's path. Ships at sea receive radio warning in time to alter their courses to avoid the worst of the storm area.

Air pilots search the weather maps for location of fair weather and foul, pressure, temperature, dew point, danger of icing, winds, clouds, ceilings, fog, and landing conditions. Weather may decide life or death. The army and the navy are intensely interested in weather. Troop movements and supplies, air support, success or failure of bomber raids, may be decided by weather. Modern aviation has brought an intense study of weather at ground levels and at high altitudes.

The weather bureau collects information from stations scattered from the equator to the arctic. It receives information from ships and from planes at sea. Airplanes are sent up to gather weather information from the upper altitudes, and balloons go higher than planes for such information. These balloons do not carry men but instruments that measure air conditions and a radio transmitter that sends the data back to the ground station. Robot stations that transmit weather data have been established from Greenland to the tropics. These stations are unat-

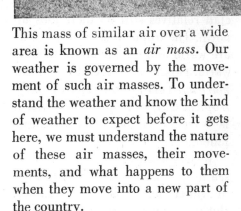

Continental polar air originates in Canada and northern United States where the air is chilled by snow-covered land. Tropical maritime air is bred over the tropic seas where the hot sun warms the air

tended for months, transmitting their data automatically by radio.

Weather information is sent by wire and radio to the main office of the Weather Bureau in Washington and to offices of the Bureau in various cities where the weather maps are issued. The weather facts placed on the maps make clear the location of storms and fair weather. Comparison of successive maps makes clear the paths of storms and their rate of advance. Storms follow rather definite paths across the country and fair weather too advances over well-known courses.

Air masses in winter. Think of the air in winter over the continent of North America. Canada and northern United States lie buried under many feet of snow. Lakes and streams are covered with ice often a yard thick. On this cold land lies the cold air, several miles thick and thousands of miles across, chilled through and through, its temperature 30°, 40°, 50°, 60° below zero, air in natural and intense cold storage.

This mass of similar air over a wide area is known as an *air mass*. Our weather is governed by the movement of such air masses. To understand the weather and know the kind of weather to expect before it gets here, we must understand the nature of these air masses, their movements, and what happens to them when they move into a new part of the country.

The air mass over the northern part of North America just described is called *polar continental air* (cP) or the air pilots may call it *polar Canadian*. At times this air mass moves to other lands. Usually it moves south and east. Less often it moves west over the mountains to the Pacific coast. When in winter the refrigerated polar continental air moves down over Des Moines, Chicago, Philadelphia, and points east and south, people turn on their radiators, pile coal on their furnaces, wood in their stoves, and load on their heaviest coats to go outdoors. The weather is clear, cold, below

127

freezing. Sometimes the polar continental moves over the mountains to Seattle. It stops the usual winter rains and immerses the country in clear, cool weather.

Now think of another air mass in winter, the air lying over the Gulf of Mexico and the Atlantic Ocean east of Florida and southward. Northern vacationists in Florida have their pictures taken lolling in flimsy and scanty attire or bathing in the sea to send home to their wool-clad relatives still on their jobs up north. The tropic and subtropic seas are warm and the air above them is warm. This air mass is called *tropical maritime* (mT) or more particularly *tropical Gulf* or *tropical Atlantic*. It is warm, even hot, and moisture-laden air.

When the air from over the tropic sea moves in over the United States in winter, it brings warm weather. But it does not bring balmy Florida weather to St. Louis and New York. It brings chill, damp, mist, and rain. Because it is warm air from the sea, it is laden with moisture. When it moves over the cold northern land and the cold northern sea, its lower layer is chilled and its moisture is condensed as fog and rain, or if chilled low enough, as snow. Our friends up north are bathed in tropical maritime air, but they do not enjoy it. The northern land and sea spoil it, at least in the lower layer of air where people live. To the northerner, maritime tropical in winter is chill and damp, but the temperature is not nearly so low as polar continental.

Thus the kind of weather we have depends chiefly upon where the air comes from and what happens to it by the time it gets here. What happens to it depends upon our particular part of the country, the land or sea over which the air travels to us, and upon the season of the year. (The weather business begins to sound complicated, but wait a moment before you decide you are "all mixed up." We will make sense of it.)

Air masses in summer. When you—from Midwest to Maine and southward—are sweltering in summer, you are probably living in tropical maritime air, air that moved upon you a few days earlier from the tropic sea. It may be tropical Gulf or tropical Atlantic, but you know it is tropical, hot, humid, the kind that soaks your clothing with perspiration a few moments after a cold bath. Such breeze as you get is southerly. You may have thunderstorms in the afternoon. Air pilots watch for them and fly around them, not through them. For an hour after the thunderstorm you may be cool, but the next day you are in tropical air again.

Then some day or night, perhaps suddenly, the wind swings around and comes from the northwest. The air is cool and the skies are clear and blue. It is beautiful summer weather. You feel like work or play. You are then in air-cooled atmos-

Black Star, N. Y., (inset) Philip D. Gendreau, N. Y.

The bathers on the beach in Florida and the people up north are both experiencing tropical maritime weather. Why is it so different?

phere, cooled in Canada. You are living in polar continental air.

Other air masses. Maritime polar air from the North Atlantic brings the famous "Nor'easter" to New England, and to regions south and west, northeast wind, dense clouds, cold rain. Maritime polar from the North Pacific, polar Pacific, keeps the northwest coast rainy and cool in summer and cool in winter but not intensely cold. Tropical maritime from the Pacific moving into California has its moisture condensed to produce fog on the coast and rain in the mountains.

Air fronts. Imagine the sea coming in as a gigantic wave, a wall of water. So the air comes in, the polar continental against the tropical mari-

time. The advancing front of air is called an *air front*. There are cold fronts and warm fronts. They may be recognized as they travel across the country because weather changes at the air front. The weatherman follows the air fronts across the map by reports from station to station. He can see them advancing at the rate of thirty miles an hour, faster or slower. He can predict the weather before the front arrives, at its arrival, and after the front has passed and the new air mass submerges the particular section of the country. The sailor and the air pilot can often see the air front coming, and you, too, perhaps still on the ground, can learn to see it coming, if you learn its "signs" in clouds, wind, and rain.

The polar continental comes in as *cold front*. When it meets tropical maritime, there may be trouble in the air, storms. The cold air is heavier than the warm air and plows under and lifts it. The moisture in the warm air condenses as it rises. Cumulus clouds pile up like great rolls of white wool. Some grow large, forming rapidly into thunderheads. So much air may rush upward at 60 to 100 miles an hour that thunderstorms form. The wind at the cold front shifts violently around in squalls until it sets in strongly from the northwest, straight from the cool land and sea. Then the sky clears, and we are immersed in polar Canadian air. In summer a cold front means thunderstorms and squalls and after them cool, clear weather.

When tropical maritime air moves in to replace polar continental, it comes in as a *warm front*. The signs tell of its approach. The tropical maritime is warm and moist, lighter in weight than the polar continental. The warm air flows in above the cooler. It can be recognized first

(1) *Philip D. Gendreau, N. Y.,*
(2) (3) (4) *Weather Bureau*

(1) Low scud clouds (fragments of cumulus) traveling under a layer of stratified clouds, common in winter and on the edge of disturbances. (2) A regular "factory of clouds" (cumulus). Notice rain at bottom of this cloud. (3) High, delicate cirrus clouds indicate an approaching warm front. (4) The familiar "mackerel sky," composed of alto-cumulus clouds, associated with a weak cold front

high above the earth's surface while we on the ground are still submerged in the polar continental. Five miles or more above us the tropical maritime moisture is condensed to form thin high clouds. In the intense cold of that great height the moisture condenses as fine crystals of ice, forming *cirrus* clouds. The warm front that is five miles above us slopes southward until it rests on the ground three or four hundred miles to the south of our position.

The polar continental air mass retreats as the tropical maritime flows closer. Perhaps the clouds thicken and lower. The third day, dark rain clouds move over us with a drizzle of rain. Another day and the rain has ceased, but the weather is warm and humid with south wind. The warm front has passed, and we are submerged in maritime tropical air. So here are the signs of an advancing warm front: (1) thin high cirrus clouds; (2) hours later or next day, heavier clouds; (3) the following day rain and southerly wind. The warm front may be followed as it moves north: Monday, Richmond; Tuesday, Philadelphia; Wednesday, Boston; Thursday, Augusta, Maine.

Cyclones. When cold air masses and warm air masses meet at an air front, disturbances often arise. *Low pressure areas* develop. The barometer falls, down perhaps to 29 inches or 980 millibars. Air moves in as wind from all sides toward the low pressure area. The wind does not blow straight in but is deflected to

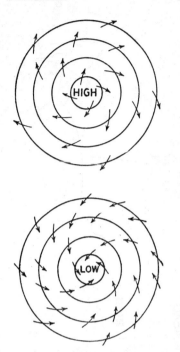

These diagrams show the direction of the wind at high and low centers

the right in the northern hemisphere by the rotation of the earth. A gigantic spiral or whirlpool of air, up to a thousand miles across, develops. Such a low with its spiral wind is called *a cyclone*. It is usually accompanied by rain. Cyclonic storms are our common storms that come with rain or snow. A cyclone is part of an air front, a gigantic whirl in an advancing front.

Following a low comes a *high*, a cold air mass surging down. The barometer may rise to 30 inches or 1016 millibars. The high brings the clear, cold weather that follows the storm. (High pressure areas are sometimes called *anti-cyclones*.)

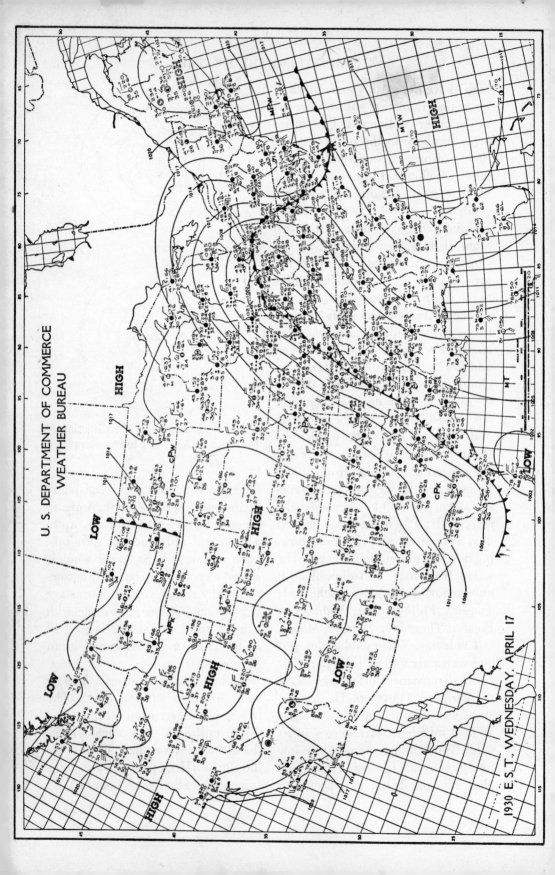

U. S. DEPARTMENT OF COMMERCE
WEATHER BUREAU

1930 E. S. T., WEDNESDAY, APRIL 17

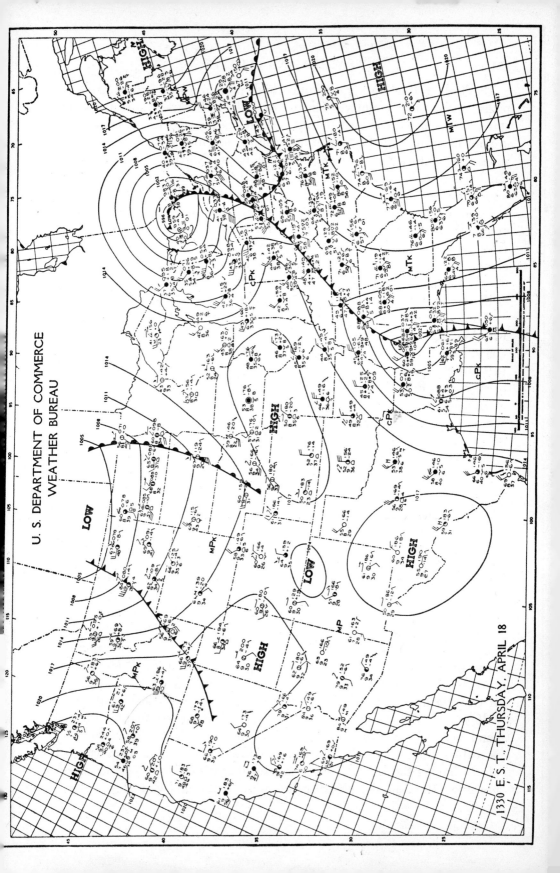

U. S. DEPARTMENT OF COMMERCE
WEATHER BUREAU

1330 E. S. T., THURSDAY, APRIL 18

The lows follow rather definite paths across the country. These storm tracks are from west to east around the world in the temperate zones. Some storms move from the Pacific across North America and onward over the Atlantic. Some swing down from northwest Canada, across the United States, and out from New England. Sometimes cyclones disappear along these storm tracks, and new cyclones may arise at the air fronts.

The weather map and your weather. Examine the weather map (page 132) for April 17, 7:30 P.M. (1930 E.S.T.). You will see that it bristles with data that the weather man needs to predict the weather. We will only attempt to understand some main features of the map.

Notice a heavy wavy line entering the United States from the Atlantic Ocean at North Carolina. The line bends northwestward to Ohio and Indiana and then southwestward to Texas and Mexico. This line marks *air fronts*. The sharp points along the line are *cold fronts* (▼▼▼▼▼▼), and the rounded spots are *warm fronts* (●●●●●●). Notice in Kentucky the letters mTk. These letters stand for maritime, tropical, colder *air mass*. In the Atlantic Ocean east of Georgia notice the word HIGH, half surrounded by a wavy line numbered 1017 at its ends. The line is called an *isobar*. It connects places having the same barometric pressure. Here in the ocean is a

high pressure area with a pressure of 1017 millibars. Above the word HIGH notice the letters mTw, denoting maritime, tropical, warmer air mass. Northwest of the word HIGH notice a half-black circle with a straight broken line extending down from it (♀). This symbol tells that here was a gentle wind, 1 to 3 miles an hour, from the south and the sky was about one-half covered with clouds.

Now look in Indiana at the word LOW. To east and south of this low pressure area you see black circles (●●) indicating cloudy weather. The wind was from the south and southwest. Now look northwest of this low pressure area in Illinois and Wisconsin. Near the low, the sky was cloudy with some rain (black dots ●●) and some snow (✶✶) in Minnesota. The wind was northerly and stronger (⚡), 19 to 24 miles an hour. Still further west and Northwest the sky was partly cloudy and clear.

Now look at the map (page 133) of April 18, 1:30 P.M. (1330 E.S.T.). You notice that the air fronts have changed and moved generally east. From the Pacific, across the northern states, a cold front has moved eastward preceded by a warm front. The high and low pressure areas have moved generally eastward. Thus you see that the weather of these days is moving eastward.

From the weather map you can read the kind of weather north, west, south, and east of you. From

Ewing Galloway, N. Y.

When the weather man predicts frost, the orchard growers light their smudge pots, hoping to save their crops

a study of successive maps you can form an idea of how the air masses are moving and predict the weather. For example, if you were in central Pennsylvania at 1:30 P.M. on April 18, you would expect for the evening and next day: cloudy, possibly light rain, wind shifting from south to southwest to northwest, followed by clearing, cooler, brisk northwest breezes as the continental polar, colder air mass moved in.

What weather does to us. Weather and climate govern our lives. Shelter, clothing, and food are dictated by weather. The production of food—farming, herding, and poultry raising—are subject to weather's governing hand. In consequence, food-processing—milling, meat-packing, fruit-packing, canning and other food industries—and transportation are subject to weather's influences.

For the white man, at least, the best zones are the temperate zones. Here nature provides abundantly, if

a man works for the products. Here the climate provides sufficient stimulus to keep him active, but is not severe enough to take all his time just to keep him alive.

The value of the weather service. In the great fruit belts frost may mean the loss of a year's fruit. Orchards are supplied with heaters, frequently burning oil. Watchmen follow the night temperatures, and government weather reports are awaited for the frost warnings. When frost is predicted, fires are lighted in the orchards to protect the fruits. When storm-warning signals fly along the coasts, ships stay in port. One storm at sea has often cost millions of dollars and many lives. By no one are the weather reports more closely watched than by the air pilots. Weather reports are constantly received at the airports and radioed to the pilots in the air. The army and the navy have their own weathermen, meteorologists, serving with the air

135

forces. The civil air services too have meteorologists in constant touch with the United States Weather Bureau.

The Weather Bureau is costly, but it pays many times over by the saving in lives and property.

How to Learn about Foretelling the Weather

I. Study the weather maps and observe the weather.

1. Secure weather maps from the Weather Bureau. Learn from the explanatory matter on the map how winds, rain, pressure, temperature, and storms are marked. Locate the storm areas (lows). Study the directions of winds about them. What is the meaning of an east wind, a north wind, a west wind, a south wind in your region?

Follow the weather maps for several days. How do the storms and clear-weather areas travel across the country?

How can you use the weather map to foretell the weather?

How can you use pressure, temperature, and wind direction in your region to predict the weather without a weather map?

2. Make a daily weather report for one month on a form such as the one at the bottom of the page.

Next day mark the prediction right or wrong.

II. Read the chapter.

III. Test yourself with the following questions:

1. How does the weatherman get the information which enables him to foretell the weather?

2. What facts should you observe to make a prediction of your own?

3. What winds "bring rain" in your region? What winds precede clear weather?

4. What are "highs" and "lows"? How does the weather map help you to tell the coming weather?

5. Tell how the weather service saves money for the country.

IV. Think these out:

1. Does the height of the muskrat houses tell the kind of winter that we shall have? Do wild animals have some means of foretelling weather that we know nothing about? If the ground hog sees his shadow on February second, will there be six more weeks of winter?

2. From what you have learned about the relation of the atmosphere to weather and climate, would you say that the seasons on the moon would be more or less severe than on the earth? Why?

3. Would you expect the difference between day and night temperatures to be greater in the desert or in a humid region? Why?

V. Vocabulary. Here are some suggestions:

air front   anticyclone
cyclone   air mass

Date	Temperature	Pressure	Wind Direction	Clouds	Humidity	Rainfall	Your Prediction	Official Prediction

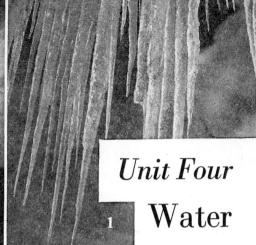

Unit Four
Water

Water is all about you and inside you. It is in the air and in the soil, even in the solid rocks. Water makes you warm and keeps you cool. It runs the steam engine and stops the fire. It makes things grow and stops them from growing. It keeps the nations apart and aids them in getting together. It furnishes power and transportation. It changes desert into farm and orchard. Cities and nations spend millions obtaining pure water. The ability of water to take other material into itself and then to penetrate to hidden places makes it valuable to life.

We shall study in this unit some of the things water can do and some of the things we do with it. We shall study how water acts when it meets other substances, and how these other substances determine its behavior. The water supply of our cities and of our farm homes may be the support of life or the bringer of death. It depends on what the water contains. We shall study how to get safe water. We shall study how to make unfit water fit for washing.

We shall see how sewage from great cities can be treated to prevent its killing the living things in our streams and turning them into great open sewers and how to prevent contamination of water supplies of village and farm.

(1) (3) Ewing Galloway, N. Y., (2) Black Star, N. Y., (4) (5) Philip D. Gendreau, N. Y.

Chapter Nineteen

The Value of Impure Water

Did you ever take a drink of pure water, absolutely pure? Water and nothing else? Probably not. The nearest we can get to such a state of purity is distilled water. Our lives depend on getting water that will not stay pure. If water remained pure, chemically pure, we should die. Water is valuable in our body because it dissolves so many things so easily. If it would not dissolve our food in digestion and carry it in the blood, we should starve to death. If it would not dissolve the waste substances in the body and carry them to the kidneys to be thrown out, we should poison ourselves.

What are solutions? Let us make sure that we agree on what is meant by *dissolving*. If you drop a spoonful of mud into a tumbler of water and stir it up, you see a glassful of muddy water. If you drop a

When this river flooded, the water dropped its load of mud which the turbulent current held in suspension

Ewing Galloway, N. Y.

teaspoonful of sugar into water and stir it up, you see a glassful of clear water. If you let the glassful of muddy water stand, it changes. The mud settles to the bottom, and you see a glass of clear water. If you let the glass of sugar in water stand, you see no change. The sugar does not settle to the bottom. The mud is said to be in *suspension;* the sugar in *solution.* Water is the *solvent* and sugar the *solute.* To form a solution a solute is dissolved in a solvent.

If you pour the muddy water through a filter paper as in Experiment No. 24, the mud stays on the filter and the water that runs through the paper, *the filtrate,* is clear. The filter removed the mud in suspension. If you filter the sugar solution through another clean paper placed in a clean funnel and collect the filtrate in a clean beaker, you may taste it. Sugar is still in the water. It cannot be filtered out. A poisonous substance in solution would not be removed by filtering. Thus, clear water may not be pure water.

Solutions are not always colorless. If you drop a little copper sulfate or bluestone in a glass of water, the solution is a clear blue. You may prove that it is a solution by filtering it or allowing it to stand. The copper sulfate does not filter out nor settle to the bottom.

Hot solutions. If you take a tumbler of hot water, you can dissolve more sugar in it than you can in cold water. This is true of almost all solids that will dissolve in water. If you keep adding sugar until no more dissolves in the hot water, the excess sugar then falls to the bottom of the glass. If you then pour off into a second glass the hot sugar solution but not the sugar from the bottom of the first glass, when the water in the second glass cools, more sugar falls to the bottom of the glass. If you warm the water, the sugar redissolves. Thus, raising the temperature increases the solvent power; that is, it dissolves more solid.

Why water is seldom pure. Water dissolves many substances. It dissolves so many substances that water percolating through the soil (passing through small spaces) and coming out in springs or collecting in wells is never pure—that is, to the chemist. It may or may not contain harmful bacteria and other harmful substances, but it always has dissolved some of the minerals through which it has seeped. Great caves in limestone countries, like Mammoth Cave, Kentucky, are produced by water dissolving away limestone. Sea water has so much salt in solution that it tastes salty, and so many other substances that it also tastes bitter.

Not only solids but liquids and gases dissolve in water. Soda water is merely water with carbon dioxide dissolved in it. It fizzes because the

Water dissolved limestone rock and left Mammoth Cave in Kentucky

carbon dioxide is dissolved under pressure. When the pressure is released as the soda clerk squirts it into the glass, some of the carbon dioxide bubbles out. Oxygen and other gases also dissolve in water.

Did you ever take a drink of boiled water? It tasted flat, insipid. The flat taste is due to the driving off of gases that were dissolved in the water. If you allow the water to stand and especially if you stir it vigorously or pour it from one vessel to another after it has cooled, it will dissolve more gases from the air and taste like drinking water again. Unlike solids, gases dissolve better at low temperatures than at high. Boiling drives the gases out of solution. If you boil water and cool it without shaking or stirring it and then place a goldfish in it, the fish will come to the surface and gasp for air. The air that had been dissolved in the water was driven out by boiling.

Freezing and boiling points of solutions. Dissolved substances change freezing and boiling points. Did you ever see the ocean frozen? No? But you have seen a pond

139

Ewing Galloway, N. Y.

Why does the ocean freeze only in the Arctic and Antarctic regions?

frozen, perhaps. The sea freezes in the polar regions but not in the warmer regions where lakes freeze. You know that alcohol, glycerin, and other substances are dissolved in the water of the automobile radiator to keep it from freezing. Solutions lower the freezing point of water. The stronger the solution, the lower the freezing point. Pure water freezes at 32° F. (0° C.). Sea water freezes at 28° F. (about −2.5° C.).

Dissolving substances in water also raises the boiling points. A solution of salt or sugar boils at a higher temperature than pure water. The boiling point rises with the quantity of salt or sugar in solution. The more concentrated the solution, the higher is the boiling point.

How to Learn about the Value of Impure Water

I. Experiment and observe:

1. EXPERIMENT No. 24. What is a solution? Mix some mud in a tumbler of water. Mix some copper sulfate or brown sugar in another tumbler of water. Set the two tumblers away for an hour or until next day. Then notice whether the water has become clear in the tumblers. Mix up two more tumblers, one of muddy water and one of copper sulfate or brown sugar. Fold filter paper as shown in the diagram. Place in funnels. Pour some clear water in to wet the paper, and pour out any that remains. Set the funnels in bottles. Through one funnel pour the muddy water and through the other pour the copper sulfate or brown sugar. Notice the water that runs through the filter into the bot-

tles. A solution runs through the filter unchanged. A suspension is removed by the filter. A suspension settles upon standing; dissolved substances do not settle.

With thoroughly clean glassware and filter paper, try another experiment. Mix some salt in water. Pour the water through a filter paper. Taste the water that runs through the filter (the filtrate).

Write a report in the required form.

2. EXPERIMENT No. 25. What effect has heat upon the power of liquids to dissolve solids? Stir sugar in water, a spoonful at a time, until it will dissolve no more and a little sugar settles undissolved on the bottom of the beaker. You now have a cold saturated solution. Place the beaker on stand and heat gently until the sugar dissolves. Add sugar, a spoonful

140

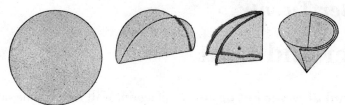

This is how filter paper is folded

at a time, until no more will dissolve in the hot water. You now have a hot saturated solution. Pour off the solution into another beaker, leaving the undissolved sugar behind in the first beaker. Cool the second beaker by setting in a gentle current of cool water. What happens to the sugar in solution? Write a report.

3. EXPERIMENT No. 26. Does ordinary water contain dissolved substances? Pour some water from faucet, well, or stream into evaporating dish or tin lid. Heat gently over the Bunsen burner until the water all evaporates. Is anything left behind in the evaporating dish?

If you can obtain sea water, try this experiment with sea water.

EXPERIMENT No. 26A. Does water carry the dissolved substances of orange juice? Squeeze the juice of an orange in a dish of water. Strain and then evaporate the solution. Write a report.

4. EXPERIMENT No. 27. How do dissolved substances affect the freezing and boiling points? Arrange apparatus as for Experiment No. 15. Make a saturated solution of salt. Place the beaker on the retort stand. Suspend a thermometer from ring of the stand so that it hangs in the solution. Slowly heat the beaker until the solution boils. Read the temperature.

Mix cracked ice thoroughly with salt. Thrust a thermometer in the beaker. Read the temperature. What is the temperature of the freezing salt solution or of the melting ice and salt solution? Write a report in the required form.

II. Read the chapter.

III. Test yourself with these questions:

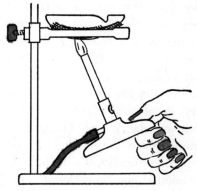

Evaporating water over a Bunsen burner

1. Name several common solutions about the house.

2. What is a solution? How can you tell a solution from a suspension? Name a common suspension that you have seen.

3. What is the effect of heat upon the power of liquids to dissolve solids?

4. Why is natural water seldom chemically pure?

5. How does a dissolved substance affect the boiling and freezing points?

IV. Think out these questions:

1. Is coffee a suspension or a solution? Find out by experiment.

2. Why does the water in a pitcher standing in a room often taste flat and stale? Try to improve the taste by beating with an egg beater or fork.

3. You sometimes see sugar crystallized on the top of a jar of jelly. What makes it collect there?

V. Vocabulary.

dissolve	solvent
solution	solute
suspension	filtrate

Chapter Twenty

Water and Heat

A pound of water hot or cold. Why does the hot water come up from the cellar to your bathroom? For the same reason that the water runs over the kettle and over the automobile radiator when they warm up. For the same reason that mercury or alcohol climbs in a thermometer tube. We need to study this commonplace happening a little more scientifically. We begin by asking another question: Does hot water weigh the same as cold water? Now do not jump at the answer. Let us see if we know what we mean when we ask the question. We might answer by two experiments. Suppose you took a large glass beaker in the laboratory, or a tin pot at home, that held about two quarts, and put in it an exact quart of water. Now suppose you weigh it, heat it, and weigh it again. Will it weigh the same when hot? You could argue about that, but by experiment you would find that it weighs the same.

Now let us try a second experiment in answer to the same question: does hot water weigh the same as cold water? Fill a quart measure exactly brimful of cold water and weigh it. Heat it. Some of the water would flow over the side and out. Wipe the vessel dry and weigh it again. Now does hot water weigh the same as cold water? A quart of hot water weighs less than a quart of cold water.

Now go back to the experiment with the water in the two-quart vessel. Start with a quart of cold water, weigh it, heat it, weigh it again. It weighs the same before heating and after. While it is still hot, measure it

Does a quart of hot water weigh the same as a quart of cold water?

142

with your quart measure. You have more than a quart of hot water, but it weighs the same as a quart of cold water.

Now let us answer the question: does hot water weigh the same as cold water? We need to speak very carefully in science. Our answer must report exactly the results of our experiment. We need to say that a *quart* of hot water weighs less than a *quart* of cold water. Now with this understanding we might say that when water is heated, it expands and becomes lighter.

Why the hot water comes up from the cellar. Water is heated and expands and then quart for quart it weighs less than the cold water. The cold water coming into the system lifts the hot water to the top of the storage tank, and when the faucet is turned on in the bathroom, the hot water runs out from the top of the tank.

If your house is heated by hot water, the cold water in the system similarly lifts the hot water to the radiators in the room, but a hot-water pump is sometimes also added to the system to secure a quicker and more certain circulation. A similar arrangement takes the water from the water jacket around the automobile engine to the radiator, and a water pump hurries the circulation of the water. The radiator in each case serves the same purpose, that is, to let the heat pass out from the hot water to the surrounding air. In the house we want to get the heat into

Ewing Galloway, N. Y.

Why does hot water come up from the basement to your bathroom? See the diagram below and explain how the system provides hot water throughout the house

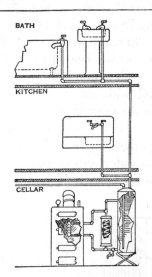

the room and in the automobile we want to get the heat out of the engine. When the heat passes out of the water in the radiator, the water is heavier, quart for quart, than the hot water

143

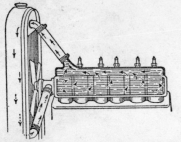

Circulation of water in the cooling system of a gasoline engine

rising from the heater. Therefore, the cold water returns down the pipes to the boiler or to the water jacket around the automobile engine.

Carrying heat around. Now we must use and learn another scientific term. When the hot water carries the heat around with it from one place to another, we say that the heat is transferred by *convection*, the word coming from two Latin words which mean "to carry with." When the air in the room is heated by a radiator and travels around the room as you showed with smoking punk sticks, we say the room is heated by convection in air. Convection in water brings the heat from the furnace in the hot-water system, and convection in the air takes it around the room.

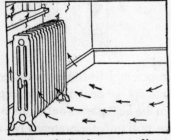

Circulation of air about a radiator

In our study of the air we found a similar convection of air about the earth. At the equator the air is being heated and expanding. The colder air from north and south flows in and raises it to high altitudes. Then, as it cools, it flows northward and southward. It descends to the surface as cold air at the horse latitudes.

Similarly in the ocean there is a convectional circulation of water. At the polar regions the water is continually cooled and becoming heavier. Then it descends and flows deep below the surface toward the equatorial regions. There the heating makes it lighter, and it rises again to the surface as warm water. Thus there is a circulation. The ocean currents, however, are not as simple as this explanation would suggest. The winds drive water before them and send the currents across in the direction toward which they are blowing. The continents turn the currents aside and further complicate the course of the currents. There is, however, a gentle and grand convection of water between the cold polar regions and the warm regions of the equator.

Solid water. You can hammer a stake with a piece of water. All you need to do is to take enough heat out of the water first to make a hammer out of it. The water changes from a liquid state to a solid state. You know that this change takes place with pure water at 32° F. (0° C.). You know also that if the water contains other substances in solution, the change to a solid state will not take place until a lower temperature is reached. The more other substances there are in solution, the lower the freezing point will be.

Invisible water. You may have water all around you and yet not see it. If it is in the state of gas or vapor, it is invisible. You experimented with water vapor in the air in the unit on air. You can hurry the evaporation of water by heating it. You know that water boils and becomes a vapor at 212° F. (100° C.). Heat changes water from the solid state to a liquid state and then to a gaseous state. In the gaseous, or vapor state, water is invisible. You may say that you have seen steam coming from the kettle. You saw a cloud of fine drops of water. The true water vapor is just at the end of the spout of the teakettle. There you will see a small area that has no cloud. That area is occupied by water vapor. Just beyond, the vapor condenses to the cloud of fine drops of liquid water that we loosely call *steam*.

Distillation. If sufficient heat is added to liquid water, it changes to water vapor. Then if heat is taken away from the water vapor, it changes back to liquid water. This is the principle of distillation.

On page 146 is shown a glass still sometimes used in the laboratory. If a solution of salt or other solid is boiled in the flask, the water vapor passes down the tube and is condensed. Cool water flowing through the outer tube takes heat from the water vapor. The salt or other solid

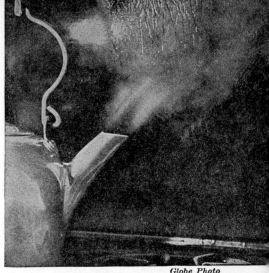

Globe Photo

In this remarkable photograph, the invisible vapor close to the teakettle spout, the cloud of droplets, and the condensed steam on the cool surface of the stove lid are clearly shown

does not become vapor at 212° F., the temperature of boiling water. Therefore, the solids are left behind in the flask and the water dripping from the condenser is chemically pure, as the experiment shows.

You learned that ordinary water is a solution of several minerals which the water has met in the soil. Such water is not suitable for many chemical processes in the laboratory. Therefore, the scientists use distilled water. You probably know also that distilled water is added to automobile batteries which would be ruined in time by solutions of the solids of ordinary water. On shipboard distillation furnishes drinking water, for distilled sea water is fresh water. Distillation has many other uses in industry and in the laboratory.

Why freezing bursts pipes. If you have taken the milk bottle from

This compact distilling unit provides fresh water for fliers forced down at sea. The operator is inserting the canned heat. The principle is that shown in the diagram below

water freezes, and since it cannot force its way upward, it breaks the bottle. Because of the expansion, ice is lighter than water. Therefore, it floats, and a pond freezes on top instead of on the bottom. That expansion gives us the chance to skate.

You may now be a little confused. You learned that as water cooled it contracted, and now you learn that when it freezes it expands. The two statements seem to disagree. If you take water at a high temperature or at the temperature of a living room and cool it, the water will steadily contract and become heavier until it is cooled to 39° F. If cooled below 39° F. water again expands and grows lighter. Water just at the freezing point 32° F., therefore, is lighter than water at 39° F. and floats on top. Therefore, water freezes at the top instead of the bottom of the pond.

the doorstep on a very cold winter morning, you probably have seen the reason freezing bursts pipes and radiators. A column of frozen milk may be standing from the mouth of the bottle. When the water in the milk froze, it expanded and forced its way upward. Fill a bottle with water to the very top and wire in the cork so that it cannot be forced out. Set it outdoors on a cold winter night, or pack it in salt and ice. The

Heat and evaporation. It takes heat to change water from a liquid to a gas. If there were no heat to pass into the water, it could not evaporate. It would remain liquid. It must get heat from somewhere to

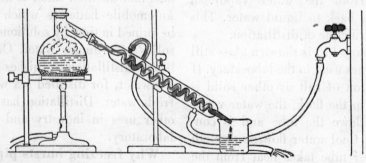

Still with condenser. How has the water changed in the flask? How is it changed in the condenser?

evaporate. On the stove it takes heat from the flame of burning gas or coal, or from the glowing electric coil. When the sweat on your face evaporates, it takes heat from your face, and you feel the cooling effect of evaporation. Your wet clothes take it from your body and may take so much that you are chilled.

You can cool drinking water by evaporation. A camper once discovered that by accident. A canvas bucket filled with water had stood in the breeze. Some water gradually oozed through and evaporated, cooling the remaining water in the bucket to a pleasant drinking temperature. The desert water bag that may be hung on a thorn tree works on the same principle. A camp refrigerator may be easily made by covering a frame with cloth which is allowed to hang in a vessel of water. The temperature inside will be several degrees cooler than outside.

Ice is manufactured by evaporation. In your home the electric re-

Hugh Spencer, Chester, Conn.

Freezing causes expansion

frigerator is cooled by evaporation. Instead of using the evaporation of water, however, liquids are used which evaporate more readily and take up more heat, therefore cooling more. In the manufacture of ice, ammonia is used. At ordinary temperatures ammonia is a gas. Ordinary household ammonia water is a solution of this gas in water. Ammonia gas may be made a liquid by

Why does the pond freeze on top and not at the bottom?

Philip D. Gendreau, N. Y.

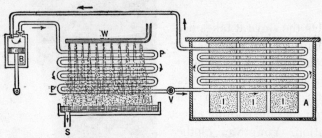

How ice is manufactured. Ammonia gas, much compressed, fills the pipes P, P'. Cold water from W flows over these pipes and carries away the heat due to compression of the gas by means of the pump B. Through a regulating valve V the liquid ammonia which results is allowed to pass very slowly into the pipes in the brine tank A. The pressure in these pipes is kept low all the time by means of B. As the ammonia vaporizes, and then as the vapor expands, heat is absorbed from the brine in the tank. Water to be frozen is in the cans I

compressing it. This compression is secured by pumps. The liquid ammonia is then allowed to evaporate in coils of pipe and cools tanks of brine (salt water). Cans of water immersed in the tanks of brine are frozen. The cakes of ice taken from these large cans are those sold by ice dealers in most of the larger cities. Such ice has the advantage of being made from purified water and so does not spread disease as often ice from polluted ponds does.

In the electric refrigerator ammonia or some other gas, such as sulfur dioxide, is compressed to a liquid and then allowed to evaporate. The evaporation takes heat from the refrigerator and, therefore, cools it.

How to Learn about Water and Heat

I. Study by these experiments:

1. EXPERIMENT No. 28. Does a quart of hot water weigh the same as a quart

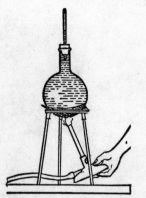

Apparatus for Experiment No. 29

of cold water? Fill a flask with cold water exactly to a mark on the stem. Weigh it and record the weight. Then pour out the cold water. Fill exactly to the same mark with boiling water. Weigh it. Write a report in the required form.

2. EXPERIMENT No. 29. Why does hot water not weigh the same as cold water? Arrange the apparatus as shown at left. Fill the flask brimful of cold water. Force in the cork so that the water rises in the tube. Heat. Write a report.

3. EXPERIMENT No. 30. How does water circulate in the hot-water system? Arrange apparatus as shown on page 149. Add some very fine sawdust, thoroughly wet. Heat the flask gently and watch the sawdust.

Apparatus for Experiment No. 30

4. EXPERIMENT No. 31. What happens to water when it is greatly cooled? Pour a little water in a beaker and set it on some "dry ice" (solid carbon dioxide). Or set a watch glass full of ether in a few drops of water on a board. Fan the ether until it evaporates. What happens to the water? Caution: Do not touch the dry ice with your hands. It will give you a painful frostbite. Do not open the ether in a room with a flame. It is highly explosive. Write a report in the required form.

5. EXPERIMENT No. 32. How to distil water. Arrange apparatus as shown at right. In the flask pour some copper sulfate and salt solution, or a brown sugar and salt solution. Examine the water that condenses in the receiving test tube. Taste it, for it is pure. Write the report and draw the apparatus.

6. EXPERIMENT No. 33. Why does freezing damage pipes? Fill a bottle brimful of water. Force in the cork. Pack the bottle in a mixture of salt and ice. Write a report in the usual form.

II. Read the chapter.

III. Test yourself with these questions:

1. Why does water circulate in a pot on the stove or in a hot-water system?

2. Where in nature do we find similar circulation of water due to unequal heating at different places? Where is there a circulation of air due to the same causes?

3. What is the term used to designate the carrying around of heat by moving air or water?

4. What effect has evaporation upon temperature? What use is made of this?

5. Why do pipes burst when they freeze?

IV. Think out the answers to the following questions:

1. In a hot-water heating system an expansion tank is placed in the top of the house or an overflow pipe is connected to take off water when necessary. Why are these provided? Without these provisions what might happen to the system? Why?

2. Does convection of heat take place inside your body? Explain.

3. On a humid (moist) summer day, why do you feel much warmer than on a dry clear day of the same temperature?

4. What scientific precaution did you learn in experiments section, "A pound of water hot or cold"?

V. Vocabulary. Did you find any new words? Watch the spelling.

convection   distil   distillation

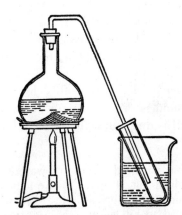

Apparatus for Experiment No. 32

Chapter Twenty-one
Water to Drink

Where our water comes from. If you live in the country, the water supply comes probably from a spring or a well or perhaps from a brook, or part of it may come from a rain barrel or cistern. If you live in the city, it seems to come from a pipe in the wall. If you traced back that water from the faucet to the source of supply, you might find a long and varied story. We shall see something of the process of providing a safe and sufficient water supply in the city and in the country. Let us see first the smaller source of supply from which the country home obtains its water.

Rain that soaks into the ground goes somewhere. It goes downward, and when it falls on a hill, it works its way underground into the lower land. If you dig a hole deep enough, water seeps in. In a dry season you will need a deeper hole than in a wet season. The level below which the water seeps in, that is, the level of permanent ground water, is the _water table_. Below this level the ground is saturated with water. If a well is dug below the water table of

the dry season, it will not go dry. If it does not reach this level, it will go dry in dry seasons.

As the water makes its way downhill, it may come to a layer of clay or other material through which it cannot go. Such a layer is called an _impermeable_ or _impervious_ layer. It may follow this impervious layer until it reaches the side of a hill in the valley. There it comes to the surface as a spring. If a well is drilled to the deep porous layers below the impervious layers, it is called an _artesian well_.

The city water supply. In cities the demand for water is so great that the supply is one of the chief costs of government. Some cities have bought large tracts of land in mountain or hill regions sometimes several hundred miles away. On this watershed, forests are preserved to help control the water supply. Lakes serve as reservoirs to hold the water, and artificial lakes are created by dams to make additional reservoirs. From these reservoirs water is led through great pipes to the cities.

What's behind a glass of water? (1) Watershed where water is collected and drained off slowly. (2) Aqueduct which brings water to users sometimes hundreds of miles away. (3) Filter beds where sediment is removed. (4) Chlorine added to kill germs. (5) Aëration to restore taste. (6) Tank where water is stored to maintain pressure. (7) The glass of water you drink

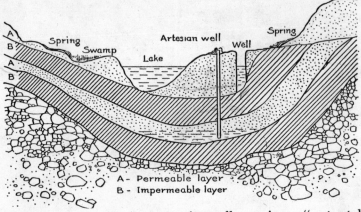

Diagram showing a surface well, an artesian well, a spring, a "water table," and an "impermeable layer"

Cities along large lakes, as along the Great Lakes, often draw their supply from the lakes. To secure pure water, cribs for obtaining the water are built far from shore, sometimes a mile or two out. Cities along great rivers with no other suitable source of supply generally use the river supply. The water from these various sources must be guarded against contamination with disease germs or freed from germs

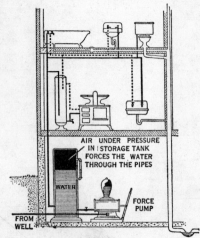

Diagram of a compressed air tank

in a manner which we shall study presently.

Why water flows out of the faucet. Usually water flows out of the faucet because it is running downhill. It seems queer that it should be running downhill when it comes up a pipe from the cellar. It is flowing from a reservoir on a hill high above the city, or in smaller towns it may flow from a tank high in the air. Water may be led into the reservoir from greater altitudes in the mountains, or it may be pumped into the reservoirs from rivers or lakes and then allowed to run down through the water mains of the city and into the houses. As the water flows under the attraction of gravity this system of distribution is called the *gravity system.*

Some cities use a direct pumping system. The water is pumped directly into the water mains. More often there is a combination of the direct pumping system with a reservoir system. During times of slack

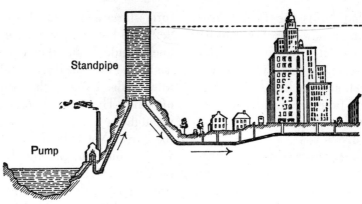

Standpipe

Pump

A standpipe, and how it serves a town

demand for water the pumps fill the reservoir. During the periods of greater demand, the water from the reservoir supplements that from the pumps.

Pumping and compressed air tanks are often used in country houses to secure distribution of water through the house. Water pumped into the tank compresses the air at the top of the tank. The compressed air forces the water out through the pipe at the bottom for distribution to the various rooms in the house.

How a faucet controls the water. Figure I shows the construction of the usual type of faucet. Screwing up the handle raises the washer and allows the water to flow. Screwing the handle in turns down the washer and stops the flow. Figure II shows another type of faucet. The handle operates a plunger which allows the water to flow.

Washers wear and faucets leak. Someone must pay for the water that is wasted by a leak. If your supply is metered, the person responsible for the leak pays for the waste. If there is no meter in the house, the people of the city must pay. Usually a leaking faucet may be repaired in a few minutes by anyone who can handle a screw driver and a wrench. Shut off the water at the main valve in the cellar. You can easily find it. Unscrew the nut through which the handle of the faucet runs. Screw up the handle and take it out. Undo the

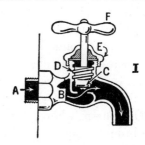

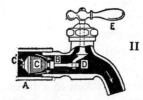

Explain these two types of faucets

screw that holds the fiber washer and put on a new one. You can buy the washers at any hardware store for a few cents a handful. Screw up the faucet, and the leak has stopped. A singing faucet is usually due to a loose washer which may be easily tightened.

Making water safe to drink. The water supply has in the past been one of the greatest sources of disease and death. Epidemics of typhoid, dysentery, and cholera have swept through cities and countries, in some epidemics killing over half of those who fell ill. These epidemics of disease and death have been stopped through the discovery that the diseases are carried by water and by the development of methods of purifying and delivering water. To look at some of the water pumped from rivers to be used for drinking, one might think that it could never be fit to drink. Yet if there is no purer and clearer water available, such muddy river water, perhaps even contaminated with sewage, can be made clear and safe to drink.

The first step is to get rid of the mud. Of course, where clear water can be brought from a good lake or mountain source, the expense of clarifying it is saved. Muddy water is allowed to stand in settling basins. Here the heavier mud settles to the bottom, and the clearer water is drawn off from the top. The water then may be taken to a basin where it is treated with alum. The alum forms large flakes which slowly settle to the bottom, carrying down the finer mud. From the top of this basin, the water is drawn and sent to filter beds. Usually they are made of sand. The water makes its way through the sand as it does through the earth. Not only the fine mud is filtered out, but practically all the bacteria are also removed. To make absolutely sure that harmful bacteria are killed, liquid chlorine or a compound of chlorine is generally added. The water is then clear, free of harmful bacteria, and safe for drinking purposes. Contantly, however, samples are taken and tested for purity.

Is well water pure? Many city people, and country people, too, have an idea that well water and spring water are pure and that city water is bad. Nowadays water of our large modern cities is generally safe and water from wells and springs may be very unsafe. To a certain spring near a large eastern city many cases of typhoid fever were traced. Many springs in a large park in this city were closed because their water was found unsafe. Where State departments of health have tested the water from farm and village wells, they have found many with water so badly contaminated that it was unfit for use. Sewage systems usually do not exist in villages and on farms, and the seepage from outdoor toilets and cesspools may contaminate the soil, and so bacteria of disease get into wells and springs.

Which is in greater danger of pollution, the ordinary well (1), or the artesian well (2)? How might the scout (3) protect himself from impure water when camping?

Look around a spring or well before taking a drink, and look especially uphill. Look for any possible sources of contamination—barns, outhouses, drainage from houses. Even if you can see no danger above ground, you cannot be certain what course the water takes underground.

Pure water in camp. If you are camping, there is one easy precaution to make sure of safe water. Boil the drinking water a half hour. Boiled water tastes flat until it again dissolves air, but a flat taste is better than a case of typhoid. If the boiled water is cooled either by ice, by placing in a deep pit, by placing in cans in a cool brook, or by evaporation from a porous water bag, it is delicious.

A convenient method of making drinking water safe on a journey or in camp is to add one or two drops of tincture of iodine to a quart of water. This quantity of iodine kills germs but does not harm healthy people.

155

How to Learn about Water to Drink

I. Study water supply by the following experiments:

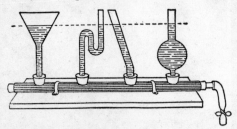

Diagram for Experiment No. 34

1. EXPERIMENT NO. 34. To show that water seeks its own level. With a piece of garden hose, some glass tubing, a funnel, corks, and cork borer—and a little ingenuity—you can arrange the apparatus shown in the picture just above. You can easily devise other simple apparatus to show the same thing.

Conclusion: 1. What determines the height to which water will rise?

2. How do the sizes and shapes of the tubes affect the height? (Be careful. No. 2 is a trick question.)

2. EXPERIMENT NO. 35. To demonstrate with a model how a gravity water-supply system works. Arrange apparatus as shown in the diagram. (The tank is a

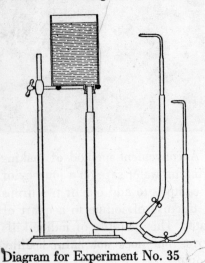

Diagram for Experiment No. 35

gallon oil can with a cork fitted to the opening and the bottom removed with a can opener. Instead of removing the bottom, a hole may be punched in the bottom to accomplish the same purpose.) The upright tubes indicate house supply pipes.

A. What represents the city reservoir? the water mains in the street? the faucets in the house?

B. Place one of the faucets higher than the other. Does the water flow with greater force from the higher or lower faucet?

C. Raise one faucet above the level of the tank. What happens to the flow of water? Why?

3. EXPERIMENT No. 36. To repair leaking faucets.

Material: Old or new faucets; washers; wrench; screw driver. Go exploring with the wrench and screw driver. Take the faucet apart and put on a new washer.

4. EXPERIMENT No. 37. To demonstrate the purification of city water supply.

Start a hay infusion by placing a little hay or dead grass in a tumbler of water. Pond or brook water, well or rain water, or distilled water will do. Water from the faucet sometimes kills many of the tiny living things. The hay infusion should be started a week or two in advance. Cover the tumbler with glass so that the water does not dry away.

Mix up some muddy water. Place in a funnel some clean pebbles, then smaller clean pebbles, then two inches of clean, coarse sand, and finally two inches of clean, fine sand. Pour the muddy water through. What happens? What treatment of the city water supply is illustrated by this procedure?

To some more muddy water add a little alum, and set aside to settle. What treatment does this illustrate?

Put a little "chloride of lime," a quarter of a spoonful or less, in a tumbler of water. Examine the hay infusion. To the slide under the microscope with the living bacteria and microscopic animals, add a drop of the "chloride of lime" solution. What happens? What water-supply treatment is illustrated by this procedure? Try also a drop of dilute iodine solution. Write report in required form.

II. Read the chapter.

III. Test yourself with these questions:

1. Where does water come from that leaves the ground in a spring? Explain the picture on page 152.

2. What is the water table? How deep must a well be dug to give a permanent water supply?

3. What is the source of water supply for cities? Why does water flow from the faucet?

4. Why does it sometimes fail to flow in the top stories of high buildings? How can the flow be obtained in the top stories? Explain the picture at the top of page 153.

5. How may running water be obtained in the country house?

6. With page 153 in front of you, explain how a faucet works. What is usually the trouble with a dripping faucet? How can it be easily repaired?

7. How is clear water obtained for the city supply? germ-free water?

8. What is a danger from well water? How can it be avoided?

9. On an automobile trip or other

Filtration of water. The water poured into the funnel passes through a layer of fine sand, coarse sand, small pebbles, and coarse pebbles

journey how can you guard against impure drinking water?

10. How is chemically pure water obtained?

IV. Think out the answers to these questions:

1. Why are filters attached to faucets unsafe?

2. Examine the water supply and the delivery at home and in school. Is your system safe?

3. Is it safe to drink from brooks flowing through a woods?

V. Vocabulary. Did you find any new words to add to your list?

Chapter Twenty-two

Water to Wash in

Use of water at home. There are three things in particular that you do with water around home. You drink it, wash with it, and cook with it. You also probably use it to carry away refuse and sewage from the home. Almost any kind of water will do to flush out the plumbing and carry away the wastes provided that it does not damage the plumbing. Water for drinking, for preparing food, and for cooking must not spoil the food, poison the family, or damage pots and kettles, and must be free of disease germs. We studied in the last chapter how to make water fit to drink. We shall now study how to make water fit to wash with, if we cannot get it that way.

Water is good to clean things with, but soapy water is much better for most things. You probably never asked why soap helps to clean things, but as a student of science you may ask the question. To answer it we shall need to understand what soap is and how it is made. Before

Why does soap clean your hands?

we succeed in answering the question about soap, we shall need to understand some things about chemistry. Soap is a chemical compound made by the joining of an alkali (also called a *base*) and a fatty acid. You have probably heard of alkali and of fats and of acids. Let us see what they are.

What acids do. Vinegar is sour. Lemons are sour. Green apples are sour. They are sour because they contain acids. The first thing to note about an acid is that it is sour. It is not always safe, however, to taste a substance to see if it is acid. It may be so strongly acid that it will burn the tongue badly, destroying some of the flesh. The chemist has a very convenient test to detect an acid. You probably have seen, growing on rocks, those crusty little plants called *lichens* (pronounced lī′kĕns). From some of the lichens a blue dye can be extracted. In fact, if you sit down on a soft bed of moist lichens, you may get up with a nice blue seat to your clothing. The blue dye is called *litmus*. If you put a little litmus in a glass of water, you get a blue solution. Then if you add a few drops of acid solution, such as vinegar, the litmus solution turns red. If now you drop in a little alkali (or base), such as lye or slaked lime, the solution turns blue again. Acid turns litmus red and alkali turns it blue. If you dissolved some common salt in water and dropped in a little litmus, the color would be a sort of violet. Salt is neither acid nor alkali. It is neutral. Litmus is a convenient indicator of acid and alkaline condition.

ˈDid you ever peel an apple with a pocketknife or a steel kitchen knife and find the blade turned dull or blackish? Did you ever leave a kitchen spoon overnight in the salad dressing? If you dropped a strip of zinc in vinegar, you might see little bubbles rise or cluster on the zinc. If you used stronger acid, such as hydrochloric acid, you would find a continuous stream of bubbles rising rapidly. In fact, you could collect bottles full of gas. Acids "react," as the chemist says, with metals and give off a gas. Now you have three tests for an acid: it is sour; it turns litmus red; it reacts with a metal.

Alkali or base. If you wet your fingers with ammonia and rub them together, they feel slippery. Lye or slaked lime will also make your fingers slippery. That is because these substances eat away a little of the outermost layers of dead skin. If you used strong lye, it would eat into the living flesh. If you added a bit of lye to a glass of water and tasted it, you would find it bitter. If you try the experiment, use a *very* tiny bit to a glassful of water, and spit out the solution. Do not swallow it. Alkalis (bases) are bitter to the taste and eat away skin and cloth. Do not soak clothes in lye to clean them.

The colonial soapmaker made his lye by wetting wood ashes

If you mixed an acid and an alkali (base) in just the right amount, you would have neither acid nor alkali left. The two substances would neutralize each other and form a salt.

What soap is. Did you ever taste old, rancid butter? It tastes sour, acid. Butter is the fat from milk. Other fats also become rancid and acid. This fatty acid may be neutralized by an alkali (base). When acids are neutralized by lye (potassium hydroxide or sodium hydroxide), they form soaps. In the old days on the farm, the farmer's wife saved all the scraps of fat and grease and all the wood ashes from the fireplace. The wood ashes contain potash. By pouring water through the wood ashes mixed with lime, a solution of potash lye was obtained. Then the fat was boiled slowly in the potash lye solution. It formed soap and glycerin. The soap made with potash lye is soft soap. It does not harden into cakes.

Modern soapmaking is fundamentally the same as the old methods.

Fats are cooked with alkalis. Chemists, however, control each step of the process. For hard soap, soda lye is used instead of potash lye. Fat and soda lye are cooked in great kettles. The heat is furnished by steam coils and steam is blown into the cooking mixture through a pipe in the bottom of the kettle. The fat and lye change to glycerin and soap.

At the proper stage salt is added. If you have ever tried to wash your hands with soap in sea water, you know that soap will not lather. The salt added to the soap in manufacture separates soap from the liquid and it rises to the top. The liquid is drawn off, the glycerin is obtained from it by distillation. The soap may have perfumes and other substances added. Then it is allowed to harden, is cut into cakes and packed.

Different kinds of soaps are made from slightly different substances. Laundry soaps are made from fats obtained from slaughterhouses, butcher shops, garbage, and cottonseed oil. Toilet soaps are made from coconut oil, palm oil, olive oil, and tallow oil. Perfumes and other substances and dyes may be added to make the soap attractive. Medicinal substances are sometimes added, but they are of little value, serving chiefly by their odors to conceal unpleasant odors due to inferior materials, or because they give opportunity for convincing "sales talks." Fine sand, powdered pumice, or other fine "grit" may be added to make sand soaps, scouring soaps, and "gritty" hand soaps. Washing soda and borax are added sometimes for household uses.

Washing powders are made by adding washing soda to the soap while it is still soft, and granulating the soap when it hardens. They clean greasy dishes more easily than soap because of the excess of soda. You can make an equally good substitute, cheaper than you can buy washing powder, by just adding washing soda to soap jelly, made by heating soap in water. However, such washing

Steps in soap-making. (1) Fats and it is just right. (3) After the various which came in contact with the mold (6) Finally the cakes of soap are cut

compounds, bought or homemade, are hard on hands, for they dissolve natural oils from hands just as they dissolve grease from pans.

How soap cleans. You cannot wash grease off your hands with plain cold water. If you put a little olive oil or butter or common grease from the kitchen in a bottle with some water, they do not mix. If you shake them violently, they may form a mixture of small bubbles, but upon standing, the oil and water again separate. If now you add soap to the mixture and shake it, you see a milky mixture. This mixture lasts much longer than the plain mixture of oil and water. Such a mixture of oil and water in fine bubbles is called an *emulsion.* Milk is such a mixture of water with substances in solution and butterfat in fine bubbles.

When our faces, hands, and bodies get "dirty" in the course of the day, the "dirt" is a collection of dust and dead skin cells, with moisture and chemical substances from perspiration, and oil from the glands of the

alkalis are "cooked" in kettles. (2) Chemists analyze the product to see that mixing processes the soap is run off to be hardened in molds. (4) The soiled sides are scraped from the hardened soap. (5) The soap is then cut into thin strips. and stamped

(1) Black Star, (2)(6) Ewing Galloway, (3)(4)(5) Proctor & Gamble

skin. Soap forms an emulsion with the oil and water and loosens the other parts of the dirt, which then readily wash away in the water. Hot water is much more effective than cold because the soap forms an emulsion more readily with melted or warm grease. Soap also adds to the power of water to penetrate the pores or the tiny spaces between the threads of clothing. Clothes wet more quickly with soapy water. Then the soapy water can float away the particles of dirt.

Hard water and soft water. You no doubt have noticed that with some water the soap remains a greasy scum on your hands until you have worked it up well with plenty of soap. If there is a lime compound (or magnesium compound) dissolved in the water, it is hard for soap to form suds. Other water forms suds very readily. Water in which it is hard to make suds is *hard water,* and water in which it is easy to make suds is *soft water.* On the farm and in villages rain water is often stored in barrels or cisterns for washing. Rain water contains nothing in solution, but gases of the atmosphere. It is soft water and forms suds readily.

You can make suds in most hard water but you will need to use much more soap than in soft water. Therefore, if you have a big wash on hand, it may pay to "soften" the water first. Laundries find that it saves money to install apparatus and supplies for softening water before adding the soap.

Some hard water, called *temporary hard water,* softens upon boiling. That is because boiling drives off carbon dioxide, and the lime compound that made the water hard is deposited on the bottom of the kettle. If you examine the bottom of your teakettle, you may find a deposit that looks like stone. It is stone, limestone. It was dissolved in the water. As long as the water contained carbon dioxide, it remained in solution. When the water boiled, the carbon dioxide was driven off and the limestone fell to the bottom of the kettle. Boilers and pipes are often coated in this manner. This coating of *boiler scale,* as it is called, adds seriously to the cost of heating.

Permanent hard water does not soften upon boiling but may be readily softened by chemical means. If you add some washing soda or borax to a bottle of hard water and then shake it up with soap, suds will form immediately. Both washing soda and borax are cheaper than soap, so that you may lessen the cost of the family wash by adding one of them to hard water. But do not put the clothes in the tub, fill with water, and throw a handful of soda on the clothes. The strong solution of soda will stay right where you threw the soda and weaken or destroy the clothes if you let it lie overnight. Dissolve a pound of washing soda in a measured jar of water. Determine by the soapsuds test just how much of the strong soda solution is needed to soften the tubful of water. To do this add a meas-

In some places primitive methods of laundering are still used

ured quantity of soda solution to the tub, stir the water in the tub, then take up some of the water and shake it with soap in a bottle. Add some more soda solution to the tub and again test. When you have added the right quantity, suds will form quickly. Remember the quantity of soda solution you added to the tub, and thereafter add that amount of soda solution to the same quantity of water in the tub. Always make up your jar of soda solution with the same quantities of water and soda. This procedure will soften your water at a trifling cost just as well as an expensive outfit, and do no harm to the clothes.

Cleaning your clothes and cleaning yourself. Almost any kind of soap will take the dirt off your hands, face, and body. But you want only the dirt taken off. If you use a soap with excess alkali, it may take off too much of the skin. Even if you use only cold water, you rub off some of the dead skin cells from the outer layers, but that does no harm, for dead skin is part of the "dirt." Strong alkali takes too much off and reacts with the natural oil of the skin, taking it out also. The natural oil keeps the skin soft and smooth. Your hands chap readily in winter when you dissolve out this oil before going outdoors. If after washing you add a little cold cream or other grease to the skin, the skin will not chap. For toilet soaps you want no excess alkali. Hard-water soaps have excess alkali to soften the

water. They are, therefore, less desirable, especially in wintertime. Perfume does no harm in the soap, if you like the odor, and dye does no harm, but both are sometimes used to conceal inferior materials. A plain soap, white or cream-colored, with little or no perfume, may be more easily judged for its purity.

Clothing, especially that which is next to the skin, must be washed frequently. Good soap and warm water are the best agents for cleaning clothes. It is usually not necessary

This modern washing machine stirs up the clothes in soapy water

to rub them continuously and heavily on a roughened board. The washing machine merely stirs them up in the warm soapy water. This is usually all that is necessary to allow the soapy water to emulsify the fats and loosen the dirt. Then thorough rinsing is necessary. White clothes sometimes develop a yellowish tint. Bluing is added to blend with the yellow and produce white.

For brushing teeth. An important part of bathing is the cleaning of mouth and teeth. A good brush is the best cleaning implement so far produced for the teeth. Tooth powder and paste are often a good grade of soap to which a little flavoring is added. Precipitated chalk is added for polishing. Sometimes a finely powdered pumice is added to furnish a fine grit to polish more severely. Chalk seems to do no harm, but grit is not advisable. In brushing the teeth, brush so that the bristles go between the teeth. Brush the upper teeth downward and the lower teeth upward. Brush both the inside and outside surfaces of the teeth, and begin the brush strokes on the gum. Rapid brushing is not necessary. Go slowly and not so long, and think what you are trying to do, to reach food lodged in any crevice.

How to Learn about Water to Wash In

I. Experiment and observe:

1. EXPERIMENT No. 38. How may acids be detected? Pour a little water (about twenty cubic centimeters) in each of three beakers. To one beaker add about fifteen cubic centimeters of dilute hydrochloric acid; to another add a little tartaric acid; to the third add a little vinegar. Taste each solution by touching the tip of the finger (after you have washed it) to each of the solutions and touching it to the tip of the tongue.

In each beaker place a strip of blue and a strip of red litmus paper. Note change in color.

In each beaker add a piece or two of mossy zinc. Note what happens.

Write up a report in required form, stating in the conclusions the three reactions by which you can detect acids.

2. EXPERIMENT No. 39. How to recognize alkali (base). Break off a piece of potassium hydroxide about one-half inch long and with forceps or piece of paper drop it into a beaker. Do not touch the potassium hydroxide with the fingers. Place about twenty cubic centi-meters (or a tablespoonful) of ammonia water in another beaker and an equal quantity of limewater in the third. Add about thirty cubic centimeters of water to each beaker.

With the tip of the finger taste each solution. Wet the fingers with each in turn and rub the fingers together. Test each with litmus paper.

Write a report, stating in conclusion how you can detect an alkali (base).

3. EXPERIMENT No. 40. How may an acid be neutralized? Put about ten cubic centimeters of hydrochloric acid in the evaporating dish. Add a piece of litmus paper. Then add sodium hydroxide solution very slowly, stirring constantly until the solution turns blue. There is now a slight excess of alkali. Now add acid, a drop at a time, until the litmus just turns. With care the color may be a violet. Then just one small drop of acid or alkali will turn the color. The solution is now neutral, neither acid nor base.

Evaporate the solution over a low flame. The substance left is common table salt.

Write a report in the required form.

Conclusion: An acid may be neutralized by ....A base may be neutralized by .... When an acid neutralizes a base, a .... is formed.

4. EXPERIMENT No. 41. How to make soap. Dissolve some fat in alcohol. This step is not done commercially but shortens the operation because the fat will not mix with water. Place in the evaporating dish about ten cubic centimeters of sodium hydroxide. Warm gently and stir in slowly the fat solution. Often the alcohol solution takes fire. Have a piece of asbestos handy. Put it over the dish, remove the flame, and the fire is soon smothered. Warm and stir until the mixture is the consistency of butter.

Put a little in a test tube half full of water and shake it. Try washing the hands with a little.

Write the report in the required form.

5. EXPERIMENT No. 42. Make up a washing solution as directed on page 160.

6. EXPERIMENT No. 43. How to soften hard water. In most cities the water is hard. To test it, put two inches of water in a test tube. Mark a medicine dropper with a strip of gummed paper so that you can easily measure out the same quantity of solution. Add one measure of soap solution to the test tube of water and shake. If a lather forms easily, the water is soft. If the water becomes cloudy and a curd of soap forms, the water is hard. Add a measure of soap solution to two inches of distilled water in a test tube. Shake and compare the results with your first test tube. If your city supply of water is soft, you can make hard water by adding a little calcium chloride to a beaker of water.

Place an inch of hard water in a test tube. Add measure after measure of soap solution, shaking after each addition un-til the lather is formed. The water has been softened by the soap. How much did it take as compared with the soft water?

In another test tube place an inch of hard water. Add a measure of washing soda solution. Then test with soaps.

Write a report in the required form. Tell three ways in which the hard water may be softened. Which is the cheapest way?

II. Read the chapter.

III. Test yourself by answering the following questions:

1. Tell three characteristics of an acid. Tell three characteristics of a base. What is the most convenient way to distinguish acid from base in the laboratory?

2. What happens when an acid is added to just the right amount of base? What new kind of substance is formed?

3. How is soap made?

4. What is in washing powder? Why does it clean greasy dishes more readily and more cheaply than does soap? How can you easily make a washing compound?

5. How can you distinguish soft water from hard water? How can you change hard water into soft water?

6. What is boiler scale? Why does it not form with all kinds of water?

IV. Think out the answers to these questions:

1. Why does soap not form a lather in sea water?

2. Why does a little ammonia in the wash water make cleaning of windows in the house or in the car easy?

3. Why is rain water soft?

V. Vocabulary. What have you found new? Can you add any to the following?

acid   litmus
alkali   emulsion
base   precipitated
     neutralize

Chapter Twenty-three

Water for Other Uses

Irrigation. There are miles and miles of fertile soil in the United States and in other continents that produce no crops because there is no water. Before the dawn of written history man had learned to lead water to fertile land to grow crops. Through Asia and northern Africa are found the remains of irrigation works of ancient peoples, now abandoned and the land gone back to desert. Areas in these lands, however, produce large supplies of food and cotton because irrigation projects have been kept open or have been revived. In our own West great areas of desert have been made rich farms by supplying water. Sometimes the water for irrigation is supplied by wells and is pumped to the surface to be stored in reservoirs or led to the fields directly. Mountain streams and lakes may be tapped, and the water led through ditches, sometimes lined with concrete. Huge dams, like the Boulder Dam on the Colorado River, and the Roosevelt Dam in Arizona, supply water to farms where without water there would be desert. The United States Government furnishes the money to build these huge structures. The farmers who use the water on their

Water is often led from mountain streams (1) through ditches and then allowed to run on fields (2)

(1) Ewing Galloway
(2) Resettlement Administration

2

Tennessee Valley Authority

Norris Dam (above). As well as maintaining water supply dams are used to develop electricity. Generators such as those below are run by falling water

fields and orchards pay water rents, but the main return to the government lies in the prosperity and wealth produced by irrigation.

Water power. Dams also furnish power. Some of the dams erected for irrigation have power plants to furnish electricity to regions within their reach. Other dams are built solely for power. Water power was used in ancient times. All down through the Middle Ages and through our colonial period the generation of power by falling water remained much the same. The water turned a water wheel, which turned the machinery, usually for grinding grain. Nowadays the falling water at the great dams turns a water turbine. The turbine turns a generator that

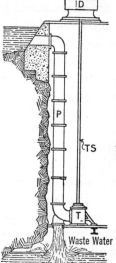

Water turns the turbine, T, which turns the generator, D. P is the penstock through which the water runs

Tennessee Valley Authority

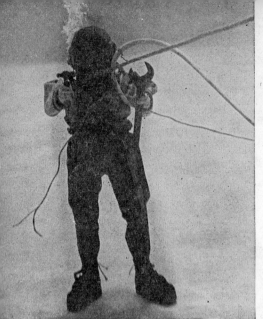

Globe Photo

In a modern diving suit air pressure equals the water pressure

sends an electric current out through the wires to cities and homes and industrial plants miles away. The electricity furnishes light, heat, and power to move machinery in homes and factories. Although most of our electric generating plants today use coal and steam to drive their dynamos, hydroelectric plants (using water to turn the dynamos) are becoming more numerous wherever the falling water is available. The white coal of falling water is one hope for the future when the deposits of coal and oil run low.

Water pressure. You have noticed that dams are thicker below than at the top. Water is heavy. Have you carried a bucket of water? It weighs 62.4 pounds a cubic foot (at 39° F., when it is heaviest). If the water is one foot deep, the pressure upon a square foot of bottom is 62.4 pounds; if it is two feet deep,

the pressure is two times 62.4 pounds; if it is 100 feet deep, the pressure is 100 times 62.4 pounds.

Water presses in all directions. If you hold a block of wood under water and then let it go, water pressing upward forces the block to the top. Water presses sidewise as you may show in Experiment No. 46. At the bottom of the great dams the lateral (sidewise) pressure is very great. Because of this pressure such dams are enormously thick at the bottom. See the picture on page 167.

The diver in his diving suit must endure the pressure of water; therefore, his air lines leading to his helmet are reinforced with steel. The diving suit is filled with air under pressure equal to the pressure of the water. The diver cannot go to great depths, for he would be crushed to death. The submarine must be sufficiently strong to withstand the pressure where it operates; therefore, the submarine cannot go to the great depths of the sea. A submarine dives by taking water into its chambers. It rises by forcing the water out with compressed air. If it went too deep, the water pressure would be so great that it could not be forced out and the submarine could not rise again.

In working on the bottom of streams or lakes men sometimes work in caissons. They are metal chambers without bottoms, into which air is forced to drive out the water. The men are thus working under great air pressure, a pressure equal to that of the water. The pres-

168

sure is so great that if the men were suddenly brought out of the caisson, they would suffer severely, perhaps be killed by the sudden reduction in pressure. On leaving the caisson, they are subjected to gradually reduced pressure until the normal pressure of the air is reached. Divers similarly on being drawn up from the sea are allowed to remain at various depths for some time to become adjusted to reduced pressure.

Fish coming to the surface from great depths must have the pressure in their bodies changed. When deep-sea fish are hauled up on deck, their internal organs are often forced out of their mouths by the internal pressure which balances the water pressure at the bottom of the ocean and not the air pressure above the water. The air bladder of fishes helps to keep this internal pressure balanced against the water pressure.

Adding up the uses of water. Our bodies are 65 per cent water. The processes of life could not go on without water. Digestion, circulation of the blood carrying food and oxygen to the cells, the carrying of wastes to the kidneys and to the lungs, the cooling of the body

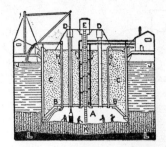

Men working in a caisson. Air pressure keeps the water out. A, working chamber under caisson; B, roof of caisson; C, concrete filling; D, bucket-hoist shaft; E, air lock; F, air-pressure relief lines; G, air-pressure line; H, water-suction line; J, water level surrounding caisson; K, mud bottom; L, bed rock

through evaporation of perspiration, in fact every process in the living body goes on only in the presence of water. We have seen some uses of water in the home: to drink, to cook with, to wash with, to flush out and carry away the wastes, to carry heat through our houses with steam or hot water. In industry it is just as important. For example, the making of wood pulp and paper, dyeing, tanning, the chemical industries require quantities of water. Then think of the part steam plays in our life. It is the chief source of power. Water power also furnishes electricity.

How to Learn about Water for Other Uses

I. Do these experiments:

1. EXPERIMENT No. 44. Why can water do work? On one pan of a platform balance, place an empty milk bottle. Balance it with weights and then add a pound weight. Pour water in the milk bottle until it lifts the weights on the other pan. How much work did the water do? (What weight did it lift? How far?) Why can water do work? Write a report in the required form.

2. EXPERIMENT No. 45. Does water exert pressure?

A. Hold a block of wood under water. Let go of it. What force pushed the block up?

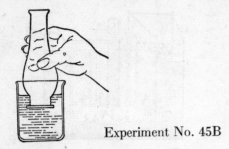

Experiment No. 45B

B. Cover the under end of a lamp chimney with a square of glass. Lower it into a vessel of water. How does the glass act? What force holds it up?

C. Pour water in the chimney. Watch carefully. What is the level of the water in the chimney when the glass falls?

D. Repeat, pouring shot into the chimney instead of water. Note the depth of the bottom of the chimney. Collect the shot and weigh it. Lower the chimney twice as far and again weigh the shot that causes the glass to fall.

Conclusion: In what direction does water exert force? (You may want to revise your answer after later experiments.) Name one thing that determines how much force. Write the report in the required form.

3. EXPERIMENT No. 46. In what direction does water exert pressure? Tie a rubber sheet over a funnel as shown in the diagram. Hold the funnel under water in various directions. Note the displacement of the rubber. Note also the water in the gauge. In what direction does the water exert pressure? Write a report of the experiment in the required form.

4. EXPERIMENT No. 47. Does pressure change with depth? Note the effect on the rubber and the water in the gauge when the funnel is lowered to greater depths.

5. EXPERIMENT No. 48. Can pressure of water cause movement? Arrange the apparatus as shown in the diagram opposite. Measure the lengths of the streams. What relations do you notice between depth, pressure, and movement? Write the report in required form, showing the apparatus in a diagram.

6. EXPERIMENT No. 49. How can water pressure be put to work? Arrange the apparatus as in the diagram at the bottom of page 171. Place it under a faucet. If you have a small electric motor attach with a belt made of a rub-

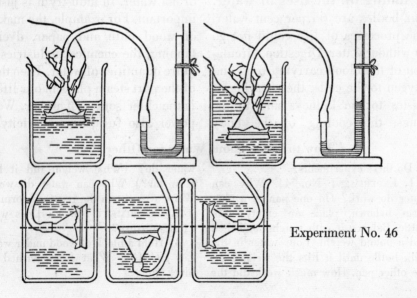

Experiment No. 46

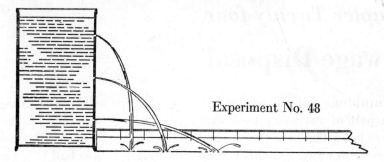

Experiment No. 48

ber band and generate a current to light an electric light.

II. Read the chapter.

III. Test yourself by answering the following questions:

1. What is the source of water used for irrigation? Why are dams used in irrigation works?

2. Name some other uses of dams.

3. How does the modern turbine differ from the ancient water wheels?

4. In olden times the mill was located at the dam or waterfall. Now the mill may be many miles from the source of the power. How is the power of falling water transmitted to a distance?

5. Why are dams built so thick at the bottom?

6. If a dam is fifty feet high, what is the pressure against the bottom of the dam?

7. Why is the diver's suit filled with air under heavy pressure? How great must the pressure be inside the suit?

8. How is the water kept out of caissons in which men work under water?

9. Can you add to the list of uses of water on page 169?

IV. Think out the answers to these questions:

1. Would it be possible to make the ocean generate power as rivers do?

2. Why do logs sometimes lie at the bottom of the pond instead of floating at the top?

3. Does rain water make good drinking water? Do you know of any people who use rain water for drinking water? How could rain water be collected for the house supply and stored with assurance that it would be pure for drinking?

4. Why do some kinds of spots not wash out in water? What then would you try on the spot? What determines whether the spots will come out?

5. What properties (characteristics) of water make it so useful?

6. How is water used in the lift at the automobile greasing station?

V. Vocabulary.

irrigation	lateral
hydroelectric	caisson

Experiment No. 49

Chapter Twenty-four

Sewage Disposal

Plumbing for flushing. A large part of the water used in a modern house flushes out wastes and carries them away. For this a good supply of water and good plumbing is necessary. Examine the plumbing under the kitchen sink. You see a crook or loop or cylinder in the drainpipe. This is the trap. Water always lies in this trap. It prevents sewer gas from coming up into the house. It also stops solid material that might wash into the pipes below and clog them, requiring expensive digging and repairs. A plug in the trap may be unscrewed and solids cleaned out.

The bathroom toilet is similarly provided with a trap. The water lying in the bowl also serves as the trap. In the diagram below the projecting piece at the rear of the bowl forms the trap. When the bowl is flushed, a large quantity of water is needed at once, more than the supply pipe will furnish. This flood of water is provided by the tank above the seat. In the diagram note the hollow rubber ball (*a*). The rubber ball is held in place by the pressure of the water, thus closing the outlet. When the handle is turned, the ball is raised and floats up. The water from the tank floods the bowl and flushes it out through the trap. The rubber ball falls in position again, closing the outlet, and the pressure of the water again flowing into the tank holds the ball down. When the water in the tank reaches the bottom, the metal float (*b*) reaching the bottom of the tank turns on the water. The float rises with the incoming water, and, when the tank is filled, shuts off the water.

Sewage in streams. Not many years ago many city people were using dilute sewage for drinking water. That seems a horrible assertion, but it is true. Cities turned their sewage into lakes and rivers, and other cities pumped out the water to drink. Rivers through cities were

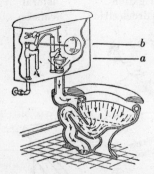

Diagram of a toilet and flush tank

The sink trap keeps solids out of the pipes and sewer gas from the house

172

Philip D. Gendreau, N. Y.

A polluted stream is unsanitary as well as being an eyesore

hardly more than great sewers. It is a common saying that running water purifies itself. We shall see how in just a moment, but the process of purification is so slow where a large river flows through a settled region that the water is always contaminated. Terrible epidemics of typhoid and cholera that were so common showed how badly the drinking water was contaminated with germs of these diseases. We have not solved the problem of keeping our streams and lakes free of disease germs, but we have learned how to purify the drinking water and how to treat sewage to make it harmless. The great expense of proper sewage disposal plants has prevented their erection in all towns and cities, but many towns have built them. We are progressing, still hoping that some day our streams will again run clear and pure as they did in pioneer days.

Running water purifies itself because of the bacteria in the water and the oxygen of the air. Many kinds of bacteria feed upon organic matter. By organic matter is meant material that is alive or has come from living things. [The chemist defines organic matter as matter that contains carbon.] These bacteria destroy the organic matter, changing it through a long series of changes to harmless simple substances. If the sewage is sufficiently diluted with water, the bacteria in time will destroy practically all of it. If the load of sewage is very heavy for the volume of the stream, the bacteria cannot destroy it completely, and the stream remains foul and unfit for drinking, washing, or industrial purposes. Fish cannot live in it. Such an overload of sewage is common in densely settled regions. Yet this can be changed, and our streams may run pure again.

Sewage disposal on the farm. The well is a constant source of danger. Water seeping in may bring in disease germs. Typhoid has often been traced to country wells. A case of typhoid occurs where germs from a person who carries them have reached another person. The commonest method of transfer to the second person is through bodily wastes, especially from the digestive system, reaching the drinking water of the second person. An outdoor toilet which consists simply of an outhouse built over a hole dug in the ground can easily contaminate the soil for many yards. If ground water from such soil can reach the well, the well may be contaminated. Care must be taken, but is not always taken, to see that such outhouses are so located that they cannot possibly drain into the well.

Where running water can be had in a country house, a very common method for disposal of sewage and waste water has been the use of a cesspool. A cesspool is simply a large hole dug in the ground and generally lined with stones or walled with concrete provided with holes on the sides and bottom. The sewage runs into the cesspool through a pipe and slowly seeps out through the bottom and sides. Bacteria destroy some of the sewage on its way through the pool and out at the bottom, but the

process is far from complete and the ground may be thoroughly saturated with sewage. The cesspool is thus a source of danger. It should be located downhill from the water supply and as far away as possible. It should be dug in well-drained land, not in low or swampy land from which the sewage and water would drain away with difficulty. A further disadvantage of the cesspool is that there is often danger of overflow and contamination of surface water. Such overflow may occur in rainy weather and especially after the cesspool has been used for a few years and the outlets are coated with grease from household wastes.

The septic tank. An improvement upon the cesspool is the septic tank. The tank is divided into two or more chambers by partial partitions. The sewage moves more slowly through the tank, and destruction by bacteria is more complete. Most of the solid material that cannot be destroyed by the bacteria collects as "sludge" in the bottom of the first chamber. In the course of a few years this sludge must be removed. A large part of the solid material, however, is destroyed by bacteria. Some kinds

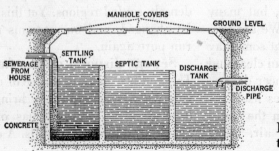

In a septic tank bacteria destroy sewage

Ewing Galloway, N. Y.

In this sewage disposal plant chemicals are added to help waste materials to disintegrate

of bacteria live at the surface where they find oxygen. Other kinds that need little or no free air live below the surface and carry on their destructive work of feeding upon the sewage. Finally only water remains in the last chamber of the tank. This water flows out through the branching drains and seeps into the soil. Although the septic tank is much more effective in destroying sewage, it must be located where seepage cannot pollute the soil through which water seeps to the water supply.

City sewage disposal plants. The principle of destruction of sewage by bacteria in the septic tank is used in the large sewage disposal plants of the cities. Generally, however, additional treatment is added. The sewage may first be sprayed into

A modern city often destroys garbage by burning in a furnace. The interior and exterior of a city disposal plant

Keystone View, N. Y.   Ewing Galloway, N. Y.

Ewing Galloway, N. Y.

This is not the best method of getting rid of refuse. The barges are towed to sea and dumped, but the refuse often washes up on the beach

the air to allow it to absorb oxygen. It is then led into settling basins. Afterwards, it trickles over coarse obstructions, such as coarse rocks where the air-loving bacteria live and feed upon it. Then it passes into settling basins where solids which the bacteria do not destroy are collected. The sludge must be removed from time to time. The liquid sewage next passes through sand filters where the process of destruction is complete and where all undestroyed material is removed. The clear water may be turned into a stream without danger. Sometimes, liquid chlorine is added to the discharge water to destroy any germs of disease that might possibly remain. Chlorine does no damage to the stream because it dissolves in the water and then combines with other substances or evaporates into the air.

Garbage disposal. Suppose the garbage man did not come to the city home for a month! What a pile of filth there would be! If it were in summer, the garbage would decay with the growth of bacteria and molds, and vile odors of gases would arise. In the warmth of decomposing material, bacteria of disease, with which garbage is very likely to be contaminated, would develop. Flies attracted to the heap of fly food would lay their eggs, the eggs would hatch in a week or so, and the place would swarm with flies. The flies walking about the garbage would carry germs of disease on their feet and, making their way indoors, would spread them over the

What would you do with your trash and garbage if the community did not remove it for you?

cake, bread, and butter on which they walked. Rats find a rich supply of food in garbage, and they would multiply at an alarming rate. A pair of rats may produce four or five litters of young in a year, if well fed by garbage, and each litter may contain from four or five to nine or ten young rats. In the course of a year rats would swarm. Rats are dangerous carriers of disease. The Black Death that killed millions of people was carried by fleas that live on rats.

Just such piles of garbage are to be found outside some of the smaller cities where the garbage men dump the collections. Garbage dumps are a constant menace to health. In coast cities garbage has been taken to sea and dumped, but the dumped garbage has been washed ashore on

bathing beaches. Suits in courts have brought the order to erect garbage disposal plants. The simplest and safest way to dispose of garbage is to burn it in incinerating plants at high temperatures, as high as 1600° F. When placed in incinerators, garbage is burned to ashes quickly. Gases produced are nearly odorless.

Some cities get money from their garbage. The garbage is placed in great kettles holding a ton or several tons. A solvent that dissolves fat is added and the air-tight lid closed. Steam is then passed into the double walls of the kettle. Machinery keeps the material stirred. In a few hours the fat is dissolved out of the garbage. The solvent containing the grease is drained off. The solvent and water are distilled and recovered

177

for use again. The grease is sold to soap and glycerin factories. The part of the garbage remaining is made into fertilizer.

In camp and in the country home it is important that garbage be disposed of every day to avoid furnishing food and breeding places for flies and rats. Prompt burial is one method of disposal if care is taken that the burial places cannot contaminate the water supply. Burning in a very hot fire is a better method.

In the city home as well as in the country it is important that garbage pails be kept clean and securely fastened against dogs, rats, and other animals. If they are not washed frequently, they are sure to breed flies and give out foul odors. If every time the garbage is emptied, a little "chloride of lime" is thrown in the pail, hot water added, and the inside of the pail washed with a rag on the end of a stick, the garbage can may be as inoffensive as the kitchen pots.

How to Learn about Sewage Disposal

I. Study by observation the safe disposal of wastes.

1. Examine the trap below the sink. With a funnel to represent the sink, a glass tube which you may bend over a gas flame, and some rubber tubing for connection, you can work out a model trap that will work.

2. Perhaps, if you are handy and ingenious, you can make a working model of the toilet tank shown in the figure.

3. If possible visit sewage and garbage disposal plants and learn of their operation.

II. Read the chapter.

III. Test yourself with the following:

1. With the model trap or with the figure, explain how the trap works and why it is necessary to put a trap in the waste pipe.

2. With the figure before you, explain how the toilet tank works, as you would explain it to pupils who were absent when you studied it in class.

3. Why is it harmful to turn untreated sewage into streams?

4. If "running water purifies itself," as is said, why is it necessary to build sewage disposal plants?

5. Why is sewage on the farm or in the country home especially dangerous?

How can sewage be properly disposed of in the country home? With the figure open before you, explain how septic tanks work.

6. Explain how sewage is made harmless in a sewage disposal plant.

7. How is garbage disposed of so that it cannot become a source of danger? Why is it not safe to feed garbage from a city to hogs?

8. In a camp or country home, how may garbage be disposed of safely?

9. When is the garbage pail a source of danger? How may the garbage pail be made harmless and inoffensive?

IV. Think out the answer to the following questions:

1. On a picnic, how can garbage and other wastes be disposed of inoffensively and without danger?

2. Suppose that you were camping for two weeks. Plan a camp, arranging tent, cooking fire, toilet, washing place, and garbage disposal with reference to the water supply and the slope of the land.

3. Make similar plans for a house in the country that is supplied with water from a well.

V. Vocabulary. Were there any new words? Perhaps you know these:

contaminated　　　　septic

Unit Five

Some Plants and Animals of the House and Garden

Imagine what would happen to you if all green plants on earth died. To understand how living things make a living on earth, we must understand how plants live. We shall study how plants grow in garden, farm, or window box.

Many things live on plants. Cows and men eat them. Many other things eat them. Plants sicken and die because microscopic things eat them. Plants crowd one another for a place to live, and often plants we want to live are crowded under and die. Farming is a long battle with insects, a battle never to be finished while we are on earth. But we have many animals fighting insects with us, not to help us but to help themselves. We can help these enemies of insects and benefit by their attacks.

If we did not know how to keep our harvest, food might disappear in a mass of ill-smelling refuse in our cellars and storehouses. The abundant supply of food throughout the winter, even perishable fruits, shows that through scientific study, we have learned preservation.

(1) Ewing Galloway, N. Y., (2) (4) (5) Black Star, N. Y., (3) Philip D. Gendreau, N. Y.

Chapter Twenty-five

A Plant and Its Life

What is a seed? You know a seed when you see it, but try to say what it is. You might say it is something that starts the plant. Yes, but other things start plants. If you make a cutting from the stem of a rose or a grapevine and plant it in moist sand, taking care that it does not dry out, it will probably grow a new rosebush or a new grapevine. If you break a twig from a willow and stick it in the moist ground, it will probably grow to be a tree. If you plant a piece of potato bearing an "eye," it will grow to be a potato vine. If you plant a piece of the root of a sweet potato or of a raspberry bush, you can raise a new plant. Even a leaf of a bryophyllum will grow new plants.

So a seed is not just something that will start a new plant. It is true that a seed will grow up into another

These seeds are miniature lima bean plants. What are the things that will make them grow?

Philip D. Gendreau, N. Y.

plant, but just what is the seed? Do not guess what a seed is. Get a seed and find out. Soak a few lima beans in water overnight. Next day examine the outside of some dry beans and some soaked beans. You notice the scar where the seed was attached by a little stem to the inside of the pod in which it grew. This scar is called the *hilum.* Close to this scar, you will notice, if you look sharply, a very tiny hole. If you squeeze a soaked bean lightly, you may see a little water ooze out of this hole. This hole is called the *micropyle.* It helps to take in water in a hurry when the bean is soaked. Water, however, will also go in through the skin.

Slide the skin, or seed coat, off the soaked bean. It sticks very tightly to the dry bean. This coat is a protection to the seed. It keeps out bacteria and molds, and helps to shed the water during the season when the bean seed is resting.

Inside the seed coat there are several things. Did you ever look to see? You find the seed made up chiefly of two big, fleshy halves. These two big halves are the seed leaves, or *cotyledons.* You see also, near the point where the halves are joined together, a little projection a fraction of an inch long like a little pigtail with only one curve. It looks like a small beginning of a root.

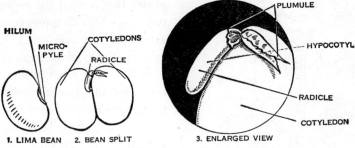

A lima bean contains a young bean plant. Name its parts or organs

This is the little stem of the seed. It is called the *hypocotyl*. The tip end of the stem is the beginning of the root, and is called the *radicle*. Now very gently open the two cotyledons, or seed leaves, part way and look in. You will see some tiny beginnings of leaves. Inside these tiny folded beginnings of leaves is a little point that will grow to be the stem. The little stem point and beginning leaves form a bud. This little bud in the seed is called the *plumule*. So here is a little plant already formed in a seed—leaves and bud that will grow into stem and leaves above ground, a little stem, and the beginning of a root.

Most of what you eat in the lima bean is seed leaf. A drop of iodine on the broken seed leaf will turn it black. That shows that there is starch stored there. There are also stored proteins. The starch and protein are food for the young plant that give it a start in life while its root is growing down into the soil and its leaves and stem are growing up into the light. In many seeds, like corn and wheat, instead of having the food stored in seed leaves, the little plant

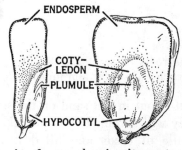

A grain of corn, showing its parts

lies at one side of the stored food or embedded in the food.

A seed, then, is a little plant with a supply of food, wrapped around with a good coat to protect it.

What starts the seed growing? The little plant in the seed is alive but it can endure hardship even though it is small and tender. The seeds of our native plants lie all winter in the frozen ground; yet the little plants inside do not freeze to death. The seeds of some garden plants lie all winter on the dry shelf, yet will grow when better times come.

The seeds that have lain all winter in the soil do not start to sprout (or germinate) until the spring sun has warmed the soil. If kept in the refrigerator they will not sprout. The seeds left on the shelf will not sprout.

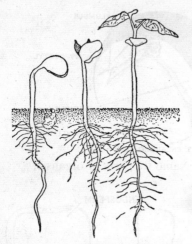

The roots of seedlings cling to earth particles for water and mineral food

But if put in wet sand on the shelf, they will sprout. If you uncorked a bottle of seeds and filled it with water, the seeds would not sprout. They must have air to breathe.

If the good things needed by the seed are supplied—warmth, water, air—the seed grows. You can try it out by putting some corn or peas in some moist sand. Set them aside in the house or outdoors if the weather is warm. Do not have the dish flooded with water, for then the air cannot reach them. Watch them as they grow. Dig a seed up every day or two to see how its underground parts are doing. Or you can follow their growth if you plant them in a glass.

What the root does. When a seed sprouts (or germinates), the root grows down. Downward, it does not grow upward. It does not make a mistake. If you turn the sprouted seed upside down, the root turns around and grows down again. If you sprout the seeds on moist blotting paper in a covered saucer, you can see almost at the end of the root a fine fuzz. With a lens or magnifier you can see that the fuzz is made up of delicate hairs. They are called *root hairs*. They are the drinking parts of the plant. All the water and all the mineral food from the soil enters the plant through the root hairs. If you gently pull up a young plant, a seedling, from your pot of sand, it will bring up a small teaspoonful of sand. With the lens you can see the root hairs entwined around the grains of sand. They are searching out the tiny films of moisture that surround the particles of the soil. That is the reason that plants

These grass roots by their extent and complexity hold the soil together

Ewing Galloway, N. Y.

can grow in soil that seems dry to our fingers and eyes. The root hairs can find moisture that your fingers cannot. [The plant drinks through the "skin" of the root hairs, although our strongest microscopes show us no holes in the skin. Not only water but also the solutions of soil minerals pass directly through the skin or membrane of the root hairs. This process of passing of water and solutions through membranes is called *osmosis*.]

Watch from day to day how the branches come out on the root. The taproot that grows straight down sends out secondary branches, and these send out branches in turn. Try gently to pull up a plant that is some inches high to see how securely it is anchored. Such an anchorage holds the smaller plants in the ground when a passing animal brushes against them. It holds the trees in the ground when a gale tears at their branches and trunks.

Dig up a plant six inches high and wash away the soil from the roots. Note how the branches of the root entangle themselves with the soil, holding it together in a ball. It is little wonder that the grass sod and the trees with the smaller plants about their roots hold the soil on the hills, while the rain washes away the soil from the bare hillside until it is furrowed with great gullies or washed down to the barren rock. The hill covered with sod, or better with woods, absorbs rain and holds it after the storm has passed, gradu-ally allowing it to come to the surface in swamps and springs that keep the streams flowing in dry weather.

When you run the lawn mower over a dandelion, you may seem to discourage it for a few days, but you do not kill it. A new crop of leaves replaces those that you cut off, and in due season a new flower stalk comes up. Did you ever dig up a dandelion by the roots? The fat root is gorged with food. New leaves to replace those cut off draw on the abundant supplies of food in the root. Similar roots are beets, carrots, parsnips, and radishes. The thick roots of the cassava yield tapioca.

Many kinds of roots have been used in medicine. Many nowadays are used only in home remedies of the back country. Bloodroot, dandelion, May apple, licorice, rhubarb, snakeroot, and yellow jasmine are some of the many. Ginseng is greatly valued by the Chinese, and collectors still go through our woods collecting it for export to China. The medicine stored in the plant does not seem to do the plant any good. It is waste.

Potatoes, swollen parts of underground stems, store food for the plant

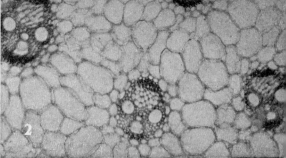

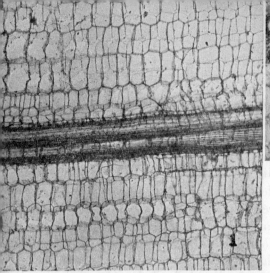

Hugh Spencer, Chester, Conn.

Magnified bits of cornstalk cut length-
wise (1) and across (2). The white
strips or dots are water tubes

What the stem does. By the
time that the roots have become well
branched, the stem has grown up a
few inches, and the cotyledons have
spread out. All parts above ground
have become green. Shortly the cotyledons begin to shrink, as their stored
food is used by the growing plant.
When their food is gone, their shriv-
eled remains drop from the stem.
By this time the little bud that lay
between them in the seed has grown
to be a stem with green leaves. The
roots and leaves have now taken over
the work of providing for the plant.

At this stage, cut off the stem and
stand it in a little red ink. Cut off
also the stems of some corn seedlings about six or eight inches high
and a stalk of celery or the stem of
a light-colored weed, and stand them
in red ink. Next day you will see red
ink has run up into the stem and into
the leaves of the corn and the celery.
You may see it also in the leaves of
the bean, although sometimes the
dark green of the bean leaves con-
ceals the red. If you cut a fresh slice
across the stems, you will see little
red dots where the ink ran up. These
red dots and the red lines going up
the stems of the plants and the
strings in the celery mark the tubes
(vessels) that carry water and dissolved minerals up from the soil.

If the young plants are growing
in the midst of grass or other plants,
the stem grows rapidly upward,
keeping the leaves spread out in the
sun even with the other plants or
above them. The stem is always
pushing upward toward the light so
that the leaves may spread out in the
life-giving sun. The stem is the support of the plant that holds it up in
the light, and through its tubes it
carries the water and mineral solutions to the leaves and flowers that
must be in the light to change the
minerals into food.

Instead of standing up in the
light, some plants climb upon others
or upon fences and walls. The pea
vine wraps delicate tendrils around
supports and so climbs up to the
light. The bean twines around poles.
Some roses just sprawl over a fence,
their thorns helping to hold them on
the fence. Ivy attaches itself to a
wall by little discs on the ends of
tendrils.

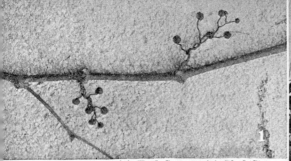

(1) The ivy climbs a wall by means of tendrils and discs while the bean plant (2) twines about its support

Why plants are green. Green is a magic color. The green color of leaves is one of the most wonderful things in the world. On it depends the life of the plant. Men and the animals of the earth owe their lives to the green-colored stuff in the leaves.

Potatoes that sprout in the cellar send out pale, sickly, spindly stems. Potatoes that grow in the sunlight become green and sturdy plants. If you take a sturdy green plant, such as a geranium, and shut it in a dark closet, it slowly loses its green, healthy color. Sunlight develops the rich green.

When sunshine falls on a green leaf, something happens inside. Pluck a leaf from a plant that has stood several hours in the bright sun, and kill the leaf by plunging into hot water. Then soak it in a corked bottle of alcohol until the next day. Do the same with a leaf from a plant that stood overnight in a dark closet. Next day the leaves are bleached white and the alcohol is a brilliant green. The green substance has been dissolved out of the leaf. [The green substance of the leaf is called *chlorophyll,* which means "leaf green."] Then soak the whitened leaves in iodine solution. The leaf that stood in the sun becomes dark or black; the leaf that stood in the dark closet is merely stained brown. The substance that turns dark with iodine is starch. The green leaf in the sunlight formed starch. The green leaf in the dark formed none. [The making of starch by the green leaf in sunlight is called *photosynthesis.*]

Food for the world. Starch is food. Plants eat it. You eat it in potatoes, corn, peas, beans, bread, breakfast cereals, and many other foods. Our starch comes from green plants growing in the sunlight. The plants also make fats and proteins. Our entire food supply comes from green plants in the sunlight. If you eat meat, you are merely eating green plants once removed, for the cow, hog, or sheep ate the green plant. Without green plants and sunlight our food supply would vanish. Neither we nor our domestic animals can live on minerals and air as plants do. Plants too need starch, fats and

185

How a leaf
develops
from a
bud

proteins as we do, but green plants in the sunlight make these food substances out of soil minerals, water, and air. The green leaves are the food factories for the whole world.

A plant spends most of its time growing. When a plant has sent its roots to find minerals and water in the soil, and when its green leaves have spread out in the sunlight, its work in life for a time is making food and using the food to grow. Some plants grow for a thousand years or several thousand, like the "big trees," the sequoias, of California. Other plants grow for less than a year, then die. Before they die, they provide for future life of their kind. [Plants that live for many years are called *perennials* and those that live for one year are *annuals*.]

What is in a bud? No guessing. Bring in a twig even in winter and place it in a jar of water on a sunny window sill. Have patience. You will see winter buds along the side and at the end of the twig. After a few days, or perhaps a week or so, the tight bud scales begin to open slowly. You see something green pushing through. The bud scales are pushed farther apart and finally fall off. By that time, if you are impatient, you can unfold the little green things and

spread them out. In a few days more they would unfold themselves. Packed up tightly in the bud were little leaves partly formed and all folded in a definite way. Encircled by the leaves is a stem.

What is a flower? Some buds have flowers folded inside them. If you bring into the house in winter some twigs of forsythia or cherry and place them in water on the window sill, you can watch them unfold. Then you may see in winter how a flower is built.

Perhaps to you a flower is a bright pretty thing of the garden. Some flowers are bright and showy and some are not. Have you ever seen the flowers of an oak tree or the flowers of grasses? The brilliant parts are missing from these and many other flowers. The red, yellow, blue, and other glorious colors of the garden flowers often do not work for the plant. Man has spoiled them for their rightful work. In other flowers the brightly colored parts are very important to the plant as are also the odor and the sweet nectar. But even on such plants the showy parts are not the most essential or necessary parts of the flower.

Before the flower bud opens, you see it covered with green parts some-

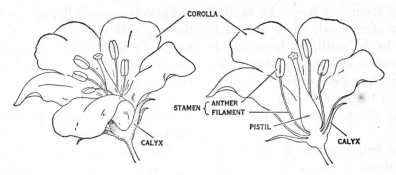

The parts of a flower

what like leaves. These green parts protect the parts within. As the flower expands, they are spread apart, and the inner parts grow out. The outer green parts are called *sepals*. [The whole ring of sepals make up the *calyx*.] They fall away from many plants as the flower opens, but in others they are retained and folded over the inner parts of the flower again when the bright-colored parts fade and fall.

The usual bright-colored parts are the *petals*. [The circle of petals makes up the *corolla*.] Inside the circle of petals you see a circle of little stalks each with a knob at the top. In most flowers these structures are either yellow or white. They are called the *stamens*. In the center of the flower is another part called the *pistil*, or there may be several pistils [also called *carpels*]. The lower part of the pistil is swollen. If you split open this swollen bottom part with a pin point or the point of a knife, you see inside some tiny objects like exceedingly small seeds. They are the beginnings of seeds, but they may or may not grow into seeds [*ovules*].

How bees help the flowers. You know that bees buzz around flowers, gathering the sweet nectar they find in them to make honey. It looks as if the plants were kind to the bees, in giving them nectar. But the bees must do work for the plant. If you touch the inside of a flower with your finger tip, you will often find a yellow dust sticking to it. The dust sticks to the bees also. As a bee backs out of a flower, you can often see her hind legs swollen out with little balls of this dust. The dust is called *pollen*. It is produced in the knobs at the tops of the stamens. [These knobs are called *anthers*.] When a bee visits a second flower, some of the dust is rubbed off on the top of the pistil of the second flower. [The top of the pistil is called the *stigma*.] The pollen from the first flower is very important to the second flower. The flower must have pollen from another flower of the same kind in order to produce seed. In most flowers no seeds will form if the pollen is not placed upon the top of the pistil. The bees do this service for the plant. They carry pollen from one flower to another of the same kind. Then the seeds grow in the pistil. So important is the service of the bees that apple growers hire hives of bees from bee-keepers to place in their orchards during the flowering of the apple trees.

The bright colors of the petals serve the same purpose as the bright lights over the store and the bright colors in the windows. They draw the attention of the bees to the flowers. The odor of flowers also attracts the bees, for bees can smell flowers at long distances, much farther away than we can. The bees seek nectar to make honey and pollen to make bee bread. The flower has much more pollen than it needs to start seeds forming, and it has no other use for nectar than to feed bees. The nectar is so placed that the bees must perform their service to the plant before they can reach it.

The egg in the flower. The most important parts of the flower cannot be seen without a microscope, and to see them even with a microscope the specimens must be carefully prepared. Inside each of the little seedlike bodies (ovules) in the swollen part at the base of the pistil (the ovary) is a microscopic cell different from all the cells around about it. This important cell is the *egg cell* or *egg*. The new plant grows from the egg cell, as the chicken grows from the egg. In the chicken's egg also is an egg cell, and it is from the egg cell that the young chick arises. In both plants and animals the new individual arises from a microscopic cell, the egg cell.

Inside the cells are still smaller parts. A very important part within the cell is a little body called the *nucleus*. Inside the egg cell is a nucleus called the *egg nucleus*. Inside the grain of pollen are two nuclei called the *sperm nuclei*.

After the pollen is brought to the pistil, the sperm nucleus enters the egg cell and unites with the egg nucleus to form one nucleus. From the united nucleus a new plant arises. All the complicated structure of the flower which you saw in the diagram on page 187 is just nature's means of bringing pollen to the pistil, after which the sperm nucleus unites with the egg nucleus. The union starts the seed which grows to be a new plant.

Where does the apple come from? In spring the apple tree is covered for a short time with bright flowers. Soon the flowers fade and their petals fall. But the whole flower does not fall from the tree. Look carefully and you will see that an important part of the flower is still on the twig. Two weeks after the petals have fallen, you will find small, round green objects where the flowers used to be. They are the parts of the flower that stayed on the tree. If you watch these round green parts you will see them grow into apples.

(1) (3) Black Star, (2) Ewing Galloway, (4) Hugh Spencer, (5) J. C. Allen
Some typical flowers. (1) apple, (2) hollyhocks, (3) cactus, (4) grass, (5) hyacinth

They are the lower parts of the flowers including the pistils. These parts of the flower grow to be fruits.

Inside the fruits are the seeds. For them the flower and the fruit exists. The seeds are to start the new plants next year. The fruits of the apple and cherry are inducements to animals to scatter the seeds about where new plants can grow. You have probably seen apple and cherry trees growing in fence corners where birds, squirrels, and boys have dropped cherry stones and apple cores.

Not all fruits are large and juicy like apples and watermelons. A pod of peas is a fruit. A cotton boll is a fruit. Fruits of maple and ash have wings upon which they flutter away on the wind, giving the young plants a chance to grow where they will not be overshadowed by the mother tree. In the fall you see many dry fruits standing on the top of weed stems in the fields. Bur fruits stick to your stockings, and you scatter the seeds in new places.

A large part of the food made by the plant is stored in fruits, seeds, and other parts which start new plants. Swollen roots and bulbs are also nature's means of starting new plants. After seeds are produced many plants die. Flowers must be cut from many of our garden plants to keep the plants blooming all season. As soon as the seeds form, many plants stop blooming.

What part of the apple blossom was the apple? What grows inside the apple?

J. C. Allen

How to Learn about a Plant and Its Life

I. Study germination.

1. Experiment No. 50. What starts new plants? In pots or out-of-doors try planting the following: a piece of potato containing an eye; a cutting from a geranium or from a rosebush or from some other plant; a bulb; a portion of a fleshy root; some seeds.

2. Study several seeds—peas, beans, grains of corn. Follow the description in the chapter for guidance.

3. Experiment No. 51. Under what conditions will seeds grow? Keep some lima beans dry. Plant some in pots of damp sand. Put one pot of seeds in the refrigerator. Put one pot on the window sill. Keep the soil moist, but not wet. Put some lima beans in a bottle and cover with two or three inches of water to shut out the air. Examine for several weeks to determine which grow and which do not.

Conclusion: Under what conditions will seeds sprout (germinate)?

4. Experiment No. 52. What grows from a seed? Plant a large number of peas and beans in moist sawdust. Keep the sawdust moist, but not wet. Every day dig up a seed or two to see how they are progressing. Compare with the seeds that you dissected (took apart). Where do roots, stem, leaves come from? Make a series of drawings showing the growth from day to day.

5. Experiment No. 53. Do roots and stems grow in definite directions? Make a pocket garden out of glass and blotting paper as shown in the figure. Lay seeds of radish or other small seeds on the paper in various positions. Stand the pocket garden on edge in the pan of water. After the seeds are well started, turn the glass on another edge. Again in a few days turn it to a third edge. Note what happens in the root and stem. Make sketches to show your findings. Write a report in the required form.

6. After the seeds are well grown in Experiment No. 52, dig one carefully, and gently wash away the sawdust from the roots. Examine with a lens and under the microscope, if you have one.

7. As you hike about the country take your camera along and take pictures which show how roots keep the soil on the hills. If you have no camera, make a written report, or make a series of sketches.

8. Experiment No. 54. What is the path of sap upward through a plant? Cut off the stem and leaves of a corn seedling six inches high or more and stand in red ink. A stalk of celery will do instead of corn, or any weed that does not have stems so densely green that you cannot see the red ink inside. Examine the plant after standing an hour in red ink and again next day.

9. Experiment No. 55. When does a green plant make starch? Stand a plant in the sun for several hours. Place the second plant in a dark closet. After the plant has stood in the sun for several hours, pull off a leaf while the

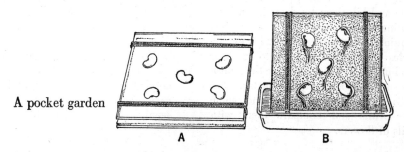

A pocket garden

A   B

plant is still in the sun. Take also a leaf from the plant in the dark. Put each in a test tube and cover with alcohol. Let stand until next day when the plants will be bleached white. You can bleach the leaves in a few minutes in hot alcohol. Do not heat the alcohol over a flame or you may be badly burned. Cork up the tubes of alcohol or place them at the far side of the room. Heat a tin of water to boiling. Turn out the fire and place the uncorked test tubes with the alcohol and leaves in the hot water.

When the leaves are white, soak them in iodine. The leaves will stain brown with iodine, but if you look through the leaf toward a light or if you examine under a microscope, you will see that the leaves contain little black bodies. Iodine turns starch black or dark blue. Note which of the leaves becomes dark blue or black.

Write a report in the required form.

10. EXPERIMENT No. 56. What grows from a bud? Bring twigs from several kinds of trees indoors and stand them in water until they begin to open. Cherry usually opens very readily. Watch what comes from the buds. Take some of the buds apart as they loosen and find what makes up a bud.

Write a report in the required form.

11. What makes up a flower? Take some flowers apart. Learn the names of the parts. Follow the description in the chapter and match your flower with the figures.

12. How do the bees help the flowers? Catch some bees in a large-mouthed bottle and kill them by dropping a little gasoline or kerosene on their bodies. Examine the bee's legs to see how she carries pollen, and her feet to see how she clings to flowers. Examine the mouth to see how she sucks up the nectar.

13. Cut open an apple and some other fruits and compare them with pistils of flowers.

II. Read the chapter and study the figures carefully.

III. Test yourself with the following questions:

1. Sketch the seeds and label their parts.

2. Under what conditions will the seed germinate?

3. Tell what grows from each part of the seed.

4. If you turned a seed upside down, which way would root and stem grow?

5. What is the name of the structures that do the actual drinking for the root?

6. Why do dandelions sprout up so quickly after they have been mowed down on the lawn?

7. What uses does man make of various roots?

8. Up what paths does the sap rise in the corn plant?

9. What does sunlight do for a plant? What food can you show made by green plants?

10. What is a bud?

11. Cover up the labels in the figures of the flower and name its parts.

12. How do bees benefit flowers? How do the bright colors of flowers benefit them?

13. Where does the apple come from? What good does the fruit do the plant?

IV. Think out the answers to the following or learn by investigation:

1. What insects in addition to bees carry pollen from one flower to another? Do any other animals carry pollen?

2. Many flowers that do not open until evening are white. What advantage is white to the plant?

3. How are seedless oranges grown?

V. Vocabulary.

cotyledon	hypocotyl
germinate	petal
sepal	pistil
pollen	

Chapter Twenty-six

Making a Garden

The right place to live. The green plants of our gardens and fields are living things. They must find certain things to keep them alive. There must be light, especially sunlight, or the green plants will fade away and they cannot make their food. They must find warmth, or they cannot live. They must have air. They must have water, neither too much nor too little. They can survive conditions that are far from the best, but there are limits.

Certain kinds of plants can make a living where others fail. Most of our garden flowers and field crops would not grow in the woods. Yet you find the ground in the woods covered with green plants. Such plants can endure the shade. Ferns and mosses grow in moist dark corners under projecting rocks and in the mouths of caves. Some kinds of plants are built to grow standing in the water-soaked soil of swamps and others in flowing water. Cactus, aloes, and sagebrush grow in the desert. Cactus has a thick skin that resists the desert sun and its thick stem stores water. White toadstools

How are the cactus (1) and the thistle (2) fitted to defend themselves? the ivy (3) to reach sunlight? How is the fern (4) fitted for the shade?

(1) (4) *Black Star*, (2) *Philip D. Gendreau*, (3) *Ewing Galloway*

and mushrooms cannot grow in soil and make their own food. These plants belong to the group called *fungi*. They feed upon the dead plants and animals in the soil. Some fungi feed upon living plants and kill them. Such is the chestnut blight that destroyed the chestnut trees of eastern United States. All plants and all animals depend in the end upon a soil that will support good green plants to make food for all the rest.

What soil is. There is more in garden soil than a back yard full of dirt. The basis of the soil is ground-down rock. You can see the bits of rock if you examine good garden soil under a lens or a microscope. Few plants, however, would grow in ground rock. Much happens to the ground rock before it will grow a garden. Weathering and the action of such coarse plants as will grow in mineral soil help to tear apart the rock substance and set free mineral compounds. Then more plants can grow. The dead plants, dead leaves and wood, dead animals, and the waste of living animals fall upon the soil and are covered over. Molds

and bacteria grow in the dead plant and animal stuff. The bacteria and molds bring about the decay of the organic matter (matter from living things). The decomposing organic matter is called *humus*. Usually it is dark in color, sometimes almost or quite black. As you dig into the ground, you usually dig first through the dark humus and then come to mineral soil very different in color and feel. Plants grow chiefly in the humus layer, although large plants send roots into the mineral soil.

The soil for the garden. A good garden differs from a poor garden largely in soil, sunshine, water, and work with the brain and muscle. Soil may be *clay*, heavy and sticky in wet weather and hard to dig and plow. Then in dry weather it bakes to brick. It holds water tightly and is wet and cold in springtime after looser soils have warmed up and sent the young plants above ground.

At the opposite extreme of soils is *sand*. It is so loose that water runs right through it. A half hour after a rain you can sit on sand without getting your clothes wet. It is easy

Have you seen these creatures around your garden? Can you tell how each

Philip D. Gendreau   *Black Star*

enough to dig and plow, but there is little use to do either. It warms up early in spring because there is little water in it. Seeds get an early start. But it lacks moisture and the mineral compounds that plants need.

A mixture of sand and clay is *loam.* It has good qualities of both sand and clay without all the evils of either. It forms the best basis for garden soil. When it contains a good mixture of humus, it is the best garden soil. It is loose enough to be worked easily. It holds water better than sand, but not so well as clay. Therefore, it warms up well in spring, but does not easily lose its life-giving moisture in summer.

A necessary part of the garden soil is the humus. It is made up of rotted leaves, leaf mold. Leaf mold gathered from the lowest layer of dead leaves in the woods is an excellent addition to the garden bed. You can make your own leaf mold, if you have a corner where you can make a compost pile of dead leaves and plants together with certain vegetable scraps from the kitchen such as lettuce leaves and pea pods. In spring you can take the lower, well-rotted part of your compost pile to spade into the garden soil. In the fields, especially in sandy fields, green crops such as rye are sometimes planted in the fall and plowed under in the spring to add humus to the soils which lack it.

Humus adds many good qualities to the soil. It makes the soil looser so that air can penetrate to the roots. It holds moisture like a sponge. And, perhaps most important of all, it is food for the soil bacteria.

Living things in the soil. Good soil is swarming with living things. You can easily find many of them by digging carefully. You readily find earthworms, beetle grubs, ants, and other insects. You often find the threads of molds among moist leaves. Most important of all are bacteria. Many of these plants and animals are feeding upon the dead things in the soil. Thus the dead things are destroyed. The bacteria and other living things give out into the soil the waste products from their bodies. These wastes contain chemical compounds which the growing

benefits or imperils your soil and plants?

Black Star   *Ewing Galloway*

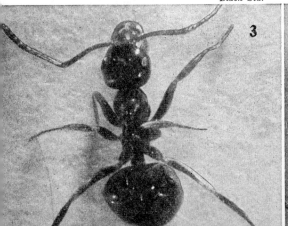
3

4

plants need. The chemical compounds become part of the mineral substances which make up the soil.

You may know that clover makes the soil rich. The ancient Romans knew that, but they did not know why. If you pull up a young plant of clover, beans, or alfalfa from moist, loose soil, you may find on the roots little bumps or nodules. In these nodules live bacteria. Somewhat similar bacteria live in the soil. These peculiar kinds of bacteria are the real plants that make the soil rich when clover or alfalfa is grown. The bacteria take a gas, nitrogen, from the air. They make it into substances called *nitrates* that green plants need in order to grow. It is because the bacteria make nitrates from nitrogen that they enrich the soil.

Feeding the soil. If you grow corn or other crops in the same field year after year, the crop gets steadily poorer. One reason for this decrease in the crop may be that the crop takes the same kind of mineral food out of the soil year after year until there is less available to the plant. If the field is allowed to rest, more mineral food will be weathered out from the rock particles of the soil. To give the soil a little rest farmers rotate the crops. One year a farmer may grow corn, the next year wheat, then clover, and then allow the field to stay in grass for pasture for a year or two. After that the sod is plowed and corn begins the rotation of crops again.

When the crop is shipped away and nothing returned to the soil, the chemical substances that the plants need to grow are steadily taken out of the soil and shipped away. Therefore the farmer must put some back in the soil. This he does by spreading manure upon the fields. Commercial fertilizers, which are mixtures of the needed chemical substances, may also be bought and spread upon the fields.

In gardens so many plants are grown in a small space that fertilizers must be added every year to get the best results. The best all-round fertilizer is well-rotted manure. However, it is not always convenient. Then commercial fertilizers may be used, but humus also should be added to the soil.

Making a home for plants. After the fertilizers have been added to the soil, the soil must be made ready for the young plant. The preparation of the soil means some hard work and an understanding of the process. The first reason for digging the soil before planting seeds is to loosen the earth and so allow the young tender roots to grow readily into the soil, but there are other reasons. The dead plant stuff lying on the ground or the sod should be turned under so that it may decay underground and enrich the soil. This adds humus. As we have seen, humus makes a looser, richer soil. In fields or large gardens, the earth is plowed. In a small garden it is usually spaded. The work must be

Many things are important to a good garden: planning, conditioning the soil, fertilizing, and mostly hard work cultivating and keeping out the weeds

thoroughly done to make a good garden soil for the plants.

After the plowing or spading, the soil is harrowed or raked. The large chunks of earth must be broken into smaller pieces. The finer the top of the soil is left the better. The first harrowing or raking should be done two or three weeks before planting time. Weed seeds that are lying in the soil will then start to grow. A second harrowing or raking then will destroy most of them.

Harrowing or raking also helps to control the water supply in the soil. You know that if the end of a towel lies in a basin of water, the water runs up the towel and wets it. Similarly, if you stand some small glass tubes in a tumbler of water, the water runs up the tubes. This running up of water into small spaces, is called *capillarity*. In the soil water runs up between the soil particles by capillarity. The smaller the spaces, the higher the water will rise. Harrowing breaks up the small spaces. If the water rose to the top of the soil, it would evaporate into the air and be lost to the growing plants. Cultivating the soil with harrow and garden rake, therefore, helps to keep the water in the soil.

Still another reason for cultivating is to get air down through the soil. Living things must have oxygen. The host of living things in the soil, including the helpful bacteria, must have air. Higher plants, too, need air. Roots breathe for plants. Air must reach them. Cultivation helps to saturate soil with air.

Thorough cultivation of the soil, therefore, is valuable for a number of reasons. It breaks the sod and allows the roots of the young plants to penetrate the surface. It kills the plants that would compete with the garden plants for food and a place to grow in the sun. It increases the supply of air. It adds to the humus. It conserves moisture for plants.

Planning the garden. If you do not plan well, your garden of flowers

Cultivating the soil helps to control the water supply and admit air

may look like a weed patch. A jumble of fine flowers may add nothing to the appearance of your home. A jumble of vegetables may bring nothing for the kitchen. Planning the garden beforehand gives pleasure on winter nights.

There are a number of things that you must keep in mind in your planning. Plants must have space, and most of the garden vegetables and decorative plants must have sun. There is a limit to the number that may be grown on the home grounds or in the kitchen garden. You must select from many possibilities. You often cannot grow all you want of one kind unless you sacrifice some other kind. Crowding too many into your space will give you inferior plants or none at all. Lay out your garden on paper and plot in the number of plants that you can grow.

See that you get the right plant in the right place. Do not plant the tomatoes where they will be shaded by the corn. Place the corn behind the tomatoes. Do not place the tall phlox in front of the short marigolds. If you run a row of corn north and south, the plants next alongside will get sun part of the day. If you run the corn row east and west, the plants just to the north may get very little sun or none at all.

You must consider the date of maturity, when the vegetable is ready for the pot or when the flower is in bloom. Select so that earlier flowers are followed by later flowers all summer long. Select your varieties of vegetables and plant them at dates that will keep fresh vegetables moving into the kitchen all summer long. Seed catalogues tell how long flowers or vegetables require to reach maturity. Garden books give you further directions for planning your succession.

In decorative gardening about the house grounds, you must also consider colors. All colors do not "go well together." See that the flowers that are in bloom at the same time give pleasing harmony of color. Again the seed catalogues and garden manuals tell you about varieties of plants and give definite plans and planting schemes. You must consider the use of bushes and perennial small plants (plants that live more than one year). The place for the bushes must be selected to add to the attractiveness, concealing a foundation of your neighbor's garage, rounding a projecting angle or furnishing a hiding place for the garbage pail. Bulbs and perennial

198

roots that send up their flowers year after year must be given positions where they need not be disturbed by planting for later flowers.

House plants. Many city homes are dark deserts within. There is not enough sunshine in them to bring a garden plant into bloom, and the air is usually dry enough to kill most plants. To add to the difficulty of life indoors for plants, as well as for human beings, these homes often have air polluted with fumes from gas stoves, oil burners, and coal furnaces. You may not notice the fumes, but the plants do, and your silverware is often tarnished by the fumes.

Grow desert plants in your home, if you find that other plants will not grow. Cactus, sansevieria, and some crassulas survive. Plants that grow in water, like some kinds of tradescantia, add a bit of living nature to a window.

For color you can grow bulbs. In the fall place some Chinese lily bulbs and some paper-white narcissus or some hyacinths in shallow bowls packed about with pebbles. Keep water about the base of the bulbs. Put them in a dark place until they have developed strong roots. Then bring them into the light.

You can add color also by bringing indoors sprays of forsythia and cherry during winter and standing them in tall jars. The winter buds will shortly open into flowers.

The city dweller can often get a diminutive outdoor garden in window boxes attached outside the window. Care must be taken to select small plants that do not need much space. Careful cultivation and frequent watering may bring a bright bit of garden to a city desert.

Test your seeds. If you plant seeds that do not sprout, you lose labor, time, money, and crop. Therefore, it is a wise precaution to test your seed. That is easily done. You should test your seed in the winter or long before it is time to plant the garden. Count out ten or, better, fifty seeds of each kind that you wish to test. To hasten the germination you may soak them overnight. Then place each kind on wet blotting paper in a separate plate. The blotting paper should be moist, but there should not be water in the plate. Cover each plate with a second plate. Set the plates in a warm place but not a hot place. In a few days examine them. If only a few seeds out of the fifty have sprouted, the seeds of the lot are of such poor

Potted plants can bring a bit of the out-of-doors into your house

quality that they should be thrown away and a new supply secured. If all the seeds on a plate but two or three have sprouted, they are a good lot of seeds. Another good method of testing seeds is with the rag doll seed tester. (See Experiment 59.)

Getting an early start. For early flowers and vegetables the seeds must be given a start before it is time to set the plants in the garden. Cold frames and hotbeds are used for early starting. A cold frame is a box without a bottom, set in the ground and covered with a frame holding windowpanes. A hotbed is prepared similarly but the earth is dug out for a foot; then manure is filled in and covered with a few inches of soil. This is done in the late fall. In the spring the manure ferments and warms the soil. At first it may produce so much heat that young plants would be damaged.

The seeds should not be planted until this stage is passed and the temperature has fallen to less than 100° F. In either cold frames or hotbeds, the covers must be raised a little during the heat of the day for ventilation and to allow excess moisture to pass off.

Whether for cold frames or for the garden directly, seeds may be started indoors for early plants. Seeds indoors are usually sown in flats, shallow boxes with holes in the bottom for drainage. Sandy soil should be used. Seeds are sown rather densely in the flats. The soil is then kept moist but never wet.

After the second leaf appears on the young plant, the plants are transplanted, for they are too dense in the flats for further growth. They may be planted in cold frames or hotbeds or out in the garden if the weather has become warm enough.

Hotbeds are used to give plants an early start. Notice how they are opened slightly during the day for ventilation

Ewing Galloway, N. Y.

The soil into which they are transplanted should be a rich loam.

Nursing the garden plants. Seeds also may be sown directly in the garden when the soil has dried and warmed sufficiently in the spring. Seeds are very often planted too deeply in the ground. This practice delays their germination and in wet weather may lead to their rotting. In general the seeds should be covered by only a very thin layer of soil, not more than their own thickness. They are usually sown more densely than they are to be at maturity. Later they are thinned out to the spacing suitable for growth. Directions on the seed packages or in garden manuals tell how much space should be allowed each kind of plant for proper growth.

After the plants are growing in the garden, they still need care. The soil should be worked with hoe or rake or small garden tool regularly to keep the surface loose and free. This loose surface is called a *mulch*. The mulch helps to retain the moisture in the soil for the use of the plants. The frequent cultivation also keeps down the weeds and grass.

Transplanting bushes and trees. If your yard is large enough for a tree or for shrubs, it looks bare without them, even if you have a good growth of showy flowers. It does not pay to grow a shade or ornamental tree from seed. You may get one well-grown from a nursery, or if you have a friend who owns a piece of land, you may get one from the woods, but beware of taking young trees from woods without permission. That is stealing, and the law so regards it.

Late autumn is the best time to transplant trees or bushes and summer is the poorest time. When the plant goes into resting condition for the winter, it will stand more abuse

An expert with proper equipment can transplant a big tree

Ewing Galloway, N. Y.

without suffering than during its active growing season. Some of the roots must be cut, but disturb them as little as possible. Dig out the plant with a ball of earth about the roots, and wrap it about with bagging. Do not lay bare the roots to let the delicate roots die in the drying air. In planting dig a hole bigger than the ball of earth about the roots. Pack loose, good soil about the roots. Water it well. A transplanted tree, if it is of any considerable size, should be supported in the ground with guy ropes tied to stakes. Where the ropes rub the bark of a young tree, they should be packed with bagging or run through sections of an old hose. The branches of the tree must be pruned or trimmed back to balance the cutting back of the roots, for a leaf surface too great will give off more water than the reduced roots can absorb, and the tree will suffer.

Propagating by cuttings and grafting. Rosebushes, geraniums, and many other ornamental plants as well as many food plants such as grapevines, start readily from portions cut from a stem. These cuttings should usually include a node or "joint" where a leaf is attached, for the new roots grow most readily from the little bud in the angle of the leaf. The cutting should be planted in sand and kept moist. Often glass jars are inverted over the cuttings to retain the moisture around them.

Fruit trees and shrubs may be grafted by cutting a twig from the

How to plant a tree

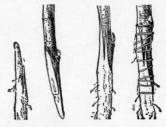

One method of grafting

desired variety and attaching it as shown in the diagram to the stock of one already growing. Care must be taken that the inner edge of the line marking the junction of the wood with the inner green bark (cambium) of both pieces is brought together. It is at this point that the two plants grow together. Buds are cut from peach and cherry trees and slipped into a new stock as shown. This practice is called *budding*.

U.S.D.A.

Steps in budding a tree. A bud is cut from a tree. In another tree a T-shaped cut is made, the bark raised, and the bud slipped under it. Then the bark is bound back in place

How to Learn about Making a Garden

I. Study garden making by observation and experiment.

1. Learning the right place to live. Make a collection of wild plants living in various situations: dry fields, woods, swamps, rich moist ground. Note also, in gardens, the kinds of plants that grow well in the shade and those which grow well in the sun. If you have no opportunity at the present time to search gardens and fields, but wish to grow plants in a city back yard or even in the house, watch what others have grown in such localities. Go to the library for suggestions. Then experiment.

2. To learn what soil is, study soil. Make a collection of soils from various places, the woods, the dry fields, the rich fields, the good gardens. Put a few handfuls from each place in a bag or bottle with a note telling where you got it. In the laboratory study it in this manner:

(a) Spread a little on a piece of paper and study with a lens or microscope. Make notes in your notebook of what you see in each sample.

(b) Throw a little of each sample in water. Shake it up. Note what sinks promptly (sand), what is slow sinking (mud), what floats even the next day (organic matter). Estimate the quantity of each and note it in your notebook.

Heat the organic matter on an iron plate to see if it burns.

3. EXPERIMENT No. 57. Which kind of soil grows the best crops? Put some of each kind in a small pot or can and plant small seeds such as ~oatseeds in each. Tend them, keeping the soil moist but not wet. Find which kind of soil produces best growth. On a second series of the same soils add small amounts of commercial fertilizer and on a third series add well-rotted manure. Number the pots and record the kind of soil, kind of fertilizer, and effects upon growth.

Write a report in the required form.

4. Pull a few clover, alfalfa, or "hog peanut" plants from moist soil, wash away the soil and look for the little bumps, or nodules, in which live the bacteria that take nitrogen from the air.

5. EXPERIMENT No. 58. How does water rise in sand, soil, and gravel? Punch a hole in the bottom of each of six test tubes with the glass rod. Put a little piece of paper toweling in each to hold the dirt. Then fill each of three test tubes with a different kind of soil. Stand the test tubes in a vessel with a little water colored with red ink. Observe the height to which the water rises in each kind of soil. Try packing the soil tightly in a second set of tubes.

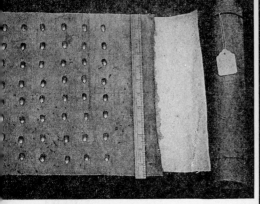

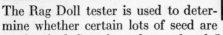

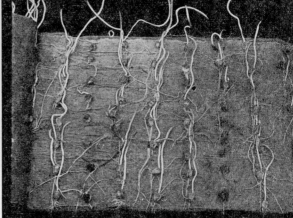

The Rag Doll tester is used to determine whether certain lots of seed are good or bad. Sample seeds are placed (left) in the tester, and then it is rolled up. After a number of days it is opened and inspected (right)

Farm Journal

Conclusion: In which type of soil does water rise most easily to the surface? What is the effect of packing the soil? What advantage would it be to loosen the top of the soil in a garden?

Write a report in the required form.

6. Lay out the plan for a vegetable or flower garden, keeping in mind the size of plants, the location of the plants, time of maturity, the color, etc.

7. Grow bulbs or other house plants.

8. EXPERIMENT No. 59. Make a rag doll seed tester. Take a piece of cloth for each kind of seed, about four inches by fifteen inches. Place the seeds about an inch apart on the cloth. Count and record the number of seeds. Roll up the cloth and wind string loosely around it to hold it. Saturate with water and lay in a moist, warm place. Examine in three or four days, then every two days until you decide how many seeds will sprout.

II. Read the chapter.

III. Test yourself on the following:

1. Name some local plants that grow in each of the following locations: submerged in water, in swamps, in moist, rich fields, in dry fields, in shady woods.

2. What kind of soil is best for the garden? What is the name for the organic material of the soil?

3. How may your garden soil be enriched with decomposing organic matter? Why does it help the soil?

4. What good is done by the little nodules on the roots of the clover?

5. Why is it necessary for the farmer to feed the soil?

6. What should be done with the soil before seeds are planted?

7. How does cultivation improve the soil?

8. Tell certain things that you must keep in mind when you plan a garden.

9. Why is the house often a bad place for growing plants? What plants may be grown successfully in houses?

10. How is it possible to get a "start on nature" in a garden in the spring?

11. What season is the best for setting out trees? Look at page 202 and tell how to set out a young tree.

12. With pages 202–203 before you, tell how budding and grafting are done.

IV. Think out these questions and, if possible, try out your answers.

1. Make out a selection of plants to grow in a sunless corner of a yard.

2. Make out a selection of plants suitable for growing in a schoolroom.

3. Suppose you had a swampy bit of ground in your yard. Plan a selection of plants and an arrangement that will improve the appearance of the yard.

V. Vocabulary.

humus	maturity	grafting
loam	perennial	budding
capillarity	propagation	

Chapter Twenty-seven

Plant Enemies of Plants

Weeds. Many weeds are beautiful. Clumps of New England asters from fence corners have been transplanted to beautify gardens. The dandelion is as brilliant as a little chrysanthemum. The toadflax is as pretty as any flower of equal size in the garden. But if they grow in too great abundance and occupy soil that we want to support some other plant, they are weeds. Many weeds have but little beauty; the ragweed and the pigweed are just weeds.

Weeds are troublesome because they can take care of themselves in the world. Many of them grow on sterile ground, on rock heaps, and railroad banks, where the pampered and petted plants of our gardens would starve to death. Many store up food in underground stems and roots which keep them alive during droughts and start them in growth again after they are cut down or their tops killed by the winter. Many produce prodigious quantities of seed. The stalk of a large mullein may produce a million seeds. Many weed seeds, like the dandelion, fly in the wind. Many stick to the coats of animals and to clothing, like the beggar ticks. Many send runners along the ground, rooting at intervals. The seeds of many may lie buried in the soil for years, and, when brought near the surface, finally germinate and produce sturdy plants.

Many weeds have ways of defending themselves. Some have thorns and prickles, like the horsenettle and brambles. Others have coatings of hair, like the mullein, that discourage cattle from eating them. Others are bitter, like the dandelion, or poisonous, like the locoweeds and Jimson weed.

How weeds do harm. Weeds in the garden occupy ground where we want other plants to grow. Their roots spread out and take the water and soil minerals that we want the garden plants to have. They grow rapidly, overtop and shut off the sunlight from more tender plants. Many kinds, like the water hemlock and wild parsnip, are poisonous if eaten. Some, like the poison ivy and poison sumac, which are shown on page 207, poison the skin if they rub against it. The pollen of some kinds of weeds, like the ragweed, is carried away by the wind and causes hay fever in persons who are susceptible (can develop the disorder).

How to battle the weeds. The first thing to do in the battle against weeds in your garden is to dig them up, and the last thing to do is to dig them up. Cultivate constantly with a small hoe or cultivator and pull

205

weeds when the ground is soft after a rain. Never let weeds go to seed. If there are too many to pull, as in a field, cut them down just before they produce seed. Do not let them lurk in fence corners, for their seeds are scattered abroad to start colonies in garden and field.

Plants get sick. Plants, like animals and human beings, get diseases. You may have found apples cracked open with the interior of the crack a velvety black. The apple is suffering with a disease, the apple scab. The disease is due to a fungus, one of the group of plants to which mushrooms, mildews, and bread mold belong. This disease plant grows inside the leaves, flowers, and fruit of the apple. Sometimes it destroys the entire crop of apples on a tree. The disease may be common in neglected orchards. It may be prevented by spraying the trees with mixtures of lime and sulphur or with copper and lime compounds forming Bordeaux mixture.

A field of cabbage is sometimes seen black and foul-smelling. The disease germs that start this trouble are bacteria. The disease is called the *black rot* of cabbage. The disease germs are sometimes in the soil, or they may be on the seed. The seed may be disinfected by soaking in a solution of bichloride of mercury. The soil, too, is sometimes treated with the same poison.

The black smut of corn is due to a fungus plant that is growing inside the ear of corn. The black mass is made of the germs or spores that are carried away by the wind to start the fungus somewhere else. The soil may contain the spores. Therefore, the disease is fought by "rotation of crops," growing crops other than corn in the field for two or three years and then raising corn one year.

There are many diseases of plants caused either by bacteria or fungus plants. Sometimes, like the wheat rust, they destroy large parts of the crop over the country. Scientists are trying to produce new varieties of wheat and of other plants that are immune to the diseases (will not take the disease). Some of these disease-resistant plants are now grown and others are being produced. In certain of these diseases, the fungus plant must have two different kinds of host plants to grow on. Thus in the northern part of our country, the wheat rust lives for part of its life on the barberry. The disease may be fought by destroying all the barberries in the wheat region. The blister rust of the white pine is a fungus that lives part of its life on currant or gooseberry bushes. The disease is fought by digging up all the currants and gooseberries near the pine woods. This is very expensive work, but the white-pine forests are well worth the cost.

Some common weeds: (1) poison ivy, (2) mullein, (3) poison sumac, (4) thistle, (5) Queen Anne's lace, (6) New England aster

(1) (2) (3) Hugh Spencer, (4) Philip Gendreau, (5) Black Star, (6) Keystone View Co.

How to Learn about Plant Enemies of Plants

I. Study weeds through observation.

1. If there is a bit of land near by not occupied by buildings or pavements, there are probably weeds to be found. Take a weed census of a piece of land near by. Make a collection of weeds. Press them between papers under a board. Try to find a book in the library naming the weeds.

2. Study the structures of weeds that enable them to succeed in life where other plants fail. Dig underground and see what is there that will enable them to rise again after cutting or crushing by the wheels of a truck. Find weeds that spread by runners. Count the seeds on a large mullein plant or other large weed. Calculate how much land they would need if all grew next year. Measure it off near your school or home to see how much land it is.

3. Study how weeds defend themselves against animals and man.

4. Learn to tell poison ivy or poison oak and poison sumac on sight. Study the pictures on page 207.

5. Search the fields, gardens, and woods for evidence of sick or diseased plants. Look for fungi growing on trees and bushes that seem to do no great harm and for others that seem to be injuring the host plant on which they live.

II. Read the chapter.

III. Test yourself with the following questions:

1. How do weeds harm other plants?

2. How are weeds suited or adapted to succeed in life in spite of the competition of other plants and the attacks of animals and man?

3. Tell how to wage successful warfare against weeds.

4. What causes disease in plants? Tell of some common diseases of plants and what causes them.

IV. Think out the answers to these questions or learn by further investigation:

1. Has any good ever come of weeds?

2. The ancestors of all our cultivated plants were wild plants which our remote ancestors learned to cultivate. Can you find among weeds any plants that look as if they might be cultivated to furnish food, fibers, or other valuable products?

3. The Indians used many wild plants which we might now call weeds. Can you learn in the library what some of the wild plants were that they used and for what purpose? Can you find some in the woods, fields, and waters?

V. Vocabulary. Do you talk over unknown words with your classmates? It is a good idea.

sterile   fungus

Chapter Twenty-eight

Insect Enemies and Friends

What an insect is. You probably think you know an insect when you see one. Is a spider an insect? No, says the biologist. You have probably seen a centipede, or "thousand-legger." Is it an insect? No. Are bees and grasshoppers insects? Yes. Then what is an insect?

You will notice that the bee has three main parts to its body: *head*, *thorax*, and *abdomen*. (Insects are so-called because their bodies are cut into three parts, from Latin words meaning "cut in" or "notched.") Look at the spider. Has it three parts? You notice that the bee has three pairs of legs. How many has the spider? The bee has two pairs of wings. Some insects are without wings. Note that the wings and legs are attached to the thorax.

Insects do not all have legs exactly alike. The grasshopper and the

cricket use the hind legs for jumping. Look at them. The butterfly uses them for holding on to the flower and clumsily walking around a little. The ant uses its legs for running, and the mole cricket uses its front legs for digging. The diving beetle uses its legs for swimming.

On the head of the bee notice the feelers, or *antennae*. The big eyes are compound, that is, made up of thousands of little eyes, which we can see with a microscope. In addition to the compound eyes, the bee has three simple eyes. They are very small and difficult to see, but with a lens and patience, you can see them like tiny beads set in the head. Not all insects have as many eyes as a bee. Some have only compound eyes. Some have only simple eyes.

Insects have their skeletons on the outside. Note the pictures on page

The bee is an insect, but the spider is not. What is the difference?

U.S.D.A.   *Wm. Thompson*

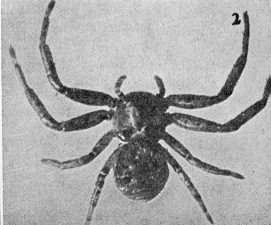

211. Their muscles and other organs are inside the skeleton. The skeleton thus serves as a suit of armor to protect the creature against other insects and other tiny animals. The armor is jointed, and the insect bends only at the joints.

Fitted to their food. Different kinds of insects choose different kinds of food. Their mouth parts are adapted or suited to the kind of food. A grasshopper chews grass and other plants. Look at his hard jaws. A butterfly sucks nectar from flowers. Look at the long tube that it carries coiled under the "chin" and unrolls to thrust into the flowers. A mosquito has a sharp beak that it thrusts into your flesh to suck your blood.

No breathing through nose or mouth. You cannot drown an insect by holding its head under water, but you might drown it by holding its head out of water and the rest of its body under water. An insect does not breathe through its head. Along the sides of its thorax and abdomen you may see little breathing holes [called *spiracles*]. Leading away from these breathing holes and branching all through the body are fine breathing tubes [called *tracheae*]. Did you ever see a hen or other bird taking a dust bath? That is to get rid of bird lice. The dust fills the insects' breathing holes and the insects are smothered. Poison-

ous powders are dusted upon growing plants similarly to kill plant lice. Soap solutions and oils fill their breathing pores and smother them.

What good is color? Did you ever see a grasshopper clinging to a blade of grass? If you have taken a hike through the country, you have probably seen many flying, but you perhaps have seen very few sitting still, unless you live in a country plagued by the devouring clouds of grasshoppers. They are hard to see when they sit still. They are green when they are young and the grass is young. When the grass is old and brown, the hoppers have become brown too. They are protectively colored, blending with their environment so that they escape some of their enemies.

Butterflies and beetles may be very brilliantly colored. But if you have tried to catch a butterfly on the wing, you know that it is a good dodger and a quick flier. It has less need for protective coloration. Yet some butterflies are protectively colored when at rest. The dead-leaf butterfly of the tropics looks like a dead leaf attached to a twig. If you look about you on your hikes, you will see many instances of protective coloration of insects, and you will see insects that seem to stand out because of their brilliant colors. Try to find out if these brilliant

Some common insects: (1) grasshopper (notice arrows pointing to breathing holes), (2) cabbage butterfly, (3) butterfly just emerged from chrysalis, (4) Japanese beetle, (5) queen ant and eggs, (6) pupa when maggot changes to fly

(1) U.S.D.A., (2) Wm. Thompson, (3)(5)(6) Black Star, (4) Ewing Galloway

Protective coloration hides the resting underwing moth

insects have other means of avoiding their enemies or of fighting them.

Taking care of their young. Many insects are famous for the care they take of their young ones. The worker bees gather food for the young, prepare it, and feed them. Ants not only feed and care for their young in the nest, but carry their young ones out from the nests in fine weather for an airing. When their nest is broken into, the workers seize the young and carry them off to safety. Watch them do it when you find an ants' nest. On the other hand, many insects take no care of their young except to lay the eggs where the young will find food when they hatch. You will see the milkweed butterfly visiting milkweeds to lay her eggs. She does not make a mistake and lay the eggs on another kind of plant where the young would starve to death. How does she know where to lay her eggs?

Butterfly enemy of cabbage. You often see a small white or yellowish butterfly flitting about the vegetable garden. Its ancestors came to us from Europe although we did not want them. You may see the little butterfly alight for a moment on a cabbage leaf or lettuce leaf or some other leafy vegetable. Each time it alights it glues a tiny egg, almost too small to be seen, to the under side of the leaf. In about a week, a little green caterpillar hatches out. These little caterpillars are very hungry. They eat and grow fast. The cabbage leaves are riddled with holes and the "cabbage worm" eats its way into the interior of the cabbage head. Often the cabbage head cannot form, so destructive are the caterpillars. For two weeks the caterpillar eats and grows. Then it attaches itself by a little silken thread to a fence, a stone, or a building. There it rests for a week or two, in a little case it has formed. [This stage is called the *chrysalis*.] Finally the case splits open, and the insect draws itself out and expands its wings, a butterfly. It flies away and the same day begins its work of laying eggs.

Because it eats its way into the cabbage head, this caterpillar is difficult to kill with sprays or poisons, or by other common methods. Fortunately for us there is a little wasp

212

that hunts the caterpillars of the cabbage butterflies. This little wasp was brought from England to this country to destroy the caterpillars. The wasp lays her eggs on the caterpillar, and the young wasps eat them. These young wasps are little, worm-like creatures. When they are full grown, they spin little cocoons and rest until they change into adult wasps. Then they make their way out of the cocoons and in turn hunt more cabbage caterpillars.

To protect the cabbage, the grower dusts or sprays the cabbage with a poison, arsenic. When the caterpillars eat the poison with the leaves, they are killed. When we eat the cabbage, we tear off the outside leaves so that we are not poisoned. In place of dangerous arsenic compounds other insect-killing substances are often used on our food plants. DDT is a powerful insecticide (insect-killer) developed during the war to kill insects that attack soldiers. By killing the lice that carry the germs of deadly typhus fever, it stopped an epidemic in Naples after our armies captured the city. DDT also has been shown to kill many insects that attack our crop plants and forests. As it is used, it is harmless to man.

The corn borer. Another immigrant from Europe that we do not want is the European corn borer. This immigrant came along on a shipment of broomcorn from Europe. Now it has spread through the eastern part of the country to the great Corn Belt of the Middle West. It is very destructive to corn and other plants. In 1943 it caused a loss of over $33,000,000 in northeastern United States. The creature that does the damage is the caterpillar of a little moth. This moth lays its eggs on the corn. The little caterpillars eat their way inside the cornstalk. There, when it is full grown, each caterpillar spins a cocoon about itself. Then it rests for about three weeks. Finally the adult moth comes out of the cocoon and lays its eggs, up to a thousand, in turn. Two generations of moths and caterpillars may develop in one summer. When the winter comes, some of the cocoons are hidden safe inside the cornstalks. Therefore, the farmers gather the cornstalks and burn them to destroy the cocoons.

Some other insect enemies of plants. Cut-worms, the caterpillars of little moths, feed on many kinds of garden vegetables and field crops. Some kinds eat the leaves,

Corn-borer larva in a stalk of corn

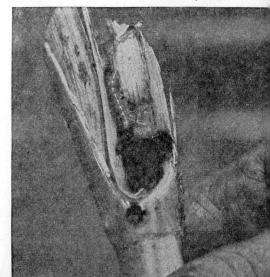

Tussock-moth caterpillar and wingless female moth

some cut off the stem just above the ground, and some feed underground. If bran is poisoned with arsenic and spread for them, many will eat the poisoned bait and die. Cutworms are attacked by many kinds of other insects. Certain flies lay their eggs on the backs of the caterpillars and the young flies eat them. Certain beetles eat them, and the eggs are attacked by little wasps.

Did you ever bite into a good-looking apple and into a worm inside? The codling moth lays her eggs in apple blossoms, and the young caterpillars are the worms in the apples. The fruit is protected by spraying the trees with poisons just after the petals fall from the flowers.

On shade trees and sometimes on orchard trees in the country east of the Rockies, you see a caterpillar with four white tufts of hair on its back and a tuft of black hair on each side of its head and one at the tail. This is the tussock-moth caterpillar.

It feeds upon the leaves until they are mere skeletons. When it has eaten all it wants, the caterpillar spins its cocoon and rests inside while it changes to a moth.

About midsummer the adult moth comes out of the cocoon. The males fly away, but the females have no wings. They stay near their old cocoon, lay their eggs on it, and die. These dirty masses of old cocoons and eggs can be found on the trees. To protect the trees the eggs should be scraped off and burned. If all the egg masses are removed and a sticky band of paper placed around the tree trunk, the tree is safe from these caterpillars unless they are blown from a neighboring tree. Fortunately for us, many kinds of insects and birds eat the tussock moth or its caterpillar.

Many kinds of beetles eat plants. The Japanese beetle, the Mexican bean beetle, and the potato beetle, or potato "bug," are some of them.

Flies that look somewhat like houseflies lay their eggs in the ground about cabbage, cauliflower, and onions. The maggots that hatch from the eggs burrow to the roots, scratch away the root tissue, and feed upon the juice of the plants. A large part of the crop may be ruined by these root maggots. Two or three broods of flies may grow up in the course of a summer. Tar paper is sometimes spread on the ground and carefully fitted around the plants to prevent the flies from laying their eggs close to the plants. Sand and

214

kerosene or ground tobacco are also sometimes spread upon the ground to keep the flies away. Sometimes in onion fields the soil is turned back from the plants and nitrate of soda added. This salty fertilizer is good for the plants and bad for the flies.

Juice suckers. Many insects do not eat the plant, but suck its sap and starve the plant to death. Plant lice, or aphids, and scale insects have sharp beaks with which they drill through the skin of the plant and then spend their lives sucking the juice. Plant lice are often found on plants in our homes as well as in gardens. They may be destroyed by washing the leaves and stems of house plants with soapy water. Those in the garden may be killed by spraying the plants with soapy water or soapy water mixed with nicotine. Scale insects similarly suck sap. Each insect is covered over with a shield of wax. Scale insects on fruit trees are fought with sprays of lime and sulphur.

How an insect grows up. Many insects go through a curious history in the course of their lives. The egg hatches into a wormlike creature, the caterpillar of the moth or butterfly, the grub of the beetle, or the maggot of the fly. An insect in this stage of its life is called a *larva.* After feeding and growing, the larva rests quietly without feeding and, in most insects, without moving. The insect in this stage is called the *pupa.* In moths and butterflies the pupa stage is passed inside the cocoon or chrysalis. It may last a

The life history of a Cecropia moth: (1) eggs, (2) larva or caterpillar, (3) cocoon, (4) cocoon opened to show pupa, (5) full-grown moth

Hugh Spencer, Chester, Conn.

As he searches for nectar, the useful bee aids pollination

week or two as in the fly or all winter as in many of our large moths of the woods and fields, like the Luna moths and the Cecropia moths. During the pupa stage the insect is remade. Wings grow, the legs become long and jointed. The inside of the body is also remade. The caterpillar chews leaves, but the adult butterfly can eat only sweet nectar from flowers. It must have new organs for new food. Some insects as adults cannot eat at all. They live a day or two, lay their eggs, and die.

Good bugs. All bugs are not bad bugs. The silkworm is the caterpillar of a moth. Worker bees gather the sweet, watery nectar from flowers. They carry it to the nest in their "honey stomachs." There they give it up again into the honey cells of the nest. Much of the water evaporates from the sweet fluid and it ripens into honey. The worker bees mix the honey with pollen from flowers to make "bee bread." Bees also furnish us with fruit. The bee visiting flower after flower carries pollen from one to another and so starts the development of the fruit. Its work

of pollination is far more valuable to us than its honey. Butterflies, too, flitting from flower to flower carry pollen and so produce the seed.

Many insects are valuable because they eat other insects. The ladybird beetle, or "ladybug," eats plant lice and scales. The ichneumon (ĭk-nū′mŏn) fly lays its eggs on other insects or caterpillars and grubs or lays them in the tunnels of the grubs. The larvae ichneumons feed upon and destroy the victims. The praying mantis catches various insects in its front legs and eats them. Dragonflies, darting across a pond, snatch up mosquitoes or gnats.

Your enemy, the fly. Look out for that fly that is just going to land on your sugary cake. A moment ago it might have walked over filth in the gutter. Its tiny, hairy feet may be loaded with germs—the germs of typhoid fever, tuberculosis, diphtheria, sore throat, and other diseases. Over six million bacteria have been taken from a single fly. Keep the screen closed. Buy from the store that keeps screen doors closed and keeps its food under cover as required by law. Swat the fly. A fly grows up from the egg in two weeks, if all goes well. The day it comes out of its pupa case, it may lay 200 eggs, and from 500 to 2000 in its lifetime. If all eggs grew to be flies, a pair of flies could leave over 100,000,000,000,000,000,000 flies in a summer, and they would cover the surface of the earth nearly fifty feet deep. Fortunately they live

216

This shows the damage a moth does to clothes (*highly magnified*)

risky lives. They have many enemies. The eggs are laid in horse manure, if it can be found by the fly. Its second choice is decaying garbage or other decaying matter. To stop the flies, keep the filth covered where the flies cannot reach it, and remember to wash out the garbage pail each time it is emptied.

Another enemy. Only a few years ago, 10,000 people died each year from malaria within the United States. In 1950 it was reported that there were fewer than ten deaths from malaria contracted within the United States. Malaria and yellow fever are carried by living mosquitoes. Millions of people in the world die each year from malaria. Every tie in the original Panama railroad, it is said, cost the life of a man from yellow fever. The disease stopped the building of the Panama Canal by a French company. Not until the United States army doctors conquered the mosquito that carries yellow-fever germs could the Panama Canal be built. Beside malaria and yellow fever, mosquitoes carry several other tropical diseases.

Mosquitoes can be conquered, if there is money enough provided. Mosquitoes lay their eggs in stagnant water in swamps, pools, and old tin cans. The eggs hatch into little "wrigglers," or larvae, and these turn into little wriggling pupae. If swamps are drained of standing water and covered with oil or dusted with poisons, mosquitoes can be destroyed or prevented from breeding and the mosquito diseases stopped.

Beating the clothes moth. Some day, if you are not careful, you will take your last winter's sweater or overcoat from the closet to find a hole in it, or perhaps it will be riddled with holes. The larvae of the clothes moth have been dining on it. The moths do not like the light. They crawl into the dark and narrow places and lay their eggs on the woolen and fur clothes. If you clean your clothes thoroughly, brushing them well, and then pack them in containers in which a moth cannot find a crack to squeeze through, the

Swamps and standing water should be either drained or covered with a film of oil to destroy mosquitoes

clothes will not be damaged. Naphthalene, the familiar moth balls and moth flakes, will kill moths and larvae, if you use enough of it in an airtight box or bag. You need never lose woolens or furs through clothes moths if you take care, but you very probably will if you are careless.

How to Learn about Insect Enemies and Friends

I. Observe insects alive and dead.

1. Catch a spider and an ant or bee or fly. Note number of legs, number of body parts, eyes, mouth parts, skeleton, breathing pores on sides. Examine the eyes with a lens.

2. Gather some caterpillars that seem to be about full-grown, together with some of the food plant. Stand the plant in a bottle of water under a cage made of screen wire or mosquito netting. Keep them supplied with food until they spin their cocoon. Then keep the cocoons until moths or butterflies emerge.

3. In wintertime gather the cocoons found on bushes, trees, and weeds. Bring them indoors and watch for the moths to come out weeks later.

4. EXPERIMENT No. 60. Catch a dozen or so houseflies without injuring them. Put them in a cage or jar covered with mosquito netting, first placing a piece of decaying meat in the jar. The jar may be covered with a piece of glass; you need not worry about the flies getting air to breathe if the jar is a quart size or larger. Keep the jar for a month, moistening the meat when it seems to dry out, or adding another piece without removing the old piece. Try also sugar and other foods. Or you may place the open jar with meat outdoors and cover it when several "blow flies" have entered.

5. In late spring and summer you can often find mosquito larvae, or wrigglers, in small pools. Take some to school in a jar covered with mosquito netting and watch them for a few weeks.

II. Read the chapter.

III. Test yourself with these questions:

1. How can you tell an insect when you see it?

2. How do the eyes of many insects differ from ours?

3. What else do you see on the head of an insect? What is its use?

4. What is peculiar about an insect's skeleton?

5. Describe the mouths of butterflies, grasshoppers, and aphids.

6. How does the color of many insects help them?

7. How do insects take care of their families?

8. Tell of several insects that have become pests. What do they attack and how may they be controlled?

9. How may harmful insects from foreign countries be kept out of this country?

10. Name some helpful insects and tell how they help us.

11. What is the best way to control the housefly? Why is the fly dangerous?

IV. Think out the answers to these:

1. Would we be better off or worse off without insects?

2. Why have some insects that came to us from foreign countries become pests, although they may not be pests in their old home?

3. Without being taught, the milkweed butterfly lays her eggs on the milkweeds and the codling moth in the apple blossom. What is the name for that tendency that guides these insects to the right food for their young? Does man have the same tendency to do the right thing without being taught?

V. Vocabulary. Here are suggestions.
antennae   thorax   larva   pupa

Chapter Twenty-nine

The Gardener's Allies

Enemies of insects. A toad is worth $20 a year in your garden. It eats insects that would destroy twenty dollars' worth of crops. A toad may be in your garden without your knowing it if you are not a careful gardener. It blends with the ground so that you do not see it. The insects do not see it either; if one comes sailing too close to the toad's nose, there is a lightninglike flip of the tongue and the insect becomes toad's dinner. When insects become scarce in the fall and the cool days come, the toad works its way backward into the loose soil until it is covered. Then it sleeps until spring.

When spring warms the soil, the toad makes its way out, and starts for a pond. It must find a pond to mate and lay its eggs. You can hear the long, trembling piping of the toads in spring. It is the love song of the males.

The eggs are laid and hatched in the water. A little tadpole comes from the egg. It spends its young life like a fish, swimming by wriggling its tail and breathing oxygen from the water through its gills. In early summer the flesh that was in the tail is all absorbed into the body and remade into new flesh. New organs, legs, arms, lungs, and a new set of digestive organs arise. Then the animal is a young toad. The toad wanders away from the ponds to live on land till its turn comes next year to sing love songs about the ponds or to lay eggs.

Frogs, too, eat large quantities of insects. Most frogs spend their lives near the ponds and streams, but some, like the wood frogs and the tree frogs, spend life away from the water, returning in the springtime to lay their eggs. Pond frogs also often travel overland long distances at night or in rainy weather. You often see many green frogs in a damp meadow.

Other animals also help the gardener and farmer. The skunks, opossums, and racoons nose about the ground at night picking up insects. Common, harmless snakes, like the garter snake, eat large quantities of insects.

Bird friends. Birds are the farmer's and the gardener's greatest friends in their battle with insects. Every few minutes during most of the day a mother bird—and often the father bird too—brings insects to the young birds in the nest. Even birds that eat seeds feed insects to their young. A little chickadee is worth $10 a year for its destruction of insects. It is estimated that the birds of the United States save us over $400,000,000 worth of crops each year by destroying the insects

219

that would have eaten them. Birds also eat weed seeds and so save the farmer money and the labor of fighting vast numbers of weeds. Our native sparrows, like the fox sparrows and tree sparrows and song sparrows, feed on weed seeds all winter long. There are several kinds of sparrows and there are other birds that eat weed seed. In a bobwhite's stomach were found at one time 10,000 pigweed seeds, and a bobwhite will fill his stomach a dozen times a day.

Hawks and owls, too, that many men with guns are eager to shoot, are good friends to the farmer and therefore to all of us who eat the farmer's food. If it were not for hawks and owls, our land might be overrun with mice and rats, and our food destroyed in the fields. Plagues of mice have eaten up miles of crops. Into the land of mouse plague the hawks, owls, and crows travel to feast upon the mice. A hawk does a farmer $30 worth of service each year by killing mice on his farm.

When winter comes most birds leave the northern countries for the south, but not all birds. About the cities the English sparrows and the starlings gather. About the woods many of our native birds hunt insect eggs and cocoons on the tree bark and twigs. About the fields many native sparrows and other seed-eat-

The gardener's allies: (1) toad, (2) skunk, (3) garter snake, (4) spider
(1) (2) (4) *Black Star*, (3) *Ewing Galloway*

ing birds are finding weed seeds. But most of the birds that feed upon active insects are gone before the cold of winter kills off the insects, and many birds that eat seeds and wild fruits go with them. Some do not journey far, but some, like the bobolink, travel to the southern part of South America.

Helping the birds. Creatures so valuable as the birds and creatures that add so much to the pleasure of life, with their song and beauty and their charming care of their families, need our protection. Their worst enemy is man, especially the man with the gun. Laws to protect our valuable birds from careless shooting have been enacted, but they are not always enforced. After man, the next worst enemy of the birds is the pet house cat. In Massachusetts 226 cats that were being watched killed 624 birds in one day, almost three birds for each cat in one day. It has been estimated that the cats of New York State kill over three million birds a year. Feed your pet cat well before you let it out in the morning. Tying a bell on its neck will do it no harm and will help notify the birds when it is about. However, the cat is so stealthy and quiet that it can steal up on a bird in spite of the bell. Homeless cats that prowl the fields should be sent to their happy hunting grounds.

More helpful friends: (1) horned owls, (2) racoon, (3) opossum, (4) bobwhites
(1) (2) (3) (4) *Ewing Galloway*

If you have some trees and green grass about your house, you can bring the birds about by furnishing them protection and the necessities of life. If there are bushes, especially bushes with wild fruits and seeds, they help furnish shelter and hiding places as well as food. Birds must have places to hide from their enemies. Bushes and dense trees also furnish nesting sites, and bird boxes should be added for the birds that prefer them. Abundant plants and thickets help furnish foods, fruits, seeds, and insects. Birds get thirsty very often. Put out a pan of water for them. You may be surprised at the number of birds and the frequency with which they come for a drink and a bath. And, finally, protect the birds from guns, air rifles, and cats.

How to Learn about the Gardener's Allies

I. Study animal friends by observation.

1. EXPERIMENT No. 61. In the springtime search the pools of water for toads' eggs and frogs' eggs. Carefully put some of the eggs in an aquarium or glass jar with some water plants. Watch them develop. You will not need to worry about feeding the tadpoles. If you have abundant water plants, the little tadpoles will find their own food. When they become frogs, take them back to the ponds and take the toads to the garden, unless you are ready to provide living food for them.

2. Become acquainted with the birds. Get a book from the library and, if possible, a field or opera glass. Go out into the woods and fields or into the city parks. In the large parks many kinds of birds are often seen in spring and early summer. In winter set up feeding stations for the birds. You may be surprised at the number of different kinds of birds that gather for food in the city where a few trees grow. Set up nesting boxes and keep a birdbath clean and supplied with fresh water. Watch what birds eat and where they hunt food.

II. Read the chapter.

III. Test yourself by answering the following questions:

1. Write down a list of birds and animals that feed on insects.

2. Give three good reasons why birds are important in keeping down the number of insects.

3. Tell of two other services birds render to the gardener and to the farmer.

4. Name two important enemies of birds, and tell how these enemies should be controlled.

5. What should be done to induce birds to live around the house and garden?

IV. Questions to think out or investigate:

1. What protection is given by law in your State to insect-eating birds? to birds that eat weed seeds, such as the bobwhite or quail or many wild ducks?

2. Is it lawful in your State to kill frogs and toads? Write to the Fish and Game Commission at your State capital.

3. Do fish of the fresh waters have any effect on insect life, especially those insects that are dangerous or annoying to us?

4. Are skunks given any protection in your State?

V. Vocabulary. Did you find any new words?

Chapter Thirty

Keeping Food

Storing the harvest. City people seldom have the problem of storing vegetables for the winter. The storage problem is solved by the storage warehouses where conditions of temperature, moisture, and light can be controlled. The cost of storage is, of course, paid by the consumer. If you have a garden of your own large enough to raise winter vegetables, it is well to know how to arrange a small storage establishment of your own. Your pile of potatoes may last for months, if you know how to store them.

A cool, dark, dry place is the place for storing vegetables. The temperature must not fall below freezing. A cellar properly protected against freezing and dampness, if it is not warmed too much by a furnace, is a good place for potatoes. Turnips, potatoes, and similar vegetables are sometimes stored in pits covered over with earth and provided with ventilating chimneys. So stored against freezing and against wetness, they will keep all winter. Potatoes stored in the cellar may start to sprout toward the end of winter. These sprouts must be removed.

Vegetables that will not keep in the cool cellar may be kept in refrigeration or preserved by canning or, less often, by drying. Fruits, other than apples, are much more difficult to store than vegetables. Even apples, the hardiest of the common fruits, are less easily kept than potatoes, but with a cool cellar, properly protected against winter freezing, some varieties of apples last all winter. Fruits of many kinds offered for sale in the large cities almost all year round are preserved by refrigeration. The method of refrigeration is in principle that of the electric refrigerator used in the home.

Canning. The grocery store with its shelves of canned goods was not known when our great-grandfathers and great-grandmothers were raising their families. A scientific discovery was necessary before fruits and perishable vegetables could be canned on a large scale. The discovery was made two hundred years ago, but then it was just a discovery in science that did not convince all scientists and that no one put into practical use. It is since the time of the war between the northern and southern States that canning of food has become important. To understand why canning preserves food, you must understand why food decays.

Food spoils because living things get into it. These are very minute living things, bacteria, "seeds" or spores of molds, and microscopic

U.S.D.A. *Campbell Soup Co.*

Giant pressure cookers (above) sterilize cans of food in a commercial cannery. The housewife (left) applies the same principle but in a smaller way

are sterile, that is, until they contain nothing alive. The containers are then filled and sealed while still hot. In the cold-pack method, sometimes used at home and generally used in commercial canneries, the food is packed in the cans before heating. The food is then heated in the can and sealed so that no living germs of decay or disease can enter.

Preservatives. Sugar or salt is sometimes used to preserve foods. Sugar is often used with fruit, and salt with meat. The microscopic organisms cannot live in either sugar or salt solutions because these substances take out the water from the germs, and nothing can live without water. Vinegar is used with some

animals. These things are so minute that they must be studied with a microscope. Most important of these are bacteria. They get into the food from human hands, from knives and containers, and from the dust of the air. When food is canned, it is heated to high temperatures until all the bacteria are killed. The cans, jars, or bottles are also heated until they

Ewing Galloway   Philip D. Gendreau

(Above) Hams hanging in a smoke-house in Tennessee. This Labrador fisherman (right) is picking up codfish that have been dried in the sun

foods. It poisons the bacteria, but if we do not take it in too great quantities, it does not harm us.

Other substances are sometimes added to foods to preserve them. You may find on a bottle of catsup the statement: "contains one tenth of one per cent of benzoate of soda." The quantity of benzoate of soda that you would get by using a little catsup on your meat or baked beans would not harm you, but if you should take it continually, it might harm you. It is not necessary in the catsup or other foods. If good, un-spoiled food is used in preserving and it is properly preserved, there is no need for benzoate or other chemical preservative.

Drying, smoking, and freezing. The Indians of the plains preserved their buffalo meat by drying and smoking. The little pygmies of the African forests also used smoke for preserving their elephant meat. Fish were preserved by drying, smoking, and salting centuries ago and by native peoples who never heard of bacteria and had no cans

Father and son place food in a freezing locker which they rent

for their food. Smoke contains substances that prevent the growth of bacteria. The smokehouse was formerly an important building on the farm and is still used in parts of our country. Country smoked meat is much more delicious than much that is for sale in the modern grocery and delicatessen store. Fruits and vegetables were also dried in the farm kitchen.

Modern dehydrated foods are the scientific products of a development of food drying begun in the Stone Age. Today extraction of water is much more rapid and more perfect than in sun drying and kitchen stove drying. Four gallons of milk are reduced in a moment to three pounds of snowlike white milk powder by spraying the liquid milk into a superheated chamber. One hundred

pounds of fresh vegetables are reduced to 10 pounds. Three dozen eggs become one pound of dehydrated egg powder. The present day list of dehydrated foods includes also meats, fruits, and breadstuffs. Dehydrated foods helped solve the acute problem of supplying food to the army and navy and to the Allied Nations in 1941 and the following years of the war. Ships were lost through submarine attack and shipping space was needed for ammunition, great guns, bulldozers, and other bulky war equipment. Dehydrated foods reduced the space needed for some foods by fully 90 per cent. These foods also solved the difficult problem of feeding the soldiers in the front line, especially in hot, wet climates. Common foods were quickly destroyed by molds, bacteria, and insects. Dehydrated foods in proper packages remained in good condition.

Cave man probably made use of nature's frozen food, and many a farm and village boy has eaten apples frozen in the orchard. The Eskimo enjoys meat processed in the Arctic's natural freezing plant. Quick freezing of a long list of our common foods at the seasons when they are plentiful is a process developed by applied science. Freezing and refrigeration solved the problem of shipping foods halfway around the world and across the Equator. Frozen foods have become common in our stores, and freezing plants and cold storage lockers are now common through parts of our country.

Pure food laws. To protect us from dishonest packers who would place on the market spoiled or decayed food or food preserved with harmful substances, Congress has passed laws and States and cities have added other laws. The Food, Drug, and Cosmetic Act of Congress prohibits the sale or sending of spoiled food, in cans or otherwise, from one State to another. It requires that, if preservatives are added to the food, the label on the container must state the kind and the amount of preservatives. You may feel reasonably safe from added harmful preservatives if the label does not mention them. However, Congress does not control foods that are not shipped from one State to another, and State laws are necessary to protect us from foods prepared and sold in the same State.

Cattle, hogs, and sheep suffer from disease, as do men. We do not want to eat their diseased bodies. To protect us from diseased meat, inspectors of the United States Government are stationed at the slaughter houses to inspect the carcasses of the animals. If they find diseased animals, they seize the carcass and destroy it so that it cannot be used for food. However, because the Constitution of the United States does not give Congress the power to make laws that apply only within a State, cattle that are killed for use inside the State may escape inspection.

Cattle that are killed by butchers in small villages and in the country, the meat of which is sold near by, are generally not inspected. Of course the States may have laws to protect the people, but very often these laws are easily evaded or they are not enforced. Some States, however, have more strict food laws and more careful inspection than does the United States Government.

Taking care of milk. Milk is an excellent food for bacteria as well as for us. Bacteria that grow in milk make it sour. Other bacteria cause it to decay. Bacteria of disease may be carried in milk. Diphtheria, sore throat, typhoid fever, tuberculosis, and other diseases have been spread by milk that has been contaminated by persons who

How is milk made safe to drink?

Philip D. Gendreau, N. Y.

suffer with these diseases. In some instances typhoid fever has occurred in the families served by one milk dealer but not those served by other dealers. Persons handling the milk of one dealer had the germs of typhoid, or the water used for washing the cans was contaminated.

We now have health laws and regulations to protect our milk supply at least in the large cities and more progressive towns. Inspectors from the cities or from the State examine the farms which produce the milk and the stations where the milk is bottled and shipped. Cows suffering with tuberculosis are killed. The open cans in which milk was formerly delivered to the consumer have been replaced by capped bottles that have been sterilized (all the germs killed). Most of the harmful

Germs may live in the refrigerator. It must be cleaned out frequently

General Electric Co.

bacteria in the milk are killed by pasteurizing the milk. In pasteurization, the milk is heated to 140° to 160° F. for twenty to thirty minutes, then rapidly cooled and kept cool.

Milk that has not been pasteurized is sometimes wanted for babies that do not thrive on pasteurized milk. Certified raw milk is provided for them. To be certified the cows and stables are inspected more frequently and the milk must contain less than a stated number of bacteria. Without sterilization it is impossible to obtain milk that is free from all bacteria, but cleanliness and care will keep the number low. Certified milk costs more than pasteurized milk and sours more easily. Even pasteurized milk will sour and should be kept in the refrigerator as soon as delivered and returned there promptly after some has been taken from the bottle. The sides and especially the top of the bottle should be carefully washed with soap and hot water before the bottle is opened.

Care of the home refrigerator. The home refrigerator may be a source of danger to food if it does not receive the proper care. Neglect or lack of cleanliness not only leads to bad odors and spoiled food but to sickness. The refrigerator should be frequently unloaded and washed out with hot water and soap, and then with clear water. Foods should not be placed back in the corner and forgotten, for the temperature does not prevent slow growth of molds and bacteria. If the refrigerator is cooled with ice, the ice must be removed often and the drainpipe cleaned out, for living things grow in the pipe and in a short time block it so that the water floods the refrigerator and runs out on the floor.

The refrigerator must be properly constructed to be effective and safe. Its walls should be insulated so that heat does not readily pass through. It should have all parts readily removable for cleaning. The walls should be so smooth that dirt does not readily stick to them and so that they may be effectively and easily cleaned. Porcelain or the better kinds of enamel are the best linings. In camp a usable refrigerator may be made by building a box with double walls and filling these walls with sawdust. This box should be sunk in the ground and properly covered. A large block of ice will make this an efficient refrigerator, but it can never be kept properly clean. Food placed in it should always be contained in pots or cans with tight lids, and care must be taken that dirty hands do not go inside the pots.

How to Learn about Keeping Food

I. Read the chapter.

II. Test preservatives.

1. If you have a quantity of potatoes and other vegetables to keep, examine the conditions in your cellar or storehouse. Is it neither too hot nor too cold? Is it dry? Is it protected against frequent temperature changes? If you have the opportunity, visit the large dealers to learn how they keep vegetables stored.

2. Examine diagrams of the working parts of an electric or other mechanical refrigerator. Your storekeeper may also show you how larger refrigerators keep meats and other foods.

3. EXPERIMENT No. 62.

Question: How may milk be pasteurized?

Materials: Several test tubes; absorbent cotton; a pan; Bunsen burner; a wire test-tube rack or tin can to hold the test tubes upright in the pan; quart of raw or unpasteurized milk.

Procedure: If you use a tin can as a test-tube rack, punch holes in it. Pour two inches of milk in each of nine test tubes. Plug with cotton. Set the rack, four tubes, and the thermometer in the pan of water. Heat to 145° F. for thirty minutes. Boil four tubes over a gentle flame. Set the eight tubes aside and set one tube of untreated milk with them. In two days, test the untreated milk and one tube each of the pasteurized and boiled milk with a strip of blue litmus paper. If the milk has soured, the lactic acid that has developed will turn the litmus red. Note the appearance of the boiled milk. Repeat the test of the remaining tubes at intervals of two days. Do you see any other evidence of "spoiled" milk?

Observation: Draw a table similar to the one shown on page 230 and fill it in. State whether sour or fresh on the days indicated.

Conclusion: How may milk be pasteurized?

What is the advantage of pasteurization?

What is the result of boiling?

What is the disadvantage?

What is the advantage of boiling over pasteurization?

Treatment	Two Days	Four Days	Six Days	Eight Days
Tube 1. Untreated	(?)			
Tube 2. Pasteurized	(?)			
Tube 3. Pasteurized		(?)		
Tube 4. Pasteurized			(?)	
Tube 5. Pasteurized				(?)
Tube 6. Boiled	(?)			
Tube 7. Boiled		(?)		
Tube 8. Boiled			(?)	
Tube 9. Boiled				(?)

4. EXPERIMENT No. 63. What is the effect of salt, sugar, and vinegar upon the keeping of foods? In a series of test tubes, as in the last experiment, pour two inches of milk. Then add to one test tube a liberal quantity of salt, to another sugar, to another vinegar. Set up also an untreated tube as a control. Examine as before to determine the keeping qualities. Write a record of the experiment as in Experiment No. 62. Why will the litmus test not show you if the vinegar preserves milk from souring?

III. Test yourself with the following questions:

1. How are potatoes, beets, carrots, turnips, and similar vegetables kept during the winter?

2. How are fruits kept during winter?

3. How may perishable fruits that do not keep well in refrigeration be preserved for the wintertime?

4. What makes food "spoil"?

5. How are meats kept during the winter or until the following summer?

6. How does the National Food and Drug Act help to secure good food?

7. By what process is milk freed from many disease germs? Describe the process.

8. What is dangerous about a home refrigerator? How should the refrigerator be cared for so that the danger is removed?

IV. Investigate and think out the answers to these questions:

1. What are the defects in the present National Pure Food and Drug Act?

2. What does your State do to protect you from spoiled or adulterated food?

3. Why is it said that mold on jelly shows that the jelly is good?

4. Make a list of all the kinds of preserved food that you see with benzoate of soda or other chemical preservative indicated on the label.

V. Vocabulary. Are you familiar with all the words in this chapter? You have probably met them, but can you say exactly what each means? Here are some suggestions:

carcass   insulated
pasteurization   sterilization

Unit Six
Health

It is no fun at all to lie abed and hear what a glorious day the boys and girls had skating, swimming, playing tennis or baseball. Usually it is not necessary to get sick. The great plagues that once swept thousands of people to the grave have been conquered in the civilized world, with possibly one exception, and even that, "the flu," in its last great visitation was a small plague compared to those of the Ancient World and the Middle Ages. The diseases that spread from one person to another are being conquered. Your health departments and your family physician, if you will consult him and follow his advice, probably will keep you free from the deadly infectious diseases.

But coughs, colds, and grippe still spoil work and play. We are learning how to protect ourselves against them, but our protection depends largely on what we ourselves do to avoid these maladies that may not kill us but may lead to pneumonia that will. How your stomach behaves, whether you have headaches and rheumatism depends largely upon what you, yourself, do to keep your body in good condition. In your own personal battles with these disorders, the departments of public health can do you little good. Each must fight his own battles. Use brains and will power.

Gendreau (both top), Galloway (side), George Bergstrom (bottom)

Chapter Thirty-one

The Control of Disease and Decay

Evil spirits. Imagine trying to cure a headache by scraping a hole in the skull with a sharp stone—without ether. Skulls of ancient Indians of Peru and ancient men of Europe, men of the Old Stone Age, have been found with holes scraped in them by stone instruments while the men were alive. These ancient men had headaches and their medicine men scraped the holes in their heads to let the ache or the evil spirit come out. Those men must have had most excruciating headaches to endure this torture in order to get rid of the devil inside.

Did you ever hear of wearing coral beads as charms to prevent sickness? Did you ever hear that you might get sick or have bad luck if you were hit with a broom or looked at the back of a hearse or left a house by some other door than that by which you entered? It sounds silly, but charms and witchcraft are still accepted by many people. The stars and planets are blamed for ill health by the superstitious.

Showing why things decay. In the old days there were notions about disease and decay that seem queer to us. Spoiled meat bred flies, cheese gave rise to worms. Dead and decayed things gave rise to living things. The mud of the Nile bred rats. Scientists who tried to show that decay was caused by things that live, were laughed at, but a scientist cannot be stopped by laughter. An Italian scientist, Francesco Redi (1626–1697), tied netting over a jar of meat and showed that flies laid their eggs on the netting, but no flies grew in the meat. Another Italian, Lazaro Spallanzani (1729–1799), one hundred years after Redi, sealed meat juices and vegetable juices in flasks and then heated them to kill all life. He showed that the juices did not spoil or develop any life until he opened the flasks, after which they promptly spoiled. That should have satisfied everyone, but scientists are not easily satisfied; they have to be shown again and again. Finally a hundred years later, the English scientist, John Tyndall (1820–1893), and the French scientist, Louis Pasteur (1822–1895), settled the question by experiments proving that there can be no decay unless living "germs" get into the substance. After that we learned how to can milk, meat, fruits, vegetables, rattlesnakes, and almost anything else you may name. The secret is to kill all the "germs" in the food and its container and let no more in. Then the food cannot decay.

Stopping "catching" diseases. Another great battle was won in the conquest of disease and ignorance

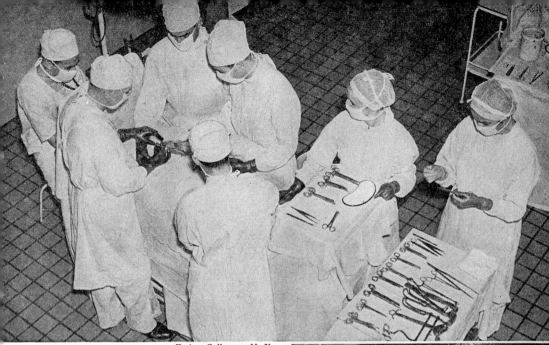

Discovery of germs and antiseptics made surgery safe in the makeshift hospital behind the lines in war and in the finest modern hospital above

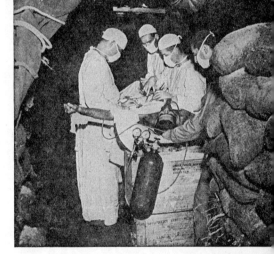

when it was shown that many diseases also were due to germs. If you keep out the germs, you cannot get the disease. Pasteur showed that germs caused certain diseases as well as decay. Robert Koch (1843–1910), the German bacteriologist, discovered the germs that cause the deadly diseases cholera, anthrax, and tuberculosis. Sir Joseph Lister at Glasgow, Scotland (1827–1912), proved that the diseased wounds, that before his time killed most people operated upon, were due to germs. He killed the germs with carbolic acid and later other antiseptics (substances preventing growth of germs of disease or decay). His patients did not die of diseased wounds. Then the safe, marvelous surgery of today began. These three men started the science of bacteriology and modern medicine.

Certain diseases are caught only from insects, and insects get the disease germs from men sick with the diseases. The English army doctor, Sir Ronald Ross (1857–1932), proved that a certain kind of mosquito carries malaria. Major Walter Reed (1851–1902), of the United States Army, proved that

233

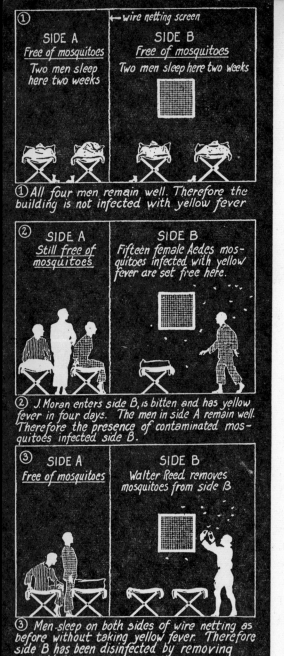

① **SIDE A**   **SIDE B**
Free of mosquitoes   *Free of mosquitoes*

Two men sleep   Two men sleep here two weeks
here two weeks

←*wire netting screen*

① *All four men remain well. Therefore the building is not infected with yellow fever*

② **SIDE A**   **SIDE B**
Still free of mosquitoes   *Fifteen female Aedes mosquitoes infected with yellow fever are set free here.*

② *J. Moran enters side B, is bitten and has yellow fever in four days. The men in side A remain well. Therefore the presence of contaminated mosquitoes infected side B.*

③ **SIDE A**   **SIDE B**
Free of mosquitoes   *Walter Reed removes mosquitoes from side B*

③ *Men sleep on both sides of wire netting as before without taking yellow fever. Therefore side B has been disinfected by removing mosquitoes*

Metropolitan Life Ins. Co.

Above is shown Dr. Walter Reed's experiment in Cuba (1900) to find the cause of yellow fever. Men who were exposed to bites of infected mosquitoes always became ill. Men who were not bitten stayed well. This proved that mosquitoes were the carriers of the germ

yellow fever is carried by another kind of mosquito. Other diseases also reach us only from certain definite insects.

We are slowly winning the battle against the "great white plague," tuberculosis or consumption. Koch discovered the germ of tuberculosis. In this country Edward L. Trudeau (1848–1915), himself a sufferer from tuberculosis, moved to the Adirondack Mountains and began in America the present treatment of rest, good food, and good air. Tuberculosis has been reduced from the first cause of death to the seventh in this country. The death rate has been reduced 80 per cent. We are still fighting. School children regularly examined for the disease in its early stages can be cured.

The cry of "mad dog" sends people running to safety. Before Pasteur, persons who suffered with the disease caused by mad dog bite were smothered to death between mattresses by neighbors who were afraid of being bitten by the patient. Always the patients died. Pasteur discovered that certain diseases could be prevented by inoculation with germs which he had weakened. By that means he cured the terrible, agonizing disease of hydrophobia, or *rabies* (pronounced rā′bĭ-ēz), the disease of mad dogs. He prevented certain other diseases by the same means of inoculation with the weakened germs. Since his day some more diseases have been added to the list that can be so prevented.

234

"Membranous croup," or diphtheria, formerly killed thousands of
children. Then a "serum," or antitoxin, was prepared that saved their
lives. Bacteria which cause diphtheria are grown in broth. The poisons, or *toxins,* which they produce
are injected into a healthy horse.
The cells of the horse's body manufacture substances which destroy the
toxins and the bacteria of diphtheria.
A small portion of the blood is drawn
from the horse, not enough to hurt
the horse. The clear part of this
blood, the serum, is injected into the
patient and immediately stops the
disease that will choke the patient to
death.

In the War with Spain we lost
more men from typhoid fever than
from shot and shell. In World War I
we lost only sixty-five out of 4,000,-
000 soldiers from that disease. In
1940 there were two deaths from
typhoid in our army. We have conquered the disease in the army but
not in civil life. We have learned
how to vaccinate to prevent the disease and how to sterilize the water
(kill the germs) and protect the
food, for water and food carry the
germs. Similar measures have reduced the typhoid death rate in our
cities from nineteen out of every
100,000 people in 1910, to two out
of every 100,000 in 1926. Yet there
are sections of the country where
the typhoid death rate is disgrace-
fully high, sections where the water
and food supply is not cared for and
there is no typhoid vaccination. The
people of such places drink filth,
for typhoid means that sewage is in
the drinking water.

The greatest single invention to
improve the control of disease was
the microscope. With it the germs
of disease could be seen. When the
germs or bacteria of tuberculosis are
found in the coughed-up sputum, it
is known that the person has this disease. When the germs of typhoid
fever were seen under the microscope, they could be used to make a
vaccine to prevent the disease. After
germs of diphtheria were found, the
antitoxin to cure it and the toxin-
antitoxin to prevent it were found.

**Stopping disease before it
starts.** Cure disease by not getting
it. Our departments of public health,
our school medical inspection, and
our family physicians are constantly
struggling to keep us well. And they
are succeeding wonderfully. In ancient Rome a baby could be expected
to live twenty-five years. Now a boy
baby has an excellent chance of living to be sixty and a girl baby to be
sixty-five. Many diseases have been
put under control.

Diseases that we "catch" from
one another are due to germs (bacteria or one-celled animals called
Protozoa or *viruses,* too small to be
seen with a microscope) that get
into our bodies. The germs live in
the body. Some of them destroy tissues. Others, although they do not
destroy tissues, send out poisons
(toxins) that poison us and may
cause death. The body has many

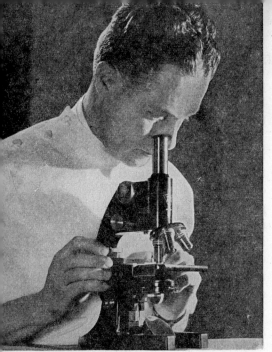

The microscope has proved invaluable to the scientist in finding causes of disease and decay

defences against disease germs. White blood cells feed upon them and destroy them. Our cells manufacture substances (antibodies or antitoxins) which destroy the poisons and the bacteria. In fighting some diseases by inoculation, we can stimulate our cells to manufacture the destroying substances.

The English physician, Edward Jenner (1749–1823), taught us how to prevent the horrible disease smallpox. Cows have a disease similar to smallpox, but very mild. Sometimes the sores of cowpox developed on the hands of those who milked the cows. The English farmers knew that after they had cowpox, which in man caused only a sore, they would not get smallpox which killed people or disfigured them for life. A milkmaid told that to Jenner. He began

the practice of taking the material from the sore on the cow and putting it in a scratch in the skin of man. This was the original vaccination.

Now the "virus" (poisonous germ) that causes the sores is grown on carefully prepared calves under scientific control, or it may be grown in fertile hens' eggs. Countries that require all persons to be vaccinated do not have smallpox. States in the United States that do not have compulsory vaccination have very many more cases of smallpox than States which require all school children to be vaccinated. Before Jenner's time smallpox was one of the commonest causes of death. Now where vaccination is enforced very few doctors have ever seen a case of smallpox. In smallpox, typhoid fever, diphtheria, and possibly in scarlet fever a person can be made immune (unable to take the disease) by suitable treatment. The Schick test for diphtheria shows whether a child can take this disease. In the test a little of the poison, or toxin, but not the germ, is placed under the skin. If a redness of the skin or eruption develops, that shows that the person will take the disease. Then he is given toxin-antitoxin or toxoid to make him immune. The Dick test shows whether one is immune to scarlet fever.

To aid in keeping all the people healthy, the various health departments of our city, State, and national governments help the family doctor and help the citizens directly. A very

236

ancient government protective measure is quarantine of patients and those who have been in contact with them during the period when they can spread the germs to others. Sanitation has controlled typhoid fever, cholera, and other diseases. Water supplies are protected from contamination, and the water is treated to kill disease germs. Sewage is treated to prevent contamination of water supplies. Inspection protects the public from diseased animals, filthy handling, diseased persons who would prepare and sell the food, and contamination of prepared food by insects and wind-blown germs. Removal of and disposal of garbage prevents the breeding of insects, rats, and mice which carry germs. Cleaning up of insect-breeding places and destruction of rats stops the spread of several deadly diseases.

Certain diseases are due to incomplete diet. Children may fail to grow because certain necessary things are not in their food. Sometimes poverty, but more often ignorance, is the reason for these diseases.

Nature sometimes gives a person an imperfect body, or disease leaves the body damaged. Such deficiency and damage must be corrected. Curved spines must be set straight. Muscles and nerves damaged by such diseases as infantile paralysis must be re-educated when possible.

Black Star, N. Y.

The x-ray is another discovery that aids the fight against disease

Faulty vision must be corrected else it may so upset the nervous system as to bring on many bodily disorders. The teeth may be irregular so that they do not bite and grind properly. They often can be straightened by the dentist if he gets the patient while his jaws are still growing, in girlhood and boyhood. The heart damaged or weakened by illness, even by a mild case of the "flu," may need proper rest, exercise, and perhaps medicine under the direction of a physician. A physician's care often produces a sound heart. A nervous child may be often calmed and restored to mental health by care of body and mind through the advice of a physician.

How to Learn about the Control of Disease and Decay

I. Read the chapter.
II. Study germs by experiment and observation.

1. Try experiments such as those of Redi, Spallanzani, and Pasteur. Do your results agree with theirs? The results

237

of experiments of different workers often do not agree. Plan your experiments carefully and write a report in your notebook as was done in earlier chapters. Use the following headings in your report: Experiment No. 64; Materials; Directions; Results; Conclusions.

2. Learn from books in the library and write down a list of diseases due to germs and some that have not been shown to be due to germs.

3. EXPERIMENT No. 65. (A further investigation following Experiment No. 63.) *Question:* What is the effect of antiseptics on bacteria of decay? Set up three series of tubes. Series I. Put small quantities of meat, milk, boiled potatoes, and other foods in test tubes. Cover with a little water. Allow to stand open for a day, and then plug with cotton to keep in any odors that develop. Set up a Series II of control tubes sterilized by heating as you did in Experiment No. 62. Series III. At the beginning of the experiment, add a drop of common antiseptic to each tube; iodine, lysol, and any other of the common antiseptics sold at the drug store, a little soap, a little salt. Write a report.

4. Search your neighborhood for places where mosquitoes can breed: swamps, pools, and even old tin cans that hold water. If you are troubled by mosquitoes, find where they breed and determine how to prevent breeding.

III. Test yourself with the following questions:

1. What makes things decay? How was the cause of decay proved? How can decay be prevented?

2. What types of disease are caused in a manner similar to decay? Name two of the first scientists to prove this. How can such diseases be prevented?

3. Name several ways in which disease germs travel from person to person.

4. Name certain diseases that are carried by insects. How can they be controlled?

5. What are the most important steps in reducing the "great white plague," tuberculosis?

6. What is the cure for diphtheria? How is the disease prevented?

7. How is typhoid prevented?

8. Tell some of the ways in which disease germs are destroyed in the human body.

9. How can smallpox be prevented?

10. For what type of disease are people quarantined and for how long?

IV. Think out or investigate the following problems:

1. List all the superstitions that you can collect about sickness and health.

2. There are still "powwow doctors" at work. Can you learn what they do?

3. Learn for what diseases especially the school medical inspector examines the pupils.

4. In recent years there have been "mad dog scares" in various parts of the country. Learn what regulations are then put into force to control the disease. What should you do with your dog during an epidemic?

5. Find out whether governmental agencies in your region provide means for protecting children against diphtheria.

6. What are the quarantine regulations governing the return to school after illness? Who sees that they are enforced in your community?

V. Vocabulary. The following are common words in the newspapers. Make sure of them.

infectious	antiseptics
rabies	vaccination
toxins	antitoxin
virus	immune
sanitation	inoculation

Chapter Thirty-two

The Wonder Drugs

Conquering pneumonia. Pneumonia is still a deadly disease. Formerly it stood number three in the list of killers, but science is making progress. Now only about one-fourth as many people die of pneumonia in our country as died twenty years ago. Let us see what pneumonia is and why the death rate has fallen 75 per cent in twenty years.

Pneumonia is caused by germs that get into the lungs, chiefly the germs called *pneumococci*. There are many kinds of pneumococci, thirty or more, but two kinds cause most of the deaths. The germs are breathed into the lungs. If you are in vigorous health, not too tired, nor chilled with wet clothes in a winter rain, you may not get the disease. If

you are run down, struggling with a cold or "flu," tired and chilled, the germs may take hold in your lungs.

If you come home with a chill, a fever, and rapid pulse, go to bed and have the doctor summoned— immediately. Keep a clinical thermometer, a doctor's thermometer, in the house, and learn how to read it. Take your temperature when you get that chill and rapid pulse. When the doctor is called, report the chill, the rapid pulse, and the temperature. If you have a pain in the chest and cough up blood, you have waited too long before taking to bed and sending for the doctor, but report these signs, or symptoms, also. The doctor will come as fast as he can. He knows that if he does not get

An oxygen tent helps a pneumonia patient to breathe

Taken for Life by Werner Wolf, Time, Inc.

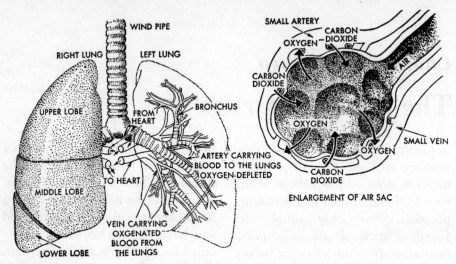

Labels on the figure (left illustration):
WIND PIPE
RIGHT LUNG
LEFT LUNG
UPPER LOBE
FROM HEART
BRONCHUS
TO HEART
ARTERY CARRYING BLOOD TO THE LUNGS OXYGEN-DEPLETED
MIDDLE LOBE
VEIN CARRYING OXGENATED BLOOD FROM THE LUNGS
LOWER LOBE

Labels on the figure (right illustration):
SMALL ARTERY
CARBON DIOXIDE
OXYGEN
CARBON DIOXIDE
AIR
OXYGEN
SMALL VEIN
OXYGEN
CARBON DIOXIDE
ENLARGEMENT OF AIR SAC

In the lungs, oxygen is taken into the blood and carbon dioxide is given off

there, the patient may die. He knows also that if he gets the patient soon enough, the "wonder drugs" will stop those pneumococci.

The lungs are among the most delicate organs in the body. Look at the figure. At the ends of delicate branches air tubes are tiny air sacs, each wrapped in a network of delicate blood capillaries. These air sacs are extremely thin tissues. Through their walls the oxygen must pass into the blood and the carbon dioxide pass out. When pneumococci get in, they irritate these delicate tissues. The minute capillaries become gorged with blood cells. The blood

Pneumococci magnified many times

General Biological Supply House, Inc., Chicago

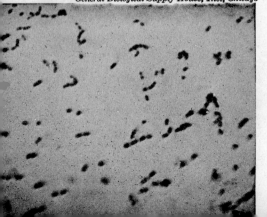

may ooze through the delicate walls into the air sacs. This mass of blood cells and fluid interfere with breathing, the exchange of oxygen and carbon dioxide. The pneumococci grow and multiply in the congested air sacs. Fibrin, or clot, is formed. The lungs begin to solidify. The white blood cells attack the germs. In the old days sometimes the white cells won. The crisis was passed, the temperature fell, and the patient recovered. But often pneumonia meant death.

The first scientific progress in overcoming the pneumococci came with the discovery that, when germs enter the body, cells within our bodies manufacture substances called *antibodies,* which react against the germs. Some antibodies weaken the germs so that the white blood cells can more easily devour them. Antibodies were then prepared in animals' bodies for use in our own. Animals were inoculated with small doses of the pneumococcus germs. A portion of the animal's blood was then drawn out and the clear part, *serum*, separated from the blood cells. The serum contained the antibodies. The serum was injected into the patient and often saved his life. One difficulty lay in the fact that only certain types of pneumonia, a very few of the thirty or more types, could be stopped by serums. Further difficulty lay in the fact that one type of serum would not stop another type of pneumococcus. The type of pneumococcus had to be determined quickly. Serums were therefore limited in their usefulness.

The next great victory came with the discovery of the sulfa drugs. Sulfapyridine and sulfathiozole often stopped certain types of pneumococci. These drugs saved lives, but sometimes they had bad effects on the patient. They are too dangerous for use by untrained persons. Some physicians have blood examinations made every day or two while sulfa drugs are being administered.

The greatest victory so far over pneumococci came from a little mold, similar to the mold that grows on bread. Alexander Fleming, a Scotsman in London, was growing certain bacteria on agar, a gelatin-like substance obtained from seaweeds much used by bacteriologists. Fleming noticed that certain bacteria did not grow around little areas of mold that had developed in his cultures. From such an observation by a trained scientist came one

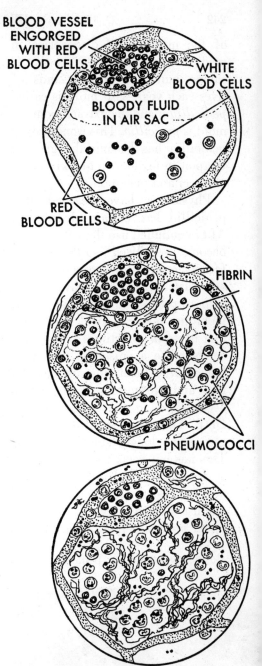

In the first stage of pneumonia (top) bloody fluid fills the air sacs. Then (middle) the fluid thickens. In the third and critical stage (bottom), the fluid becomes still thicker, with an increased number of white blood cells fighting the pneumococci

of the most useful discoveries in medical science, a discovery that is saving hundreds of thousands of lives each year. This mold is called *penicillium* and the extract from the mold is *penicillin*. This wonder drug penicillin has become the greatest weapon so far to stop quickly pneumococci and pneumonia.

Physicians have learned that penicillin has certain drawbacks. After continued use the patient may become "sensitized" so that he suffers a "reaction" when penicillin is administered. He may have violent skin eruptions and fever. Scientists, including medical men, know also that bacteria sometimes become accustomed to a poison so that it no longer kills them, just as races of flies and mosquitoes have become accustomed to the insect poison DDT. Then just as with flies, the remedy no longer stops the germs. This has not been a serious danger so far with penicillin, but it may develop. Doctors, therefore, advise against the use of penicillin except under medical supervision. Penicil-

lin is a valuable remedy that may save our lives some day, if we have not spoiled our body and armed our germs. We must do exactly as our doctors direct and not take penicillin without their advice.

The antibiotics. Penicillin is one of the drugs called *antibiotics*, the germ killers. *Anti* means "against" and *bios* means "life." Antibiotics are used against the lives of disease germs. Penicillin was the first great antibiotic and is still, perhaps, the greatest. It kills some other germs in addition to pneumococci. It kills staphylococcus or "staph" as the laboratory workers say. There are several kinds of staphylococcus that attack the human body. (See figure.) Some are found in boils, abscesses, and diseased wounds filled with pus. Some also may cause the painful disease osteomyelitis, an inflammation of the marrow of the bones. In World War II penicillin was used to stop infection of wounds, for infected wounds often kill when a wound free of germs heals and the patient recovers.

Besides pneumococci, penicillin kills staphylococci (left) and streptococci (right)

General Biological Supply House, Inc., Chicago

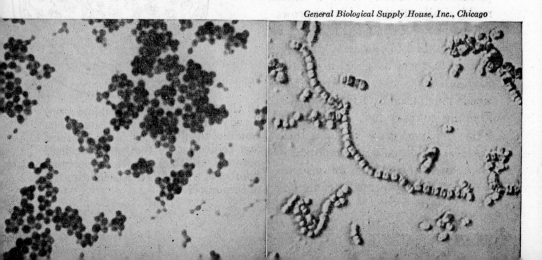

"Staph" also causes blood poisoning and meningitis, a disease of the lining of the spinal cord and brain. Penicillin has stopped these dreadful diseases, not always but often. Penicillin also stops streptococcus or "strep," which causes bad sore throats, bronchopneumonia, inflammation of the intestines, and certain other diseases. But penicillin has its limits. It will not stop tuberculosis, typhus fever, and some other bad diseases.

A newer discovery is *streptomycin*. It is prepared from a little plant-like thing that grows in the soil, a thing part way between a mold and a bacterium, called *streptomyces*. Streptomycin was originally prepared at Rutgers University, New Jersey, by Selman Waksman, born in Russia, an immigrant to the United States in boyhood. Streptomycin stops some kinds of tuberculosis attacks. In experiments it stopped typhoid fever and cholera, both killing diseases seated in the intestines. Streptomycin has been so promising that it has been flown from the United States to various other parts of the world for use against diseases.

Chloromycetin, from a similar moldlike plant, has been used to stop typhoid fever and Rocky Mountain Spotted Fever, a fatal disease that occurs in many parts of the United States outside of the Rocky Mountains. It has been used against typhus fever, one of the great plagues.

These antibiotics, only a few of the hundreds of products prepared in the laboratories, show how scientists are studying disease. Most experiments turn out to be failures, or part failures. Tyrothricin, for instance, dissolved the protective coating of pneumonia germ, but it also destroyed the red blood cells. It could, however, be used on skin ulcers. So bit by bit our information about the things of nature grows. Now and then a brilliant discovery like penicillin is made, and then follow the limitations of its use. Science grows by success and failure.

The sulfas. It is reported that the death rate in diseases in which sulfa drugs could be used has dropped 60 per cent in New York City. Before the sulfas, meningitis usually brought death. After the sulfas became generally used by physicians, the patient usually recovered. Before the sulfas, the operation to cure mastoiditis, an infection within the bony bump behind the ear, was very common. Since the sulfas, the operation has become rare; sulfas stopped the germs.

These sulfa drugs were developed from a red dye. The German scientist Gerhard Domagk tried it against germs in living tissues and showed that the germs were stopped. Then began a great study of substances produced from that dye. Over two thousand have been made and tried. A few of them have been valuable in controlling disease. We have seen how some of them have saved the lives of pneumonia patients. Some have stopped other diseases: blood-poisoning, septic sore throats, tonsillitis, "bloody diarrhea" or dysentery, boils and carbuncles, infected skin diseases. They have saved thousands of lives in war and peace.

The original sulfa drug was *sulfanilamide*. It performed wonders, but it sometimes poisoned the patient. It sometimes caused nausea (sickness of the stomach), dizziness, anemia (loss of red blood corpuscles) and destruction of white blood corpuscles, rashes, and fevers. This drug was followed by many other sulfas in attempts to reach other diseases and find a drug that did not poison the patient. *Sulfapyridine, sulfathiozole,* and *sulfadiazine* were prepared, each an improvement in some way upon earlier drugs.

Sulfa drugs were tried in pills, powders, ointments, and chewing gums. If you get a chance to try a sulfa drug chewing gum, don't, without the doctor's direction. It may poison you seriously. Let the doctor prescribe these successful but dangerous drugs. Many doctors make bloods tests daily when they give patients sulfas and watch for bad symptoms. Leave sulfas to the doctors.

The hormones. A young woman suffered with arthritis for four years. Her joints were stiff, swollen, and painful. She could hardly get out of bed. Then *cortisone* was injected. In three days she was out of bed, and on the eighth day she went downtown shopping.

Rheumatic heart disease, "the greatest killer of children and young people," has been controlled by cortisone. It has also been stopped by ACTH, another drug, in every one of eleven patients in which it was first tried. That raised the hope of doctors and laboratory workers.

Cortisone comes from two little, wrinkled, yellowish pads on top of the kidneys. They are called *adrenal glands,* which indicates that they are the glands attached to the kidneys. They are very complex glands. They are known to produce twenty to thirty different substances. These substances pass into the blood stream and control action within the body. From the interior part of the adrenal gland (called the medulla) comes a secretion called *adrenalin*. Surgeons have kept adrenalin ready in the operating room. If the patient's heart stops during an operation, an injection of adrenalin has often started it and saved the life of the patient. Adrenalin has often been used to stop bleeding. It constricts the small blood vessels and so stops bleeding. This constriction also increases the blood pressure and so stimulates the heart. From the outer part of the adrenal gland (called the cortex) come several substances, one of which is the valuable drug *cortisone*. That drug has controlled rheumatic fever and the painful inflammation of the joints—arthritis.

ACTH stands for the adreno-cortico-tropic hormone. (Do not try to remember that.) That means that it stimulates the outer part of the adrenal glands. ACTH is produced in a tiny gland no bigger than a grain of corn, the *pituitary gland,* located under the middle of the brain and embedded in bones of the skull. The pituitary gland produces several products that stimulate other parts of the body to do their work. All these products from glands that stimulate other glands and other activities are called *hormones* or chemical messengers. The pituitary is a master gland that stimulates many others. ACTH stimulates the adrenal glands to produce cortisone. So either ACTH or cortisone may be used to fight arthritis and rheumatic fever.

Another gland that regulates happenings within the body and furnishes a product for the doctor is the *thyroid.* It sits like a little saddle astride the front of the neck. If this little gland is not doing its work, a young child does not grow properly in body or mind. He becomes a misshapen dwarf and an idiot, with "less intelligence than a dog and less decency than a hog." The doctor can save such a child from that sad state, called *cretinism,* by regular injections of an extract from the thyroid glands of animals killed in the slaughter houses for our meat. If the extract is injected regularly, the child grows normally in body and mind. Now *thyroxin* is made by the chemist, so that the supply is greatly increased and the price much reduced.

Lying close to the stomach is another very important gland, the *pancreas.* This gland produces digestive fluids that pour into the

The thyroid and pituitary glands (below) and the pancreas and adrenal glands (right) help to regulate the activity of our bodies

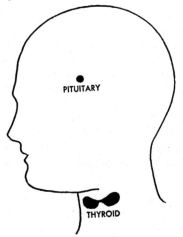

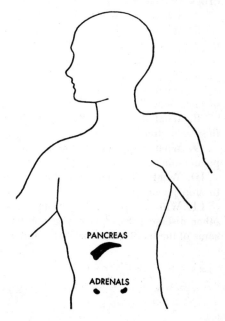

intestine. It also makes another substance that is not poured into the intestine, but taken up by the blood. This hormone regulates the sugar in the body. It has been said that we run and think on sugar. At least sugar is a necessary fuel to keep us going. But if the hormone *insulin* is not produced by the pancreas in the right quantity and quality, *diabetes*, the sugar sickness, results. Formerly that meant death. Now the patient can be saved to old age. He must, however, inject insulin regularly into his body. Insulin is extracted from the pancreas of slaughter house animals.

How to Study about the Wonder Drugs

You are not expected to remember everything that this chapter tells you about the wonder drugs. Read the chapter carefully to understand it. Study the figures; every one tells a story. Ask yourself what each picture tells you. Put it into words.

1. Can you mention some drugs of this chapter that are derived from animals?

2. Can you mention some that are produced from the chemical substances?

3. Can you mention some wonder drugs derived from plants?

4. What causes pneumonia?

5. When is a person likely to contract pneumonia?

6. What should you do to avoid pneumonia?

7. What are the symptoms or signs of pneumonia?

8. What should you do if you show these symptoms?

9. What happens to the lungs in pneumonia?

10. What drugs may the doctor use to stop pneumonia?

11. Will the pneumonia drugs stop other disease germs? Can you mention some of these other diseases? If not, read about them again in the book. It is not necessary to remember them.

12. Can you recall any other drug of the same class as the "greatest" pneumonia drug? If not, read about them again. You do not need to remember them.

13. What is the famous group of drugs developed by the chemists that first stopped pneumonia? Can you mention other diseases stopped by these drugs? If not, read about them.

14. Why is it unsafe to take these drugs without the care of the doctor?

15. What are hormones?

16. Name three glands that produce hormones and name a hormone from each.

17. Can you name a dangerous condition corrected by each of these hormones?

18. What can the doctor hope will stop rheumatic fever and arthritis? If you have forgotten, look it up.

19. Where does the drug come from that saves a child from cretinism?

20. What causes diabetes?

21. What is the name of the substance that saves the life of a diabetic patient?

22. How is that substance obtained?

Chapter Thirty-three

Your Framework and Power Plant

What bones do for you. Without your bones you would be a mass of jelly. They hold you up like a man or a woman, or like a boy or girl. If they do not hold you up properly, you are misshapen, queer in your posture and movement, and probably partly sick. You cannot breathe properly if your chest sags over in front like a bag of meal. Your stomach and intestines cannot do their work if they are cramped between the backbone and the mass of organs pushed down by your ribs and breast bone.

If bones are not properly built, they may be partly or entirely corrected when you are young. Misshapen skeletons are often due to lack of proper feeding. We shall study something about feeding the skeleton and the rest of the body presently. If feeding is corrected when one is very young, misshapen bones will often shape themselves properly. Properly fed bones will be properly built.

Bones alone cannot hold you up. The muscles act with the bones to hold you up. Bones and muscles together cannot hold you up unless both are fed properly, exercised properly, trained and rested properly. When they are properly fed and rested, they may be trained, and it is fun then to make them work.

Did you ever see a mass of bones that make up a skeleton of an animal or man? There is a great assortment of shapes. Each shape has a meaning of its own. Each bone is fitted to do its own work. Think of the bones of the skull. The brain case is roofed with flat bones curved to fit together. They form a curved, hard box that protects the most delicate tissues in the body. The very curvature helps to make a blow glance off. Notice the projections over your eyes that protect those delicate organs. The inner ear, which contains the delicate parts by which we hear, is buried deep in a mass of hard bone. Work your jaws while you hold your fingers just below the cheek bones at the sides of your face. The

How are the eyes protected? How is the jaw attached? The dark lines show where the bones grow together

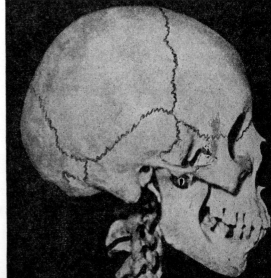

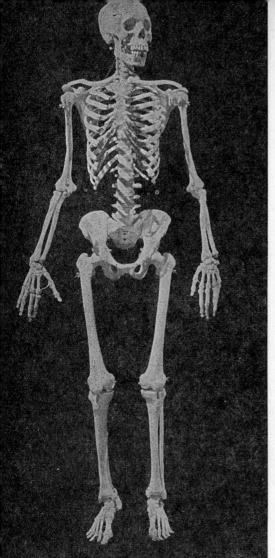

A man's skeleton

muscles, and serve as levers to give strength and speed.

How a bone is built. A bone is a wonderful thing. It is built of a tough stuff called *connective tissue*, filled in with and enclosed in mineral matter. This mineral matter is chiefly a compound of lime and phosphorus. In babies a large part of the bone is only connective tissue. Later the mineral parts are taken out of the blood and built into bone by the cells of the connective tissue. Because there is so little mineral in the baby's bones, they bend easily but do not break easily. Because in old people's bones there is a great deal of mineral matter, they break very easily. In certain parts of the body the connective tissue, or cartilage, remains without the mineral matter, as in the tip of the nose, the outer ears, and about the breast bone. Those parts can be bent more easily.

Another remarkable feature of bones is that they are not solid bone but spongy or hollow inside. This makes them lighter and stiffer. An iron tube is stiffer than a solid iron bar of the same weight. Here and there along the side of a bone you will see a small hole where a blood vessel enters, for a bone must have food and oxygen brought to it to keep it alive. Inside the big bones, in the red marrow, the red blood corpuscles are born. Surrounding the bone is a living membrane that helps to build new bone substance when you break a bone.

cheek bones furnish strong attachment bases for your chewing parts. You can bite hard. The long bones of your arms enable you to swing an ax or a baseball bat, and those of your leg enable you to get over the ground rapidly. The many little bones in the wrist and ankle make possible a great variety of movements. Bones thus protect, furnish projections for the attachment of

How bones are joined. Tough *ligaments* tie the bones together and tie the ends of muscles to the bones. The ligaments are elastic. They allow the bones to move at the joints. When you have eaten a chicken leg, you probably have noticed a long, tough, bony string. It is a ligament or tendon. You can feel a similar tendon just above your own heel. It connects the big calf muscle to the heel and pulls your heel up when you walk.

Bone meets bone at the joints. Some joints do not move. The joints, or sutures, of the skull do not move, but are necessary to let the skull grow. In a young baby's head there is a spot on top where there is no bone. Later bone grows in to cover the spot. Not until one is about twenty-one years of age, when the head has reached its adult size, do the joints of the skull grow together. The skull bones make a tight, strong box. The edges are grooved, fitting together so that there is no chance for a slip of one bone on another, which would be bad for the brain.

How joints work. Suppose you had an elbow joint at your shoulder. How could you throw a baseball? If we had been built that way, the game would never have been invented. The hinge joints at the knee and elbow are good, sturdy joints for backward and forward movement. The hinge joint at the knee makes standing safer and less tiresome than would a looser joint. The hinge joint at the elbow enables one to hold things out at arm's length

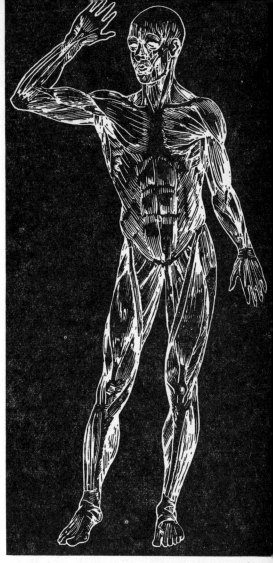

A man's muscles

without rapid tiring. Notice on page 250 the projecting bone from the lower arm that prevents bending in the wrong direction. Hip and shoulder have ball-and-socket joints that allow free play for baseball, skating, or work.

The jointed backbone is a wonderful device that allows bending and keeps rigidity. A single joint in the backbone does not allow very much

249

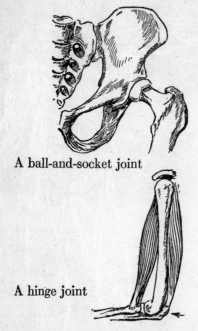

A ball-and-socket joint

A hinge joint

movement, but the whole column has enough joints to allow considerable bending. Between the vertebrae that make up the backbone are cushions of cartilage, or gristle, that prevent painful jars with each step.

What muscles do for you. You can walk because one set of muscle cells gets shorter and thereby pulls bones; and then those cells let go and another set pulls the bones back again. Sets of muscles work in pairs. One set pulls your leg bones forward and another set pulls them back. So it is with your arms. Muscles can only pull and let go. When not attached to bones, as the muscles around your mouth, they pull the lips together and pucker them up. When the heart muscle contracts, it squeezes the blood out of the heart; when it lets go, more blood flows in

from the veins. The great muscles around your arms and legs and around your abdomen also serve to protect the parts hidden inside. A bump on the calf of the leg is not pleasant, but it is not half so bad as an equal blow on the shin. The abdominal muscles bend and squeeze the abdomen and also protect the important organs inside.

How a muscle is built. A muscle is a bundle of slender, living cells. Little bundles of such cells are held together and protected by a surrounding sheath. Then a great number of little bundles are bound together by the sheath which surrounds the whole muscle. From the muscle sheath, long tendons may stretch to the bones or short broad tendons may anchor the muscle to a bone.

Watch your shoes. A very great many women—most city women—have painful feet in middle age because they wore tight shoes that were the wrong shape. With poor feet, come pains in the legs and back and then in the abdomen—all because of those fancy and ugly little shoes. If your feet are forced out of shape when they are growing, they can never be remade into the shape they should be. Correctly shaped shoes, sufficiently long, will save many pains.

Making your skeleton stand up. You do not want your back and shoulders rounded like a potato and your head sagging out in front. You will need to train the muscles to hold you up like a man. Only when your muscles hold you in the correct posture, can your bones grow as they should. Roll back your shoulders and throw out your chest.

Muscles must be exercised to keep them healthy. That is the life they are meant for. Make them work every day. That makes them feel well. It sends the blood through them to bring food and oxygen and to take away the wastes. It makes them strong and lively.

The day must not be all work for your muscles, however, for they need rest too. When they feel fatigued, tired, they should be rested. Do not work tired muscles. Keep them lively, by rest and exercise. The most complete rest is sleep. You need lots of it—nine or ten hours out of every twenty-four. Your muscles must also be properly fed with the right kind of food in the right quantity.

"Stiff" joints. Pain on bending may be due to injury or to disease. If painful joints are due to injury, time, rest, and the doctor can repair them. If they are due to disease or infection, it may take a long hunt by the doctor to locate the seat of infection. *Arthritis,* or inflamed living membranes of the joints, may be due to poisons from bacteria growing in the throat, gums, intestines, or elsewhere. When the doctor locates the bacteria, he may be able to get rid of them and cure the arthritis.

There are diseases that attack the bones. One of them is tuberculosis.

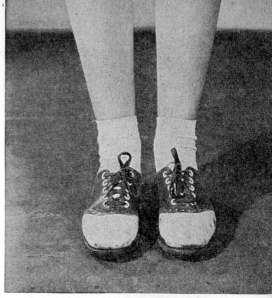

Are the shoes in the picture the shape of the feet as shown in the prints below the picture?

Another is a "deficiency disease" *rickets,* due to the lack of certain food substances. The bones fail to grow properly and become bent, and the body grows misshapen. We shall study these necessary food substances presently and find what we should eat to make bones grow.

The skin. Take care of the skin. You may never think of your skin unless it gets sunburned or itchy or needs washing, or it may be that you think a great deal of your skin and spend a good deal of time trying to make it beautiful. In the former case you probably forget it too long, and in the latter case you do not forget it long enough. A little

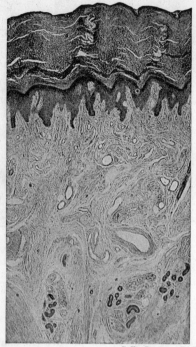

Sally Pepper, Phila.

Skin from the finger tip magnified 32 times. The dark part is the epidermis, the lighter part the derma. The open spaces in the derma are blood vessels, and the dark spots are sweat glands

soap and water every now and then helps to make the skin feel well and look well. As for powder and paint, they make you look like a wild Indian dressed for a war dance. Powder, paint, and other kinds of dirt interfere with the work of the skin, a very important work for the body.

The work of the skin. The first work of the skin is to protect you. If you have barked a knuckle, you know how painful the raw skin is. If you have had an infected finger, a running sore, it is because bacteria have entered where the skin has been broken or punctured. The skin keeps out bacteria, and there is danger from a scratch that goes through the skin. The skin also protects the delicate tissue beneath from heat and cold. A raw knuckle on a cold day may leave you with a very painful finger.

The skin also is your refrigerator, your cooling machine. If the cooling mechanism quit work, you would probably die quickly from a heat stroke. Heat passes off the skin as it does from the radiator of an automobile. The skin also has another means of cooling, more efficient than the automobile. It gives off perspiration that evaporates. The evaporation cools the skin. You know how it cools a sweating face to fan it. Fanning increases the evaporation of the moisture. On a humid summer day the perspiration does not evaporate readily, and you feel much warmer than on a dry, clear day of the same temperature. When the air in our homes in winter is too dry—as it usually is—we must keep it at a much higher temperature than when the air is moistened. The dry air causes ready evaporation of perspiration, and this evaporation results in cooling of the skin.

Furthermore, perspiration carries waste out of the body. Wastes similar to kidney wastes pass out of the sweat glands of the skin. If the wastes are not frequently washed from the skin, they give an unpleasant odor and lead to irritation of the skin. For people who meet others indoors, a daily bath is necessary to avoid odors. Warm water and soap are cheap, pleasant, and effective. A cold bath is stimulating but should be followed by a pleasant reaction of warmth if taken in winter. A warm bath is not wise immediately before going out on a cold winter day.

How the skin is built. The outer layer of skin is dead. It is made up of flat dead cells of skin. [This layer is called the *epidermis*.] The dead cells are constantly being worn and rubbed away. More cells are being constantly added from layers of living cells below. Under the outer layer is the true skin [the *derma*]. It is alive. In it are capillaries and nerves, sweat glands, and oil glands. Oil from the skin glands keeps the skin soft and moist. In the inner skin, also, are cells that grow up into hairs and cells which grow out into nails. There are also color-

Philip D. Gendreau, N. Y.

Perspiration is the body's method of controlling overheating. It also removes waste material

ing materials in the skin. This coloring material becomes darker and more extensive if the skin is exposed to the sun. That is the reason you get tanned.

How to Learn about Your Framework and Your Power Plant

I. Study your bones and muscles.

1. Try this. (a) Stand up straight with the shoulders rolled back and the ribs thrown out, or sit in a chair with the hips against the back of the chair, the shoulders back, and the ribs up. Breathe. (b) Sit forward in the chair, lean back against the back, and let your back sag and your shoulders roll forward. Breathe. In which position did you breathe more comfortably? Then read the section entitled, "What bones do for you."

2. Examine your bones as suggested in the last paragraph of the section, "Bones alone cannot hold you up." With a pencil draw a line curved as the spine (backbone) is curved. What advantage has such a backbone over a straight backbone? Look at the pelvis or hip bones on page 248. Then feel the pelvis in your own body while you raise your leg. What advantage is the great crest of the pelvis? Look also at the picture of the abdominal organs on page 260. What further advantage do you see in the arrangement of the pelvis? In the same way you can examine other bones in your body.

3. Read the section, "How bones are built."

4. Double up your fist and examine the tendons on the underside of your wrist. Examine the tendon above the heel. Read the section, "How bones are joined."

5. What kind of movement can you make with the first and second joint of the fingers? These joints work like what common piece of hardware? Now consider the joint at the base of the finger. What additional movements can you make at this joint? What advantage does this give you? Similarly examine the thumb joints. Suppose you had at the base of the thumb a joint like the outer joint of the thumb. What motions could you not make?

Now read the section, "How joints work," examining the motions of the joints as you read about them.

6. Take hold of the biceps, the big muscle on the front of your upper arm. Raise the forearm. What happens in the biceps? Now take hold of the muscle of the back part of the upper arm. Again move the forearm. How do these two muscles work together? What would happen if both of these muscles contracted at the same time? Where else do you find pairs of muscles that work together?

Read the sections, "What muscles do for you" and "How muscles are built."

7. Remove your shoe and stand on a piece of paper. Have someone trace the shape of your foot on the paper, while your weight is on the foot. Compare the tracing with the picture on page 251. Is your foot still the shape that nature made it? Now compare your shoe with page 251. Will your shoe allow your foot to grow as nature makes it grow? Read the section, "Watch your shoes."

8. Stand up in front of a mirror. Watch your shoulders and chest. Raise your arms sidewise with palms down. Roll your arms over, palms up. Note what it does to your shoulders. Now

read the section, "Making your skeleton stand up." Do you need the advice on rest and sleep?

9. Read the section on "stiff joints."

10. Read the rest of the chapter. How do your habits agree with what is said about washing and bathing?

II. Test yourself with the following questions:

1. What holds you up like a human being?

2. What good are bones? What should you do for misshapen bones? How do bones grow?

3. What system works with the bones to hold you up?

4. Tell three things you must do to keep the muscles lively and well-trained.

5. Draw a sketch of the shape of the correct shoe to keep the feet and the back feeling fine. Note particularly the line on the inside of the foot.

6. What makes "stiff joints," and what should you do about them?

7. Tell two important things the skin does for the body. How often should you take a bath? What is the value of a cold bath and what of a warm bath?

III. Think about these questions:

1. Is it better to have very strong muscles or lively, well-trained muscles? Which type will be developed by lifting heavy weights?

2. Look at your shoulders in the mirror and the shoulders of others. Are they even? What exercise will help to make them even?

3. What will eventually happen if you do not keep the shoulder muscles well-fed, well-trained, and well-rested?

IV. Vocabulary. Did you find new words?

ligament　　　　　　rickets
suture　　　　　　　deficiency

Chapter Thirty-four

What to Eat and How Much

At home you eat what is served. At the lunch counter you choose. Perhaps you help to choose the food for the home. To choose wisely you must understand what foods do to you, and what each kind of food does. Advertisements of this kind of food and that scream at you about proteins, carbohydrates, and vitamins. There is so much talk that, as the saying goes, you can't make head or tail of it.

What good is food. You usually eat because the food tastes good or because you are hungry. Now let us see how the food benefits you. It builds you. You were rather small when you came to earth. You grew from what you ate. The main foods that built you were the substances called *proteins*. You are largely proteins and water. Therefore, see that you get proteins—eggs and milk with breakfast, perhaps a piece of meat and milk at lunch, and meat —the equivalent of two chops—and more milk for supper.

You need some *fat* but probably get sufficient if you take butter, milk, and the small quantity of fat that is served with meat. Fat's chief use is to supply fuel which gives you energy.

You eat largely of starch and sugar, that is, *carbohydrates*. Breakfast cereals, bread, potatoes, peas, beans, and many other plant foods contain starch. Most fruits contain sugar, and so do cakes, pies, jams, and most desserts. Sugar and starch

What you eat is important to your health. Variety is essential

Ewing Galloway, N. Y.

These foods will give you a variety of vitamins

are energy foods, giving you the power to keep going and to keep alive.

Vitamins. From the advertising of certain products you might infer that if you did not immediately buy them and absorb the vitamins they are said to contain, you would become crippled and deformed or would die. Yet your great-grandfather, or perhaps your grandfather, never heard of them.

Meat should be in every diet

Black Star, N. Y.

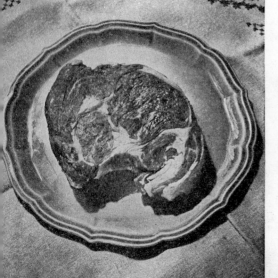

Vitamins control in different ways the growth and workings of our bodies. Several vitamins are known, and have been named vitamins A, B, C, and D. If vitamin A is not in our food, the eyes become sore, ulcers may develop, and blindness result. Vitamin A is present in butter, in milk, in the yolk of eggs, and in green vegetables like lettuce and spinach. In yellow vegetables, like carrots and sweet potatoes, there is a substance from which the liver makes vitamin A.

A group of several vitamins form the B complex. B vitamins are in fresh fruit, vegetables, fresh meats, milk, yeast, in whole wheat but not in white bread, and in other whole grains. In the Far East where many people live almost entirely on white rice for long periods, they may develop a disease, called *beriberi*, from the absence of B vitamins. In some parts of our country where people live largely on pork, cornmeal, and molasses or a similarly restricted diet, they often develop *pellagra*, due to a lack of other B vitamins.

Among the poor and ignorant of our large cities children sometimes suffer with *scurvy*. This disease is due to lack of vitamin C. Fresh fruits and vegetables contain it, but cooking usually destroys it. Canned tomatoes and tomato juice, however, may contain vitamin C. Raw milk contains vitamin C, but pasteurization destroys it. Orange juice is a rich source of vitamin C.

Lack of vitamin D is common in large cities. Children fail to develop; they suffer from the disease called *rickets*. The bones, especially, do not grow healthy and straight. The child may become deformed. The teeth also fail to develop properly.

When children spend most of their time in the sunshine with little clothing, their bodies manufacture vitamin D. This vitamin has been called the *sunshine vitamin*. If children, and older people too, are not sufficiently in the sunshine, they must get the vitamin from food. Not many foods contain it in sufficient quantity. It occurs in butter, in milk, in yolk of eggs, and especially in cod-liver oil and other fish livers.

Choosing your food. First choose protein—lean meat, fish, eggs, cheese, and milk. There are vegetable proteins too, especially in peas and beans, where you get them with starch. Bread also contains protein and starch. The vegetable proteins are not complete proteins. They lack certain substances that are needed in the body, especially when it is growing. Therefore, some animal protein is needed—meat, fish, eggs.

Next select your vitamins. Fresh fruits and vegetables, including leafy vegetables, especially when eaten uncooked, butter and fresh meat and eggs will furnish your supply of vitamins. Eat plenty of salads made of green things like lettuce, tomatoes, and uncooked fruits.

Ewing Galloway, N. Y.

Salads are excellent for us

Afterwards you may satisfy your hunger with carbohydrates, such as sugars and starches. Bread, cake, pie, potatoes, cereals, peas, and beans will supply starch.

When to stop eating. How much shall you eat? Well, healthy, active people, if they do not gorge themselves to discomfort, will probably eat about the right amount. There is more danger that you will not get enough of every kind, than

At the school cafeteria choose a healthful selection

U.S.D.A.

that you will not get enough in general. Eat a great variety, not a variety of cakes, breads, biscuits, and pies, but a variety including proteins, various fruits, fresh vegetables, milk, and butter. After that take your cakes and pies.

There is sometimes danger that young girls will do themselves lasting injury by starving to keep thin. When underfed, they fail to develop, and later in life the body cannot make up the loss of the growing period. Active boys do not worry about keeping thin. Excessive fat needs the attention of the doctor. Starvation does not correct the difficulty but brings on others.

How to Learn What to Eat and How Much

I. Read the chapter.

II. Study your food.

1. Keep an account of the food that you eat in a day. Fill out the table below, indicating: Little; Enough; Very much.

2. After studying the table for several days, decide what you should do, if anything, to improve your diet.

3. Make up menus for breakfast, lunch, and dinner that would give you a properly balanced diet.

III. Test yourself:

1. Name several protein foods; several carbohydrate foods; several foods containing the different vitamins.

2. Tell what value each of the following foods has: cereals, including bread and cake, bacon, eggs, oranges, ham sandwich, chicken sandwich, cinnamon bun, ice cream, beef, butter, potatoes, carrots, spinach.

3. Without referring to your previous work or to the book, draw up ideal menus for breakfast, lunch, and dinner.

IV. Think out answers to the following questions:

1. In the old sailing-ship days, the food of the men was largely "salt horse and sea biscuit," that is, salt pork and white-flour crackers. From what disease do you suppose they suffered? Why do men at sea not suffer now with this disease?

2. When the Mississippi River flooded the lowlands and drove the people from their homes, the Red Cross served yeast along with the food in the refugee camps. Why this yeast?

V. Vocabulary.

protein　　　　　　cereal
carbohydrate　　　rickets
　　　　vitamin

Food	Quantity	Proteins	Carbohydrates	Fat	Vitamins			
					A	B	C	D	G

Chapter Thirty-five

Preparing Food in Your Body

Food, as you eat it, does you no good at all except to excite you and "fill you up." The parts of your body that need food are the microscopic cells of which you are built. Food, as you eat it, cannot reach them. But food in your mouth or even the odor of it starts digestive juices flowing. Your mouth "waters." It is anxious to get at the job of digestion.

Mouthing your food. Chew food to a pulp. Work in the saliva to make it a soft and slippery mass. Enjoy it; do not shoot it down as a dog does. It doesn't hurt a dog to bolt chunks of meat. He has a heavy flow of saliva. You perhaps have seen the saliva trickle from your dog's mouth as you put his food on a plate. He has so much saliva poured out from the salivary glands, that his mouth will not hold it. That makes the food so slippery he swallows it easily. Then a dog's stomach and intestinal juices are much more active than yours. He easily digests bones. Do not eat like a dog. Chew food thoroughly. The saliva not only wets food but digests certain kinds. It changes starch to sugar as you chew it. Get as much digestion out of your saliva as you can.

Why you swallow and how. When the chewed food is worked by

Why can the puppy bolt his food and you cannot?

Harold M. Lambert, Phila.

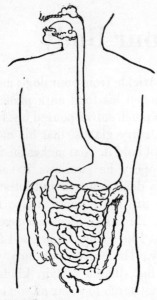

The digestive tract

the muscles of the tongue and cheeks back to the rear of the mouth, suddenly it is gone. You have little to do with its disappearance. That is the reason marbles, nails, and safety pins in children's mouths are dangerous. When they reach the back part, nature takes charge, and the muscles of the throat swallow without one's taking thought. [We say that kind of swallowing is by *reflex action*, action without willing.] The food—or marble—is sent down the tube called the *esophagus* or *gullet* to the stomach.

What the stomach does. When the food arrives in the stomach, it is churned back and forth. The stomach has layers of muscles in its walls. The muscles contract and squeeze the food downward toward the lower end. The lower end is closed by a little valve or gate [called the *pylo-*

rus]. When the food meets this closed gate, it is pushed back for more churning.

Meanwhile *gastric juice* (meaning "stomach juice") is poured into the stomach from glands in the walls of the stomach. The juice is mixed with the food and partly digests it. The gastric juice cannot digest the food completely. Indeed it does not digest at all the starch or sugar or the fat. It partially digests the protein.

When the food at the lower gate [pylorus] of the stomach is liquid and digested as far as the stomach can digest it, the gate opens for a moment and a little of the liquid passes into the intestine.

What the intestine does. The intestine completes the digestion. A great gland, the *pancreas*, pours in digestive juices that digest proteins, fats, and starches. The *liver* also pours in a fluid, bile, that aids in digestion. Very tiny glands in the walls of the intestine also pour in digestive juices.

While digestion by these various juices is going on, muscles in the walls of the intestine squeeze down on the food and move it along as well as churn it back and forth. As the food moves gradually downward, all of it that can be digested is digested. There remains a mass of indigestible material to be passed out of the body.

Getting the food out of the intestine. When the food is all digested, it is liquid. As it is digested, it is absorbed by the walls of the intestine. The walls have many folds and many tiny projections through which they can absorb the liquid, digested food. In addition, the intestine is very long, about twenty-six feet in a man. This great length gives time for digestion as the food passes along, and time and space for absorption of the digested food.

When the digested food is absorbed from the intestine, it is taken by the blood. Digestion gets the food ready to be carried to the places where its work is to be done. Carrying the digested and absorbed food is a work of the blood.

Care of the grinding force. To chew well you need good teeth. Perhaps you never think of your teeth unless you bite on a cherry stone or have a toothache. Toothache means that a tooth has become decayed, that a hole has been formed and through it the sensitive part inside the tooth has been exposed. In a healthy tooth nature covers up that sensitive part with hard enamel. The enamel makes a hard biting surface. If you let it decay and you have a toothache, it serves you right. A toothache is due to neglect or ignorance, both inexcusable. Eat the proper food, keep the teeth clean, and see a dentist once or twice a year. In spite of your cleaning, decay may start, but your dentist can stop it at the start. He drills away the decaying substance and fills the cavity with substance that does not decay.

The bristles of your toothbrush should go in between the teeth and

Ewing Galloway, N. Y.

Brushing the teeth is an important part of oral hygiene

push out the food material caught there. Keep that in mind as you brush your teeth. Brush your upper teeth

The dentist knows what should be done to your teeth. See him often, and he will not hurt you

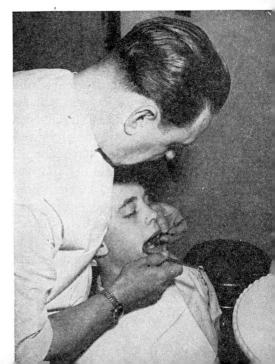

down and lower teeth up, inner surface as well as outer surface. If a shred of meat is stuck between teeth, get it out with a wood toothpick or better, a thread of dental floss.

You should have a tooth powder to do the cleaning work well. It does not need to cost much. Precipated chalk, bought cheaply at the drug store, will do. After brushing, rinsing the teeth with a weak solution of baking soda, two teaspoonfuls to a quart of water, will help to neutralize acids. Ammoniated tooth powder with careful brushing twice a day reduced decay 20.5 per cent in a two-year experiment with pupils in the schools of Peoria, Illinois. Twice a day, or better after each meal, scrub the teeth and see that they are clean before you go to bed, for the bacteria will have a long time to work before morning. Even with your regular scrubbing there may be hard deposits on your teeth which your toothbrush will not remove. Therefore your dentist should clean them when you visit him.

Sometimes the teeth grow irregularly. This irregularity may bring about a misshaped jaw and face. Irregular teeth should be straightened when the jaws are young and growing. After the bones have stopped growing, little can be done to correct the results of neglect. Sometimes babies develop such strength and persistence in sucking their thumbs that the jaws become distorted. Patience in removing the thumb from the mouth may correct the habit, but sometimes a mitten placed on the baby's hand is used to discourage this habit.

Diseased teeth are dangerous. Bacteria growing in pockets about the bases of the teeth poison the whole body. "Rheumatism" has been cured by pulling bad teeth. To locate pockets of pus due to bacteria hidden by the gums, the dentist X-rays the teeth and gums. Hidden pockets must be treated until they are drained of pus and bacteria. Often a diseased tooth must be extracted.

Taking care of the digestive force. For the active boy and girl, there are only about two precautions to take in keeping a good stomach and a good intestine. The first is, do not keep putting little bites into them all day long, a bit of candy, a cracker, a piece of cake or one of pie, a banana, an apple, and so on, without rest between meals. Give your organs a rest. They deserve it. The second precaution is like unto the first. Do not put too much in at any one time. If you eat until it hurts, you have eaten much too much. A few years of that kind of treatment may produce a permanent hurt. Stop when you have had enough; do not gorge.

Another care of the system is attention to ridding the intestine of indigestible material. Teach your intestine good habits. Train it to evacuate regularly, and do not discourage it by neglect when it demands attention. It can learn bad habits and become lazy.

How to Learn about Preparing Food in Your Body

I. Experiments in digestion.

1. EXPERIMENT No. 66. Take a dry, unsweetened cracker. Chew it slowly and thoroughly. Keep at it. How does it change in taste? Describe the cracker when it is just ready to slip down the throat. Is it necessary to stop and think that it is time to swallow? What usually happens when the food is well-chewed? Can you stop a swallow after it starts?

2. EXPERIMENT No. 67. Take a small piece of hard-boiled white of egg. Put it in a test tube and cover it with dilute hydrochloric acid. Let it stand. Cover another piece of egg with pepsin obtained from the drug store. What happens? Hydrochloric acid and pepsin are formed in the glands of the stomach. What effect have they upon the food?

3. Practice brushing the teeth with your toothbrush dry. Start with the brush on the upper gum. Brush slowly downward so that the bristles go between the teeth and dislodge particles of food. Is your toothbrush the right shape? Does the stroke actually reach every particle of food? If the brush is not effective, try some dental floss or a wooden toothpick. Try brushing with tooth powder and without. Which seems to be more effective in removing the traces of food?

4. Stand in front of a mirror and, if possible, illuminate the teeth with a flashlight. Look at all the teeth. Are they arranged well or poorly?

II. Read the chapter.

III. Test yourself:

1. What food substance is digested in the mouth? Into what is it changed?

2. When is food ready to swallow?

3. What happens to the food in the stomach? The digestion of what kinds of food begins there?

4. What happens to the food in the intestine?

5. After the food is digested, what happens to it?

6. How can you prevent toothaches? Why is it necessary to see the dentist when you have no toothache? What are you trying to do when you brush your teeth? Is your method successful?

7. Tell of three things easily done that will help keep your digestion in good condition.

IV. Think these out:

1. Can you recall a certain dinner or certain food that was followed with discomfort? What did you decide was the cause of the discomfort? What did you do about it thereafter?

2. Many people suffer discomfort after eating and then take a heavy dose of baking soda. What is a better thing to do?

3. Count the number of advertised remedies for "indigestion" that you see in one day in newspapers, store windows, and other places. Would you conclude that there is much "indigestion"? Why do you suppose it occurs? Do the remedies prevent "indigestion"? What would be a better plan than taking medicine frequently?

4. Eskimos living on native foods have very few decayed teeth. Eskimos living on white man's food have badly decayed teeth. Do these facts suggest anything about the care of our teeth?

V. Vocabulary. Watch the spelling.

saliva　　　　　　reflex

esophagus　　　　gastric

Chapter Thirty-six

Transportation Inside Your Body

The round trip. A hollow muscle, the heart, squeezes the blood that flows into it and forces it out through the blood vessels. The blood vessels branch and branch until they are a vast network of microscopic tubes, the *capillaries*. These tiny vessels unite again with others and still others until they form large vessels leading back to the heart. The blood vessels that carry the blood from the heart to the capillaries are *arteries*, and those that carry the blood from the capillaries to the heart are *veins*. All the vessels—arteries, capillaries, and veins—unite into a continuous system of tubes. Around and around through this system the blood flows.

The heart is constantly forcing blood into the arteries, and the on-coming blood behind it forces it

What does your heart do when you exercise violently?

Black Star, N. Y.

through the capillaries into the veins. But there it cannot rest. More blood still coming behind forces it through the veins to the heart. Little flaps of tissue along the veins float out and prevent the blood from flowing backward, much as a piece of paper in the sink stops the water from flowing out the drain pipe. These flaps of tissue are called *valves*. Arrived back at the heart, the blood is almost immediately forced out again into the arteries.

Receiving and delivering stations. The blood's real work of delivering goods is done in the capillaries. These tiny vessels wind everywhere among the living cells that need the supplies. There are so many capillaries that you cannot stick your finger with a needle point without breaking some and drawing a drop of blood.

As blood passes through the capillaries, some of the liquid part of the blood passes out through the walls to bathe the cells. This liquid is the *lymph*. The digested food brought by the blood also passes out through the capillaries. From the lymph bath the cells absorb the food which they need. Lymph vessels gather the lymph again and lead it back to the large veins where it becomes once more part of the blood. As the lymph and blood leave the cells, they take

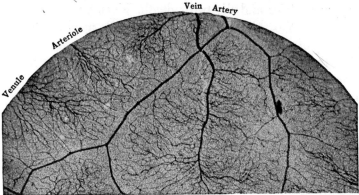

Dr. P. F. Swindle, Milwaukee

The retina of the eye enlarged thirty times. The interlacing of capillaries shows how the blood gets from the arteries to the veins

along waste materials which the cells cast out of their bodies.

Some blood vessels go to the intestines where they branch to form a set of capillaries that are wrapped around and through the walls of the intestines. These capillaries take up the digested food from the intestines and carry it away. The intestinal capillaries unite to form veins which again break up into a second set of capillaries in the liver. There some of the food is taken out and stored in the liver. Also some of the waste matter that the blood brought is taken up by the liver to be cast out of the body. Another set of vessels breaks up into capillaries in the kidneys where more waste matter brought from the cells is cast out of the body. The capillaries unite, and the blood continues to the right side of the heart.

Out of the heart, immediately it goes to the lungs. Another set of capillaries distributes the blood around the lungs. There the blood loses carbon dioxide brought from the cells and receives oxygen to carry to the cells. The capillaries of the skin allow waste material to pass to the sweat glands, which send out the wastes dissolved in perspiration.

Thus there are several stations in which the blood receives substances to carry to the cells and several where the blood gives up waste materials to be cast out of the body. It receives digested food in the capillaries of the walls of the intestines and oxygen in those of the lungs. It gives up waste to be cast out of the body in the capillaries of the liver, kidneys, lungs, and skin. In addition, as the blood passes through the capillaries of several glands in the body, it receives substances called *hormones,* or chemical messengers, which it carries to the cells of the body. The hormones regulate the cell activities, speeding or slowing as needed.

How the heart works. The heart is divided into four chambers, the two upper *auricles* and the two lower *ventricles*. No blood flows from one side of the heart to the other. When the heart beats, the two auricles contract and a moment later the two ventricles contract. The auricles squeeze blood into the ventricles. When the ventricles contract, they force the blood into the arteries. When the heart contracts, valves prevent blood from flowing back from ventricles to auricles and from arteries to ventricles.

In adults the heart beats about seventy-two times each minute. If it stops beating, the cells smother to

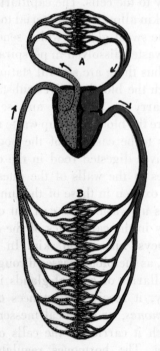

How the blood circulates. *A*, pulmonary (lung) circulation; *B*, systemic (body) circulation. Blue indicates blood carrying carbon dioxide; red, blood carrying oxygen

death. When you exercise and your muscle cells need more oxygen, the heart pumps the blood around faster. In children the rate of heart beat, or pulse, is faster than in adults, and in old people it is slower.

Take your pulse as you have seen the doctor do. Here is the idea: Arteries carry the blood away from the heart. They have muscular walls that stretch as a wave of blood goes through and then squeeze down on it, helping to push it along. You can feel the wave with the finger tips pressed against an artery near the surface. Turn your hand palm up, and firmly, but gently, place the finger tip of your other hand on the inside of your wrist just inside the bump on the bone of the forearm near the base of the thumb. Have patience. When you have found the spot once, you can easily find it again. Count the pulse.

Bad for your heart. Sudden, violent exercise to which you are not accustomed may set your heart struggling at such a rate to keep up with the demands of your cells that the heart may be injured so that it never again becomes normal. Many "headache powders" and tablets damage the heart. They should not be taken without the doctor's orders. Nicotine, one of the poisons of tobacco, has such bad effect on the heart that athletic trainers and doctors speak of "tobacco hearts." Most diseases are hard on the heart. Therefore, the doctor orders you to stay in bed after you think you have recovered from

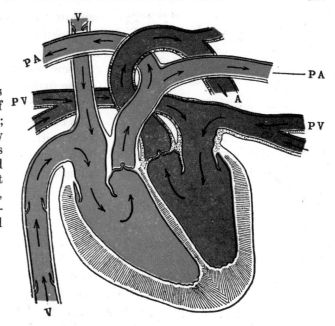

The heart. Arrows show direction of blood flow. *V*, veins; *A*, artery; *PA*, artery to lungs; *PV*, veins from lungs; *RA* and *LA*, right and left auricles; *RV* and *LV*, right and left ventricles. Can you find valves?

an attack of grippe. Alcohol makes the heart beat faster and is therefore used sometimes as a stimulant. Its continued use, however, causes heart disorders as well as damage to other organs.

What is in the blood. Blood looks like a thick red liquid until you see it under the microscope. Then it is seen as a straw-colored liquid [the *plasma*] with round red bodies in it. The red bodies are *red corpuscles*. The red corpuscles carry oxygen from the lungs to the cells. When the blood gives up its oxygen to the cells and takes carbon dioxide from

The correct position for feeling the pulse

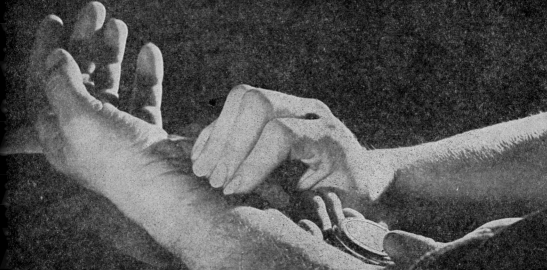

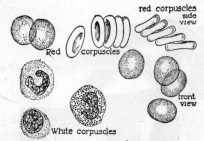

red corpuscles
side
view

Red corpuscles

front
view

White corpuscles

Red and white corpuscles

the cells, it changes from red to blue. You can see the blue in the veins on the back of your hand or on the underside of your wrist. This blood is moving back toward the heart.

Among the red corpuscles are several kinds of *white corpuscles*. They are no particular shape, like microscopic blots of jelly, and they change shape as they move along. Some white corpuscles ooze right through the walls of the capillaries and move around among the body cells. If you jab a splinter in your finger and bacteria start to grow in the flesh, great numbers of white corpuscles come to eat the bacteria. They form the whitish *pus*, or "matter," that sometimes oozes from a sore. So many white corpuscles have rushed to defend you against the invasion of bacteria that the blood cannot carry them all away. They then break out through the skin.

[Sometimes a person does not have enough red corpuscles. Perhaps he does not have enough iron to manufacture the red material in the corpuscles; he may be very pale. The condition is called *anemia*. The doctor may then prescribe certain medicines and foods containing iron

and urge the patient to stay as much as possible in the sunlight to stimulate the body.]

New corpuscles are continually being manufactured in the red marrow at the ends of the long bones. The corpuscles are carried away by the capillaries that pierce the bones. Red corpuscles are also being continually destroyed in the spleen and liver.

The blood contains other things. There are tiny objects called the *blood platelets*, and other substances which start the formation of blood clots. Antitoxins and antibodies which protect the body against germs also circulate through the body.

The air supply. Stopping the breath brings death. Oxygen must continually reach the cells of your body, and carbon dioxide must continually be taken away from the cells. The lungs secure fresh oxygen to supply the blood, and send out carbon dioxide brought to them by the blood. Blood is brought to the lungs by a great artery [the pulmonary artery] which sends a branch to each lung. The arteries branch and branch to form capillaries which are wound around the tiny air sacs of the lungs. In the air sacs is air, and in the capillaries is blood. Only the extremely thin walls of the capillaries and of the air sacs separate air from blood. The blood arriving from the cells has a heavy load of carbon dioxide and is hungry for oxygen. The air in the air sacs is heavy with oxygen. The oxygen passes from the air sacs into the blood, and the carbon dioxide passes from the blood into the air sacs. Then we breathe out the air heavy with carbon dioxide and breathe in fresh air heavy with oxygen ready to purify more blood.

The air leaving the air sacs of the lungs passes into small tubes. These tubes join others and still others, until a large tube [*bronchus*] leads up from each lung and the two tubes [*bronchi*] join to form the windpipe [*trachea*]. Incomplete rings or "horseshoes" of gristle, or cartilage, prevent the windpipe from collapsing. The rings are missing on the inside, where the windpipe lies against the esophagus, the tube through which food reaches the stomach. At the top of the windpipe is the cartilage box called the *larynx*, or "Adam's apple," which contains the vocal cords. In swallowing, the opening to the windpipe is closed by a lid [the *epiglottis*].

Just about where you get a sore throat, the windpipe and the gullet, or esophagus, join and here is only one passage, the *pharynx*. When you open your mouth and say "Ah" in front of a mirror, you can see the upper end of the pharynx. From the upper end of the pharynx, the mouth and the nasal passages open. In the nasal passages are scrolls of bone [the *turbinate* bones] and forests of hairs. The membranes lining the nasal passages and the scrolls of bone help to warm the cold air drawn in from outside, and the hairs help

to screen out the dust. If you breathe through the nose, you warm the air and clean it before it reaches the delicate membranes at the sore-throat level.

Did you ever have tonsillitis? In the throat, or pharynx, is a pair of tissues that sometimes become diseased and must be removed to prevent poisoning of the body. These bodies are the *tonsils*. When not diseased, they probably help to remove bacteria or their poisons from the body.

Perhaps you cannot breathe through the nose. Near the inner end of the nasal passages are growths of delicate tissue, the adenoid tissue, or the *adenoids*. Sometimes this tissue

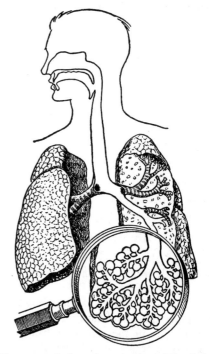

Diagram of the air passages. The left lung is laid open to show air sacs

becomes overgrown and swollen and blocks the passage so that the person must breathe through the mouth. Then it is necessary to remove the adenoids to preserve the health, and in children, to secure proper growth. Their removal is not a serious operation when done by a surgeon who understands the work.

How the air gets into your lungs. You may think that you draw air into your lungs, but really the air pushes its way in. You raise the ribs by means of muscles that lie between them. That makes your chest bigger around. At the same time you pull down the big muscle, the *diaphragm,* that forms the floor of your chest. You thus make your chest much larger. The air outside then pushes in through the nose and throat and forces out the lungs to fill up the chest. When you breathe out you let go the diaphragm, and it rises. The ribs fall and are pulled back by another set of muscles. The chest is made smaller and the air is forced out.

Why you get colds. If you spend most of your life indoors where people are crowded together, you probably have colds. If you spend most of your life outdoors and avoid people, you probably have few colds. Colds are due to germs that come from someone who has them. If the germs do not come, you do not get a cold. Also, you may not get a cold, if the germs do come, when you are vigorous and generally healthy. Most people would rather risk colds than live alone like a wildcat in the woods. By keeping in vigorous health, one can live with others without fear of colds and other illness. Good food, warm and dry clothing to protect the body, fresh air, plenty of exercise in the sun and wind, and then plenty of rest and sleep will go a long way toward keeping you in vigorous health. Then play your part of the game. If you get a cold, try not to give it to others. When you feel a sneeze or a cough coming, cover your mouth with a handkerchief. For your own good and the good of others, use your own drinking cup and your own towel only, even in your home. Alcoholic drinks do not ward off a cold. Tobacco and alcohol do your breathing no good and they make you short of breath under exercise because of their poisonous effect.

How to Learn about Transportation Inside Your Body

I. Read the chapter.
II. Study your circulation and breathing apparatus.

1. If you have a microscope, you can see the blood flowing through the capillaries in the tail of a fish or the web of a frog's foot. Wrap the fish in wet cotton and lay it on the slide. Focus on the thin parts of the tail. Do not keep the fish more than a few minutes out of water. Unwrap it and put it back in the aquarium and take another fish.

2. Put a drop of your blood on the slide, smear it out, and examine it under the microscope. Look for red and white cells. Red cells may not look very red, but you can recognize them by their round, flat shape.

3. Take your pulse. Count it first while at rest, and then after exercise.

4. Listen to the sound of a classmate's heart. Lay your head on the chest. Listen for two sounds. The first is the contraction of the auricles and the second, of the ventricles a moment later. "Lub-dub." If you can borrow a stethoscope from a physician, you can hear the heart better.

5. Count the number of times you breathe in a minute at rest and after vigorous exercise.

6. Put your fingers on your larynx, or Adam's apple, and say something. Do you feel the vibrations? What causes them?

7. Look into a mirror, open your mouth and say, "Ah." A flashlight will illuminate the inside. Do you see the tonsils on each side? Do you see where the air passes up to the nasal cavities?

III. Test yourself:

1. How does the heart pump?

2. What prevents the blood from going in the wrong direction?

3. Where is the work of delivering and receiving done by the blood?

4. What does the blood give to the cells? What does it take from the cells? Where does it get each of the supplies it carries? Where does it give up the wastes it carries from the cells?

5. What does the blood receive in the lungs? What does it give up to be cast out of the body?

6. What does the blood get from the intestines?

7. What does the blood give up in the skin?

8. What happens to the blood in the kidneys?

9. How many times a minute does the heart beat in an adult? What will make it beat faster? How can you find how fast your heart is beating?

10. What do tobacco, alcohol, and many kinds of headache tablets do to the heart? injuries

11. What is in the blood? (Many things.)

12. What is the work of the red corpuscles? of the white corpuscles?

13. What is the disadvantage of breathing through the mouth?

14. What are some simple precautions to take that will reduce the chances of your getting colds?

IV. Think these out:

1. Why are colds usually more common in winter than in summer? What can you do about it?

2. Draw a diagram of the circulation of the blood, using red and blue pencils. Locate the various loading and unloading stations and note what supplies are loaded and unloaded at each station.

3. Why does the heart beat faster when you exercise?

4. Why do the cells of the body suffer when for some reason there is a severe loss of blood?

5. Look up *blood transfusion* in the library. Learn how one person gives blood to another and why? What precautions must be taken in selecting the donor (giver)? Look up the meaning of "blood bank."

V. Vocabulary. These words are not new to you, but are you sure of their scientific meaning? Be careful of the spelling.

capillaries	tonsillitis
valve	pulse
ventricle	vein
cartilage	auricle
diaphragm*	pus
artery	adenoids
lymph	larynx
corpuscle	

* A hard word to spell.

Chapter Thirty-seven

Your Body's Government

Getting news. You know things by your nervous system. You know some things that happen outside your body and some that happen inside. The news is picked up by a receiver and sent along a nerve somewhat as a telephone message is sent along a wire. At the outer end of your nerve of hearing is a receiver in your inner ear. Vibrations (trembling, swinging) of the air shake the eardrum at the bottom of the canal you see running down into the ear. The eardrum vibrates a chain of three little bones in the middle ear and thus causes vibrations in a membrane covering an opening to the inner ear. The membrane starts the vibration of a liquid in the inner ear which is felt by the fine nerve ends. These nerve ends are fine branches of nerve cells. Other branches of the cells extend

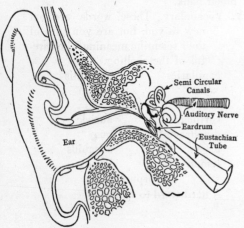

Diagram of the ear

back through the head to the brain. The bundle of branches make up the nerve of hearing.

The nerve takes the news to the brain. The brain is a great mass of nerve cells and nerves. You do not learn the meaning of the message until the brain decides what it means. Then you may decide to do something about it. That is also the work of the brain. You do what you have decided to do also by means of your nervous system.

Other sense organs gather information about what is happening outside. Branches of the nerve of sight end in the rear surface of the eye; those of smell in the lining of the nose; those of taste in tastebuds scattered over the tongue. Through the skin are nerve endings that send information about heat and cold, roughness and smoothness. In the muscles are those that tell you about the weight of things.

Your nerves also get you some inside information about your body. The semicircular canals in your inner ear send you word whether you are right side up or upside down or sprawling flat. These are the organs of balance. A pain registered about the stomach may be interpreted as a warning to stop gorging.

The eye. The eye is a delicate organ easily injured by abuse. It is

272

How do the semicircular canals of the ear help the tightrope walker?

a hollow ball filled with fluid. Near the front end is a lens that focuses the light from objects on the nerve ends, the *retina*, in the rear of the eye, as a camera lens focuses the light from objects on the film. But the lens of the eye has certain advantages over the lens of the camera. You focus the lens of the camera to make the image sharp by moving the lens backward and forward. The lens of the eye changes its curvature becoming thicker when you look at near objects and flattening a little when a moment later you look at mountains miles away. Tiny muscles squeeze the lens to make it thicker, and relax to allow it to flatten again.

The iris, the colored ring around the eye, contracts when the light is too bright, and dilates, thus admitting more light, when the light is weak. Muscles move the eye around so that it will receive the light from the objects that are of especial interest to us.

Eyelids protect the eyes from light, dust, rain, and objects that threaten. Eyelashes help keep out the dust and raindrops. Tears, from tear glands, keep the surface moist and wash off dust. You know how your eye waters when a speck of dust gets in it. If the tears do not wash out the particle, you should not rub it; that may scratch the delicate tissues and may let in bacteria. Have someone help you, or stand before a mirror. Instead of rubbing, pull down the lower lid and look for the particle. Pull out the upper lid and turn it partially inside out over a toothpick. If you see the particle, remove it with a tuft of sterile cotton or a clean, fresh handkerchief.

273

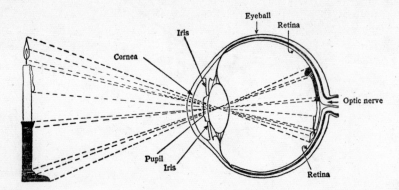

Diagram of the eye

The eye needs such delicate adjustments to make it perfect that frequently nature falls down on the job and makes one or more adjustments slightly imperfect. Generally the defects can be corrected by glasses. Therefore, school children's eyes are examined, and glasses are prescribed when necessary. Eyes should

Cross section of the retina of the human eye. Note its complexity

Bausch and Lomb

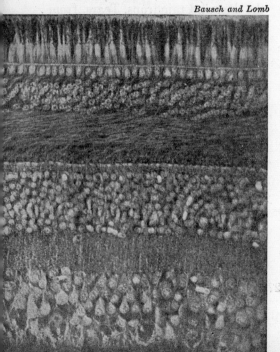

be rested frequently when reading by looking far away or by closing them for a few moments. One should never read in a dim light, nor in a light that is too bright, nor with a glare on the book. Try out the position of the book and the light. A few minutes' trial may save a great deal of eyestrain, headache, and damaged eyes.

Doing things. Nerves from your eyes, ears, tongue, fingers, nostrils, and elsewhere gather information. Other nerves enable you to do something about it. Light flashes on the inside of your eye. The information travels instantly to the brain, and you see an automobile swing around the corner. The brain sends messages instantly through other nerves to many muscles, and you jump back. Sometimes, as when you are asleep, if something tickles the feet, the information reaches the spinal cord which sends out orders to the muscles to move without your knowing anything about it. When you go from a dark room into the bright sun, you are dazzled for a moment until the pupils of your eyes contract and shut out some of the light. You do not need to remember to contract the pupils. Your nervous system takes care of that. [Actions caused by your nervous system, when stimulated, without your taking thought, are *reflex actions*.]

You breathe, your heart beats, your stomach and intestine carry on their business of digestion without your taking thought. They are involuntary actions, going on without your having to will them. The nerve centers in your brain and spinal cord take care of them.

You can train your nerve centers to take care of other actions. When you learned to write, to skate, to ride a bicycle, you had to think about every movement. Now they have become habits, and you think of other things while you do them. You can easily train yourself to good habits, such as washing your hands before eating and brushing your teeth after each meal, and then you do them without wasting thought and effort and with enjoyment.

Glands also govern. Did you ever see a circus giant? or a dwarf? They are not fakes. They are the result of the disorder of that little gland under the brain, the pituitary. Some of its hormones influence growth. Too much growth hormone makes a giant, and too little makes a dwarf. They also control fat and water in the body, and when out of order they make a mountain of

flesh. Sometimes in adults growth hormones start work again. Bones and flesh of face, hands, and feet become enlarged. This condition, called acromegaly, gives the person an ugly, misshapen appearance.

The thyroid gland in the neck also governs. Overactivity is sometimes shown by staring eyes, extreme nervousness, and "high-strung" disposition. Too little thyroxin may reduce the person to sluggishness physically and mentally, to loss of hair and puffiness of skin.

The adrenal glands too govern. When angry or scared, the heart responds by quick action. Blood pressure rises. The liver pours stored sugar into the blood fuel for fight or flight. The blood clots more easily.

The circus tall man and midget are the result of improper functioning of the pituitary gland.

How to Learn about Your Body's Government

I. Read the chapter.

II. Study your nerves.

1. Locate the nerve endings on the back of your hand. Take a fine needle and touch gently with the sharp point one spot after another over the back of the hand. On a diagram of the hand indicate the pain spots with a + sign and the painless spots with a — sign. The signs will then indicate the locations of nerve endings.

2. Cross your knees and have someone strike your leg just below the knee with the edge of the hand. When the right spot has been struck something will happen. What kind of action is that?

3. Select some good habit that you want to develop, such as always washing the hands before touching food, always brushing the teeth after meals, improving your handwriting. Do the thing exactly right each time it should be done. You may be surprised how quickly and easily the right habit is formed.

III. Test yourself:

1. Just why do you decide that you heard something? What happens between the dropping of a book and your "hearing" it? Cover the labels on page 272 and name the parts of the ear.

2. How do you learn when you are not right end up?

3. Cover the labels on page 274 and name the parts of the eye.

4. What precautions should you take when reading?

5. What kind of action takes place when you accidentally touch a hot pipe?

6. How can you train yourself to do many things without taking thought?

7. Besides the nerves, what other structures govern the body? How?

IV. Think these out:

1. Do you always think before you act? What actions must be done without taking thought?

2. If the eardrum is broken, deafness will probably result? Why?

3. Suppose you were out alone on a hike and got a speck of dust in your eye. What would you do?

V. Vocabulary.

vibrations	sterile
semicircular	ductless

Chapter Thirty-eight

Accidents

It need not happen. Someone spread a mat at the foot of the stairs. Grandmother stepped down on it, the mat slipped, grandmother fell and broke a leg. Little sister reached for a pair of scissors, fell on them, and the point went into her eye. Little brother swallowed some round white tablets from a bottle left within reach, or he started a fire in the living room with matches found on the ash tray. Big brother pulled the trigger of an "unloaded" gun, and an ambulance dashed up to the house. The cook reached in a hurry for the kettle, the handle came out—and the flesh came off with the shreds of stocking. Big sister thought she knew the headache tablets in the dark and swallowed poison tablets; big brother thought he put out the cigarette stump before he dropped it in the waste basket. The firemen found a worn lamp cord under the remnants of the burned rug. The milkman detected the odor of gas; the police broke in the door and found the gas stove had not been turned all the way off. A neighbor, alarmed at the continuous running of the car in the closed garage, found a death from carbon monoxide.

Many other dangers lurk about the careless home. Coal gas creeps up from a furnace door left open or a leaky flue that was to be repaired next summer. Sharp knives are left within reach of children. A broken glass or bottle is not removed when seen on the walk. A bucket or a dustpan is set down for a moment on the step and left for someone to step on. The electric iron is not switched off when the telephone rings. Medicine or poison is put in a bottle without a label. A hatchet or an ax, swung carelessly, bounces and strikes the shin. A stick of kindling wood, struck by the hatchet, flies up and strikes the eye. A wet bathtub is slippery and dangerous. A thousand and one accidents daily are due to thoughtlessness. The fool behind the steering wheel is only a little more dangerous than the thoughtless or indifferent person at home.

Lack of play space at home and outdoors in the city is one cause of accidents. If the only playground is the street, there is always danger. If the only playroom is the kitchen or the workroom, there is also danger. We cannot always remedy these conditions. Then we must do our utmost to train ourselves and others in carefulness. It takes patience and persistence until habits of safety are formed. It takes conscience, a desire to do the safe thing. We must learn to recognize possible dangers and to force ourselves to avoid them though

Don't take a chance while riding a bicycle on the street

it takes a little more time. "Accidents never happen. They are caused."

If you break a bone. A tumble from a bicycle, or slip on an icy pavement, a landing on the arm— and a broken arm. If you learn to

Ladders cause many accidents around the home

let yourself go when you fall, you will probably not break anything. Football players are trained how to fall, for they have many falls. An arm thrust out to save yourself must stand the weight of your falling body, and sometimes it snaps under the weight.

If the patient must be moved before the doctor arrives, apply a splint to the broken arm or leg so that the broken end of bone will not cut through flesh and perhaps become infected. Tie the broken limb to a narrow strip of board or wrap it firmly in a folded blanket so that it will not bend.

The second step is to get the doctor, the sooner the better. He may be able to feel what has happened to the bones or he may need an X-ray picture to show him. He must put the broken surfaces together as they grew to prevent a crooked or stiff limb. When the bones are in place,

Philip D. Gendreau, N. Y.

Carelessness behind the wheel results in an appalling loss of life every year

the doctor puts on a splint or cast to hold them there. The ends are alive, and new cells will form, joining the two broken ends so that the bone is as good as it was before the break occurred.

What to do when it happens. If it is a scratch, put a daub of iodine on it and then replace the bottle where the baby cannot reach it. If it is a cut, clean it with freshly boiled water, for boiling kills the germs. Wash your hands first with soap and water. Put on a wad of sterile gauze or an absolutely clean handkerchief which has been wet with a few drops of iodine. Usually pressure with a piece of gauze stops bleeding. If an artery or vein has been cut, however, pressure may not stop it. A cut artery sends out spurts of blood as the heart beats. A vein sends out a steady stream of blood.

Press an artery between the cut and the heart. A tourniquet with a

wad of material or a stone under the bandage may be needed to get sufficient pressure. If a vein is cut, put the tourniquet beyond the cut, on the side away from the heart. Every fifteen minutes loosen the tourniquet

Notice how the pole vaulter relaxes so that he will not break a limb

Black Star, N. Y.

and, if the bleeding has stopped, remove it immediately.

A *bleeding nose* usually stops in a short time without treatment, but sometimes it may be troublesome to stop. A strong solution of salt water sniffed up the nose will often stop it. Ice held on the outside of the nose or slivers of ice carefully thrust up the nostrils will sometimes stop the bleeding. A slight shock, such as that of a cold key dropped down the back, will sometimes stop it. Keep quiet; sit up. Pressing the nostril firmly for five minutes or gently packing the nostril with an inch of cotton may stop bleeding. If the nose bleeds frequently and without apparent cause, see the doctor.

A *bruise* may be relieved by cold cloths, the colder the better. The more prompt the treatment after the injury, the less the discoloration and pain. A bruise about the eye, "a black eye," may be prevented, or reduced, if treated the moment after the accident happens. If very cold water is not available, water as hot as can be borne will do. Both cold and intense heat cause contraction of the capillaries and so reduce the swelling and the gorging with blood which may leak out from broken capillaries and cause discoloration.

A *sprain* needs rest. Keep weight off a sprained ankle until the swelling subsides and it can again bear weight without pain. A ligament has been torn loose from the bone, and only rest will allow the wound to heal. The doctor, however, may sometimes prescribe exercise instead of rest for a sprain.

Cover a small *burn* with "burn ointment" from a drug store, for example, picric acid and sterile gauze. Cover an extensive burn with sterile gauze soaked with baking soda solution two tablespoonfuls to a quart of slightly warm water. Then let the doctor see it.

If *acid* is spilled on the hand, get it immediately under flowing water to dilute and wash away the acid. Afterward, baking soda, milk of magnesia, chalk, or other alkaline substances may be poured over it to neutralize any acid remaining. Speed is necessary. An *alkali*, such as lye, may be neutralized by vinegar or other weak acids.

When a person *faints*, it is not necessary to dash cold water in the face. Let the patient lie with the head a little lower than the feet, if possible. Loosen the clothing. Fan the face and let the fresh air come in. After the patient has returned to consciousness, let him rest for half an hour.

If a person has lost consciousness through *suffocation* or *drowning*, artificial respiration or resuscitation should be used. Learn how to do it; it is not difficult. Look at the pictures, page 281. Press down with your hands on the small ribs. Say while you press, "Get the bad air out." Then release the pressure on the lower ribs and say while you rest, "Let the good air in." Keep at it, about fourteen times a minute.

If your hands *get numb* with cold, do not put them into warm water. If you do it once, you will not have to be told not to do it again. It is exquisitely painful. Rub them, work them, and let them warm slowly. Warm a frostbite very slowly as by holding a frozen finger under the armpit until the circulation has started again.

If a person *takes a poison* into the stomach, get it out. Mustard in water or tickling the throat inside will cause vomiting. Although vomiting is not best for all poisons, it is the nearest right thing to do for poisons in general. Send for the doctor as soon as the poisoning is discovered. If the label of the poison bottle tells you what to do—as it should —do it while the doctor is coming.

You can often avoid *ivy poisoning* by washing the hands promptly with soap and water. Carry a small cake on your hikes. The poisonous substance is contained in an oily secretion of the plant. A wash in alcohol will remove the oil much more effectively than soap and water. If poison develops, the drugstore clerk or the doctor can prescribe a remedy, but the best remedy is to avoid getting poisoned.

Artificial resuscitation: (1) correct position for the victim's head, (2) the hands are placed around the short ribs, (3) pressure is firmly applied to force out bad air and water, (4) quick release of pressure allows good air to enter the lungs

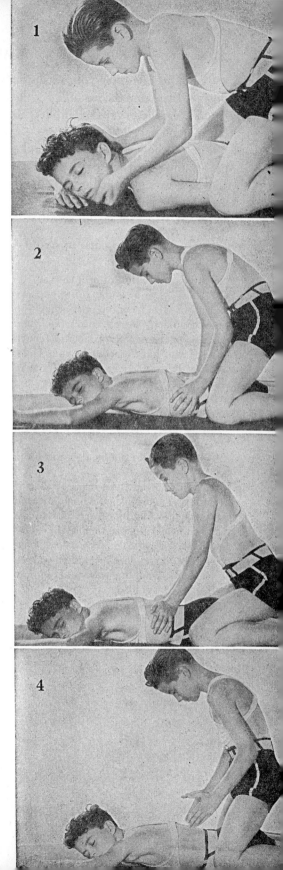

If a *mad dog* bites you, wash the dog's saliva from the wound, dry the wound with clean gauze, daub it with iodine, and speed to the doctor.

For poisonous *snake bites*, make the wound bleed and tie a bandage above the wound. Suck the blood from the wound. Better still, if you hike, camp, or live in a snake country, a syringe full of antivenin should be always at hand. It may mean saving a life. Your druggist or doctor can get the antivenin for you. Instructions with the packages tell you how to inject it. Potassium permanganate, daubed freely on the wound, is sometimes used to treat snake bites. Always rush the patient to the doctor.

How to Learn to Avoid Accidents and Give First Aid

I. Read the chapter.

II. Study prevention of accidents.

1. Search your home for the possibilities of accidents. Report what you find. Similarly search the school and make a report. Watch traffic and report.

2. If you have a scout in your class, get him or her to demonstrate how to splint a broken bone.

3. Examine a first-aid kit such as is sold for autos or provided by the Red Cross. Decide what you would put in a first-aid kit for a camping trip.

4. Demonstrate artificial respiration. Study pages 280, 281.

5. Study the pictures on page 207 of poison ivy and poison sumac. Search for them on your hikes and make sure that you can recognize them.

III. Test yourself:

1. Mention a dozen common causes of accidents about the home and tell how each may be avoided.

2. What should you do with a broken bone?

3. What is the first-aid treatment for the following: a small cut; a cut that flows with a heavy stream of blood; a cut that gives out spurts of blood; a bleeding nose; a bruise; a sprain; a burn; an acid burn; hands that are numb with cold; a snake bite?

4. What would you do with a person who had fainted? one who had lost consciousness from suffocation by fumes or water? one who had accidently swallowed poison?

IV. Think out the answers to these questions:

1. Suppose you were alone in the woods and you fell and broke your arm. What would you do? Suppose you broke your leg?

2. Suppose you were left alone to take care of a little brother or sister at home. If the child fell downstairs and was knocked unconscious, what would you do?

V. Vocabulary. Do not forget to make up your list of new words.

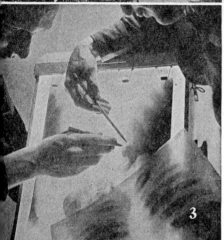

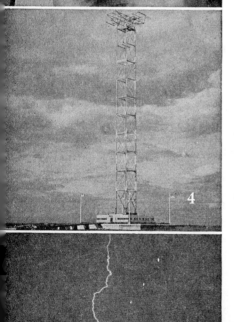

Unit Seven

Energy Around Us

In our following units we shall look still farther into the nature of things and ask what it is that makes all this amazing world of life and nonliving keep in action. What energy runs the world? What keeps the living things alive and enables us to do our work in the world? We shall see something of the source of all our energy and its transformation that enables us to control some of it. We shall study gravitation, light, heat, magnetism, and electricity.

We must find energy; we cannot make it. Our environment must supply it.

We have put light to work. You have seen its work in the movies. You have heard its work as the picture talked. You and all living things live because of the work of light that comes to the earth from the sun.

We shall study something farther about the nature of light. We shall see that it is much like certain other forms of energy, some of which have been raining down upon the earth through its long history. Others are the invention of man. Some we meet every day. Others are in daily use in laboratories and hospitals. At first you might see little connection between your radio and the X ray, between the sun's rays and radium, but all seem to be connected in nature. We shall study a little about the nature of these forms of energy, and how living things adapt themselves to energy.

(1) Philip D. Gendreau, (2) (3) (4) Black Star, (5) Ewing Galloway

Chapter Thirty-nine

The Energy of Light and Other Rays

We must gather together in our minds some things that we learned in earlier chapters. Students of science must repeatedly call to mind the ideas which they have formed, to use them and revise them in new studies. Our ideas grow as we study. They change as we learn new things. Often the scientist sees that his earlier ideas do not quite agree with new facts that he discovers. Then he makes sure that he has observed accurately, that his new facts are facts. When he is satisfied that his new observations are giving him new facts, he often must revise his ideas even if they have become "laws of science." So let us review the facts that we have learned about energy and about the energy of light in particular. Then we may add some new facts and perhaps change a little our ideas of what light is and does.

You may recall that we said that *energy* is the capacity to do work. Heat changes the water in the boiler of the engine into steam which drives the piston. Heat is energy, the capacity to do work. Electricity turns the motor which drives the trolley car, the electric locomotive, and the machinery of the factory. Electricity is energy, the ability to do work. We learned also that light is energy, that it can do work. It enables the green plants to make the food that we find in the potato, wheat, and corn. Perhaps you have used light to make a picture, or if you have not used a camera yourself for this work, you have seen the picture after it has been made.

Rays. Now let us enlarge the idea of light. Light is only a part of something. We can get the idea best by talking of the light of the sun. You learned that white sunlight is really made up of many kinds of light that reach us together. If the sunlight passes through a glass prism, it is divided up into the various colored lights: violet, indigo, blue, green, yellow, orange, and red. These colors are spread out in a band called the *spectrum*.

If you use a camera, perhaps you have used a color filter to shut out some colors of the light. If you put a yellow filter in front of your lens, you shut out blue rays. You can then take pictures which show much better objects colored white, orange, and yellow. With special plates, pictures may be taken in the dark by rays that we cannot see at all. These are the infrared rays, the name meaning rays "below red." These infrared rays are sometimes called the *heat rays*. The rays are "seen" by a special photographic plate but not by our eyes; that is, they affect the plate but not the eye.

284

Philip D. Gendreau, N. Y.

This photograph was taken by infrared rays. The camera "saw" things that our eyes cannot see

You have heard of ultraviolet rays. They are rays beyond the violet. They also do not affect the eyes and so we cannot see by them, but they do affect a photographic plate. Sometimes they are called *invisible light*. They are the rays that cause most of the tan that develops in your skin during summer vacation. They may cause painful sunburn. If you do not get badly sunburned, these rays are very beneficial as we shall see presently.

There are also other invisible rays that can be sent out from machines built for the purpose. You have heard of X rays and perhaps have had X-ray pictures taken of your teeth or other parts of your body. These rays also affect the photographic plate. They have the power also of penetrating flesh and many other substances that we cannot see through because light rays cannot go through them. Like the ultraviolet rays, the X rays may burn the skin and even flesh below, but they burn much more quickly and severely. They are, therefore, used to kill the growths of cells that we call *cancer*. Radium rays also penetrate the flesh and burn it.

There are, therefore, several kinds of rays, including kinds that we have not yet mentioned, for example, the radio rays. Of all these rays we can see only a few; only those few affect our eyes so that we see light. We can detect some of the invisible rays by photographic plates. We can detect still others by electrical instruments, for example, the radio rays, or you

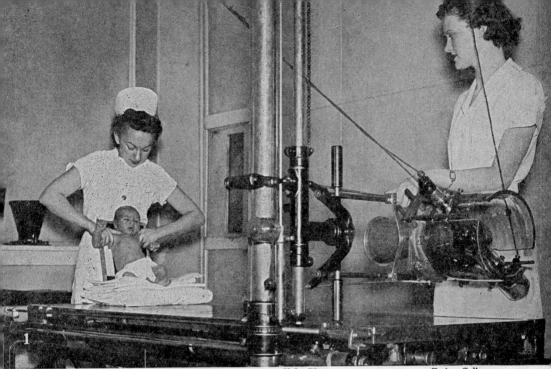

Globe Photo   Ewing Galloway

(1) This baby is having its picture taken soon after birth. X rays are used and will not harm the child. (2) An X-ray picture of a fish. Variations of shadows are caused by varying density of structures through which rays pass

may be more familiar with them as radio waves.

The waves. All these rays seem to travel in waves. You have heard of wave lengths, if you are at all interested in radio. You know that radio waves of different wave lengths can be sent out at will, and that definite wave lengths are assigned by the Federal Communications Commission to different stations. The wave lengths of all the rays that have been mentioned are known. Radio rays have the longest wave lengths. Shorter than the radio waves are the heat waves. Shorter than the heat waves are the light rays or visible rays. We cannot feel them, but we can see them. We detect the radio waves with instruments, the heat waves with our skin, and the visible rays with our eyes.

Shorter still are the ultraviolet waves. We cannot see them, but they are detected by the skin, although we may not know it at the time. We may get a bad case of sunburn before we know it. Still shorter than the ultraviolet rays are X rays. They affect the skin and flesh, but we cannot see them, nor feel them when the dentist or doctor turns them on our flesh. Even shorter are radium waves which will burn very severely, although we cannot see them nor feel them. There are still shorter rays that scientists are busy studying.

How living things are adapted to the rays. So far as we know, living things are not affected by radio waves. All living things are affected by heat waves. They are a necessary part of our environment. If there were not heat, there would be no life. We can see this in the polar regions. We shall study heat in another unit.

Passing over, for a moment, the light rays and the ultraviolet rays, we may consider the X rays and the radium rays. We do not know that the X rays occur in nature. We know that they are very destructive to living things, if they last for more than a moment. If the earth were bombarded by X rays, there would soon be no life. Radium rays do exist in nature, as well as other similar rays. However, they are not so concentrated in nature as in the hospitals and in the laboratories. We know from experiment that they may be very destructive, but in nature probably so few of them strike a living thing at any one time that they usually have very little effect.

Now let us consider further the light rays. We know that these rays are absolutely necessary for life. A few animals live in the great depths of the sea where it is totally dark. Some of the queer fish from the great depths have lights of their own. These dwellers in the perpetual dark could never live there if it were not for food continually coming down

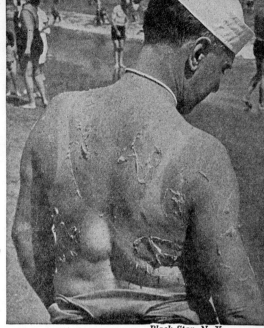

Black Star, N. Y.

A bad case of sunburn. We may not feel at the time the rays that burn us, but they can be painful'

to them from the realm of light near the top of the water. Certain kinds of bacteria seem to thrive only in the dark; some bacteria are killed by the sunlight. In spite of fading carpets, curtains, and covers, due to sunlight, it is wise to make sure that every room of your house gets a liberal dose of sunshine.

You have learned that if it were not for sunlight the green plants could not make food. You showed that by experiment. The energy that the sun sends down to us in its light rays enable the green plants to use the soil water and air to make food. Green plants make food for the world. Mushrooms, molds, and bacteria must get their food ready-made. Animals, too, must get their food after it has been made. Animals, and plants not green, do not have the power of green plants to use the sun's rays in food making.

Most animals with which we are familiar use the light rays, but for a very different purpose. They use light rays for finding food and locating their enemies, for finding their way home and for finding their mates and young ones. This is what we call *seeing*. Eyes are adapted to light waves. Let us remember that using the light rays for seeing is only one way that living things use them, and perhaps not the most important use. Many kinds of animals do not see. Earthworms, clams, and oysters do not see. Perhaps animals could get along without seeing, but they could not get along without food. Food making of green plants is the most essential adaptation to light waves.

Using the ultraviolet rays. When small children are kept indoors in the big cities, they often become sick and their bones and bodies become deformed. The disease called *rickets* develops. If children suffering with rickets are taken out and exposed to the sunlight or are exposed to special lamps that give out ultraviolet rays, the rickets is cured. These lamps do not have glass globes but globes made of quartz sometimes called *rock crystal*. Ultraviolet rays do not go through glass, just as visible rays do not go through stone or brick walls. Hospitals sometimes have rooms fitted with windowpanes made of quartz instead of glass in order to allow the ultraviolet rays of the sun to pass in-

doors. Sitting in the sun behind glass windows does not give the patient ultraviolet rays.

Instead of letting ultraviolet rays fall on the skin, rickets may be cured by taking cod-liver oil and the oil from the livers of some other fishes. These fishes store up in their livers a substance that is made inside their bodies. This substance cures rickets. When ultraviolet rays fall on our skin, our bodies also make this substance. If persons live indoors away from the sun, they may not develop rickets, but their bodies may be suffering from the lack of this substance which would be manufactured by their bodies if they were in the sunlight. This substance, which has been called the *sunshine vitamin*, can be extracted from cod-liver oil and may be bought at the drug stores at a high price. Lamps to give ultraviolet rays may also be bought. Such lamps should never be used without the doctor's orders, and should be used then only as directed. They may cause severe burns and perhaps permanent damage. The vitamin [which is marketed in the product *viosterol*] also should not be used without the doctor's orders. It is much too dangerous to be used by one who does not know about its work in the body.

Ultraviolet rays kill many kinds of bacteria. They have been used successfully to sterilize glassware in restaurants, milk bottles in dairies, and bottles for soft drinks. In experimental rooms 75% of the bac-

Philip D. Gendreau, N. Y.

Ultraviolet rays are used to sterilize glassware in this restaurant

teria and other living organisms of the air, floor, and walls have been killed. Rays from lamps in the ceilings have been used for killing bacteria and molds in the air of bakeries. They have been used in hospitals for sterilizing the air of wards and operating rooms.

Rays from atoms. Radium rays come from bursting radium atoms. An atom is the smallest particle of an element that can exist and remain the same element. It is supposed by scientists that all elements such as iron, lead, gold, carbon, radium and the rest, are each composed of the tiny particles that they call atoms. Such particles, the atoms, are much too small to be seen by the most powerful microscopes. If the atom can be split apart, the element, iron, lead, radium, is no

longer the same element. It changes to another substance. Powerful electric and magnetic machines, "the atom-smashers," have been built to bring about such changes in atoms, to change one element into another. Some elements have so been changed into other elements.

An atom such as an atom of sodium is composed of still smaller particles (protons, electrons, and neutrons), but these smaller particles are not sodium. Powerful forces hold these tiniest particles together to make an atom of sodium. When these forces are broken by the atom smasher, the tiniest particles fly out of the atom.

A few elements are known in which the tiniest particles fly out of the atom without outside aid. Radium, for example, is constantly

International News Photo

This is a cyclotron, a complicated device for smashing atoms

sending out particles from its atoms. Particles and waves of energy are its waves. The atoms of radium by giving out these tiniest particles change to a series of other substances becoming finally lead.

The atomic bomb. On August 6, 1945 an American plane dropped one bomb—only one—on the city of Hiroshima, Japan. Over one-half, 60%, of the city was instantly destroyed, turned to dust. That bomb exploded by bursting of its atoms. American scientists working with Canadian and British scientists, had learned the secret of breaking apart the atom and releasing the energy that holds together the tiniest particles.

The element uranium sends out rays as does radium. The scientists learned the secret of releasing the tiniest particles inside the atom of uranium in such quantity and with such speed as to explode the atomic bomb, the most terrible bomb ever known to man. One more bomb was dropped on the Japanese city of Nagasaki, and the Japanese surrendered their empire. Atomic energy, the energy that holds together the tiniest particles to make the atom, could soon have been released to wipe out every city in Japan.

Scientists have yet to learn how to release such energy in a manner to put it to constructive work in machines. Atomic energy is now terror and death. Even the preparation of the materials to be used in atomic bombs was deadly. The materials of the bomb were prepared behind walls several feet thick of steel and concrete, inside which no man dared to go while the process of preparation went on. Deadly rays were sent out by the changing elements. These deadly rays, rays from the splitting atom, were controlled to destroy man and his work. The energy of the atom is yet to be controlled to work for man.

How to Study about the Energy of Light and Other Rays

I. Read the chapter.
II. Study light.

1. Let us study for a moment how an idea changes. Before you studied science, what color would you have said sunlight is? After your experiment with the glass prism and the sunlight, what color do you say sunlight is?

Before you studied science what would you have said to the following question: What is light? Can you now answer the question?

Before you studied science how would you have answered the following question: Does light do any work? Has your idea changed?

2. EXPERIMENT No. 68. To show that light produces chemical change. Secure some blueprint paper. Place on it a leaf or other object or a photographic negative. Cover with a piece of glass and place in the sun. Do you see any evidence that light has produced change? In a few minutes wash in water. To get a good photographic print, you will need to experiment until you learn the right time to expose the negative and the blueprint paper.

3. EXPERIMENT No. 69. You can easily show that light makes plants green by placing one plant under a dark cover and one in the sunlight. Or you may cover a portion of the lawn with a board until it turns pale yellow and then remove the board and watch what happens.

4. If you have not had experience, learn what the sunlight does to the skin, but expose the skin a short time at first, lengthening the time of exposure on successive days.

III. Test yourself with these questions:

1. What is meant by energy?
2. Why is light said to be energy?
3. How can you show that light is energy?
4. How is the energy of light used?
5. How can you show that the light of the sun is composed of several lights of different colors? Prisms
6. Besides the rays that we see, what other rays come to us from the sun? How can you show that rays that we do not see come to us from the sun?
7. Name some rays other than light rays that we use.
8. Mention two things that the plant does with light rays.
9. Mention ways in which we benefit by the sun's rays falling on us.
10. What use do we make of rays that are not light rays?
11. Why should ultraviolet-ray lamps not be used except by the direction of the doctor?

IV. Think these out or investigate:

1. Where does our energy come from?
2. Where does the energy come from that lights your town?
3. Can there be a black light?
4. Is "invisible light" a good scientific expression? Your reasons.
5. What is the "electric eye," or photoelectric cell?

V. Vocabulary. Remember to make your own list. The following are suggestions:

energy   infrared   ultraviolet

Chapter Forty
How Light Acts

Traveling light. We have already learned that light travels fast —186,000 miles a second. That is a figure to remember. Some scientists tell us that nothing can have a greater speed than light. Radio waves have the same speed, and so have X rays. Radio waves can travel around the earth, 25,000 miles, seven times in one second.

Light travels in straight lines. It does not turn corners. If it did, we should never see a shadow. The sunlight or the electric light would illuminate the far side of an object as it does the side toward it. If light turned corners, you could see around corners. You have probably been in a darkened room where a little crack or hole allowed a beam of sunlight to come in. You have noticed the dancing dust specks floating in this beam of light. You may have noticed also that the beam traced by the lighted dust specks is a straight line. If you have not noticed the straight beam of sunlight in the darkened room, Experiment No. 70 will show it.

How we see objects. Light comes from somewhere. Most of the light that we have on earth comes from the sun. At nighttime when we are turned away from the sun, there is little light. Some light comes to us from the stars, but all the stars together give us little light, not enough

to read by. Bodies that give off light, like the sun, the stars, and the glowing wire in the electric bulb, are called *luminous* bodies, which merely means "light-giving bodies."

If you go into a totally dark room, you see nothing. If you snap on a flashlight, you see objects on which you turn the beam of light. You realize that the light by which you see the objects of the room comes from the flashlight. If you look into the bulb of the flashlight, you see that the light comes from a glowing wire in the bulb. You see luminous bodies by their own light, but non-luminous bodies by light from luminous bodies which falls upon them.

You know that when sunlight strikes a mirror or the surface of a lake it is reflected, and if you stand in the direction toward which it is reflected, the reflected sunlight may be blinding. If you hold a piece of white paper in the light, it also reflects light, though not so much light as the mirror. If you hold a piece of wood or your coat in the light, it also reflects light. When you turned the flashlight beam about the darkened room, the furniture and other objects reflected light and you saw them. When they did not reflect light, you did not see them. You see objects by their own light or by light that they reflect. A mirror or a lake

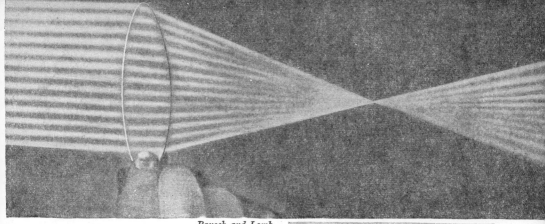

Light passing through a lens. How does this show that light travels only in a straight line? Lenses and prisms bend the rays. In the cut-away drawing of a pair of prism binoculars (right), the dotted lines show the course of light

is a good reflector, a white shirt is a fairly good reflector, a black coat is a poor reflector. We say the black coat absorbs the light.

Catching the sun's heat. We feel warm when the sunlight falls upon us. The soil warms up in spring when the long days and the bright light come. If you put your hand on a sunlighted windowpane on a cold day, the windowpane is cold. But if you withdraw your hand from the pane and allow the sunlight to fall on your hand a foot from the window, the sun's rays make your hand feel warm. The rays pass through the glass without warming it appreciably, but the rays make certain other things warm.

The sun's rays pass through the glass in a greenhouse for growing plants, and strike the soil inside. The glass does not become warm but the soil stops the rays and becomes warm. Objects that transmit

the sunlight (send the sunlight through) do not become warm. Certain objects which stop the light become warm.

But there is a difference between objects that do not transmit the sunlight. A dark suit is much warmer in summer than a light suit. Black shoes are warmer than tan shoes or white shoes. The tan and the white reflect more of the sun's rays. We say the black absorbs more light.

The objects that absorb most of the sun's rays or energy become warm. The objects that transmit or reflect most do not become warm. Good reflectors and good transmitters do not get very warm. Good absorbers get warm.

Glass in the window or greenhouse readily lets the sunlight pass, but it does not let the heat readily pass through. The sun porch inclosed with glass "traps" the heat thus: The glass transmits the sunlight. The sunlight falls on the objects inside the inclosure. The objects absorb the rays and become warm. The glass does not easily transmit the heat, or let out the heated air. So the porch becomes warm. The greenhouse similarly traps heat.

What color is sunlight? Now let us call to mind certain facts that we learned in the study of sunlight. Then we shall add new facts. Thus scientific thought grows. On a day when the air is somewhat misty, sunlight seems quite yellow, while on a perfectly clear day it seems more white. At sunset, it may seem red, yellow, and green. You have shown that sunlight is made up of many colors. In the spectrum of sunlight obtained by using a glass prism, the colors are spread out in a definite order, always the same order. Near-

est the base of the prism are the violet and then blue, the short wave lengths, and near the thin edge of the prism are yellow and then red, the long wave lengths. On a hazy day the droplets of water in the atmosphere stop to a great extent the short wave lengths, the violet and blue. The light reaching us has an unusual proportion of yellow and red, and we say that the sunlight is yellow. At sunset the rays of the sun pass through greater thickness of atmosphere and lose more of the short wave lengths than at midday, leaving the red and yellow of sunset. When sunlight falls on droplets of water in the air, the white sunlight may be broken up into the spectrum of sunlight, forming the rainbow.

Color of lights and of objects. Not all luminous bodies (bodies which give out light) have the color of sunlight. If you soak a string in washing soda, dry it, and then burn

A greenhouse traps the heat from sunlight

Black Star, N. Y.

it, a brilliant yellow light is produced. Each substance has its own
spectrum. Our electric lights, oil
lamps, and candle lights have little
of the blue light but have abundant
yellow. Often colors of clothing and
paper do not look the same by these
artificial lights as by daylight. A
blue coat may appear black. White
paper may appear yellow. If the artificial light has no blue light to be
sent back by the coat, the coat cannot be blue. If there is no blue light
for the paper to send back mixed
with the other colors, the paper cannot make white light. We say an object is blue when it sends blue light
to us. It is red when it sends red light.
It is white when it sends violet, indigo, blue, green, yellow, orange,
and red all mixed together as they
are in sunlight. When no colors come
back to us from an object, we say it
is black.

How to Learn How Light Acts

I. Study light by experiment and observation.

1. EXPERIMENT No. 70. What kind
of path does light make? Allow a narrow
beam of light to enter a dark room. A
flashlight with the lens covered with a
black paper having a small hole in front
of the lens will do. Dust some talcum
powder or chalk dust in the path of the
beam of light. Is the beam of light
straight, curved, or broken? Write up a
report of the experiment as in Experiment No. 1 using the headings: Question; Materials; Procedure; Observations; Conclusion.

2. EXPERIMENT No. 71. What happens
to a beam of light when it strikes an
object? Use the same materials as in
Experiment No. 70. Hold a mirror in
the path of the light. (1) Rotate the mirror to see what happens to the reflected
beam. (2) Hold a pencil or ruler at right
angles to the mirror at the point where
the beam of light strikes it. Blow some
chalk dust into the beam of light. Compare the angle between the original beam

In the tropics light clothing is worn that will reflect and not absorb the sunlight

Black Star, N. Y.

and the pencil with the angle between the reflected beam and the pencil. (3) Replace the mirror with a white card. How is the reflected light changed? (4) Replace the white card with a black cloth such as the sleeve of a coat. How is the reflected light changed? Write up a report as in Experiment 70.

3. EXPERIMENT No. 72. Where does the light come from by which we see objects? Darken a room. (1) What do you see? (2) Turn a flashlight about. What do you see? (3) Can you see the lighted flashlight bulb or lens? (4) Light a Bunsen burner. What do you see? (5) Heat an iron wire red hot. Hold it away. Can you see it?

Conclusion: You see objects by .... (?) light or by .... (?) light. Write up a report as in the preceding experiments.

4. EXPERIMENT No. 73. (Optional.) Is sunlight hot? (1) On a cold day place your hand on a sunlighted windowpane. Is the glass hot? Hold your hand a foot inside the window. Is your hand warm? (2) With a lens, focus the sun's rays on the head of a match until the head takes fire. Touch the lens. Is the lens warm?

Conclusion: Is sunlight warm? Does sunlight make certain things warm? Does it make all things warm? Write a report in the usual form.

5. EXPERIMENT No. 74. What kind of objects are heated most readily by the sun? Take three tin cans. Polish the outside of one, wrap a white cloth around the second, and wrap a black cloth around the third. Pour the same quantity of ice water without ice in each. Place a thermometer in each and set the cans in the sun. At five-minute intervals take the temperatures. Write a report.

6. Experiments on the color of sunlight and other lights are found in Chapter Eight, Experiments No. 2 and 3.

7. EXPERIMENT No. 75. What determines the color of objects that we see?

Darken a room and cover the lens of a projection lantern with red, green, yellow, orange, and blue glass. In each light hold paper or cloth of blue, green, yellow, orange, and red. Write a report.

II. Read the chapter.

III. Test yourself on the chapter by answering the following questions:

1. How fast does light travel?

2. Why can you not see around a corner?

3. What did you learn by Experiments Nos. 70 and 71?

4. Can we see any object if no light falls on it? (Think about this.)

5. What did you learn by Experiments No. 2 and 3?

6. You can see objects if they .... or if they ....

7. Is sunlight or starlight hot? Describe an experiment that supports your answer.

8. What kinds of objects are heated most when sunlight falls upon them? What kinds are heated least? Describe an experiment supporting your answer.

9. What colors make up sunlight? How can you show that your answer is correct?

10. What determines the color of lights that we see?

11. How can astronomers find out what the sun and the stars are made of?

IV. Think out answers to these:

1. Could you make a black light?

2. If a star gave out no light, could we know where it was?

3. Can we locate any body in the sky that does not give out light? (You may revise your answer to this question later, but make a trial answer now.)

4. Can you tell what the moon is made of by its spectrum? (You may want to revise your answer later, but make a trial answer now.)

V. Vocabulary.

luminous	spectrum
prism	transmit

Unit Eight

Heat in the World

What sends the starlight through millions of light-years of dark and empty space? How does the heat reach us from the sun? By what means does it cross those 93,000,000 miles of emptiness?

Where does the heat come from that runs our steam engines? Where do our coal and oil come from? Calculations by scientists do not all agree exactly, but it would seem that before you are old men and women, the oil that is now being pumped from the ground will be all pumped out. Later the coal will all be dug out. Then what will supply heat?

What does heat do to things that makes it so pleasant and so useful? Why do we cook our food when animals get along just as well without cooking? What does cooking do to the food?

Muscular labor built the pyramids, but the great pyramid was twenty years in building. Our great dams and bridges are built in a year or two. Muscular power has been replaced by other force. The chief source of the power that does so much of our work today is heat.

Even muscular power cannot be had without heat. Your body constantly produces heat. You are aware of it on the winter day when you put your hands in your pockets or when you hike uphill. What makes heat in the body?

Ewing Galloway, N. Y.

Chapter Forty-one

How Heat Begins and Travels

How do we get heat? If you were shivering out in the street on a bitter cold day, you would no doubt think of going into some building where fires were furnishing heat. If you were out in the woods, you might build a fire. Fires are the usual sources of heat whether to warm ourselves, cook a meal, or run an engine. Something burns. You have learned that when things burn, something unites with oxygen. If you shut down the draft, the fire slows down. If you smother the campfire with sand, shutting off the air supply, it goes out. You have learned that the part of the air necessary to burning is the oxygen. The greater the supply of oxygen the more intense the fire, so that in pure oxygen even iron will burn brilliantly. Air is the great source of supply of oxygen. Fires need air.

Fire is a source of heat. The welder uses a very hot flame which he obtains by feeding it oxygen. Every camper knows how welcome fire is for comfort and cooking

Philip D. Gendreau *Ewing Galloway*

Caterpillar Tractor

Philip D. Gendreau

Black Star

In cities three kinds of fuel are used to heat our homes. (1) Great oil wells are tapped to release nature's buried fuel. (2) Coal is shown being loaded into cars at the mine. (3) Natural gases, when they have been released from underground wells, are stored in tanks under pressure for future use

To make fire, there must also be something to burn, some fuel. Out of doors, the fuel is usually wood, although the modern automobile camper often carries a stove that burns gasoline. Admiral Byrd in the Antarctic uses oil, and the Eskimo at the opposite end of the earth uses oil and fat from seals and walruses. The fuel in most of the homes of the United States is still wood. Within the cities the fuel is usually coal, gas, or oil. Often the coal is first heated in retorts and the gas driven off to be led through pipes and burned in the kitchen stoves.

Within our bodies, also, something burns or oxidizes to keep us warm. You perhaps have noticed that when you are hungry on a cold day, you are also cold. When you are well-fed, you are warm. The rabbit, the fox, the wildcat, and the birds seem to pay little heed to the cold so long as there is plenty of food. When there is food to burn within their bodies, they keep warm.

How heat travels. Did you ever take hold of the end of a spoon that had been standing in a pot on the stove? And did you drop it quickly? Or perhaps you have burned your fingers on the handle of a frying pan. You probably did not stop to ask how the heat got to the end of the handle. You just know it got there and said something about it.

Did you ever step out of doors on an early spring morning and find a delightful, warm spring wind coming up from the south? You knew that the wind was bringing the heat of the south up to you. You know also that the warm air carries the heat from the radiator up to the ceiling of your room, and if you have a hot-air furnace, you know that currents of air carry the heat from the furnace in the cellar. You know also that the warm water of a hot-water system carries the heat from the furnace to the rooms upstairs, and that the ocean currents carry the heat of the tropics far toward the poles.

How does heat travel from an electric heater to you?

You have stepped out from the house or out from the shade of a tree and felt the warm sun instantly on your body. What brought the heat through 93,000,000 miles of cold, empty space?

Heat travels in different ways. Experiments Nos. 76, 77, and 78 will demonstrate them further. When the wind travels up from the warm southland, it carries along the heat. When the warm water or warm air comes up from the cellar furnace, it car-

ries the heat with it. We say that the heat travels by *convection* (from Latin meaning to "carry with").

When you put a spoon in a hot pot and the outer end gets hot, no metal has traveled from the inner end of the spoon to the outer end. We say that the heat in the metal spoon travels by *conduction*. We might compare conduction to passing a pile of books from one side of a room to the other by handing the books along from one person to another. We might compare convection to moving the books by each person's carrying an armful across the room. In conduction, the person does not travel but the books do. In convection, the person travels and carries the books along. In conduction, the iron does not travel, but the heat does. In convection, the air or water travels and carries the heat along.

When you step out into the sunlight and feel the sun's heat, something entirely different must take place. There is no substance stretching the 93,000,000 miles from the sun to the earth to pass the heat by conduction, and that empty space is

Here heat is traveling by conduction

Here heat is traveling by radiation

intensely cold. There is no substance traveling those 93,000,000 miles of empty space to carry the heat along by convection. The heat you feel must reach you by some other means than conduction or convection.

We say that the sun's energy is *radiated,* which simply means that it is given off as rays, and we speak of the energy passing out in this manner from the sun as *radiant energy.* Stars, comets, and other heavenly bodies also send radiant energy. Bodies upon the earth also radiate energy. A hot iron radiates energy. You can feel it by holding your hand near the hot iron. With the proper kind of photographic plate, you can take a picture in a totally dark room by these rays of radiant energy.

Heat thus may be transferred by conduction, by convection, or by radiation.

What heat does to substances. You have learned what heat does to mercury or alcohol in a thermometer. It makes the liquid expand and rise in the tube. You know that heat also makes iron expand. The rails on a railroad do not touch end to end, but a small gap is left between the rails. If the rails were placed in contact in winter, they would expand when the summer sun warmed them, and the track would be so badly twisted that trains would be derailed. You know that gases, like the air, expand when they are heated.

You have learned that the difference in temperature is responsible for the ocean currents and winds

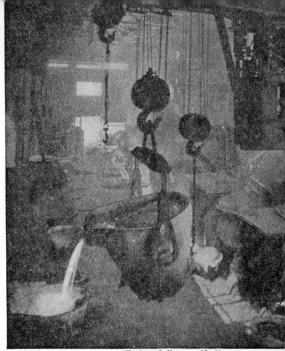

Iron melts at 1530° C., and slag (impurities) can be poured off at the smelting plants

upon the earth, for the circulation of air, hot water, and steam in our houses. These movements are due to the expansion and reduction in weight of air or water when heated or cooled.

If water is heated to high enough temperature, it becomes steam, and if enough heat is taken away from it, the steam changes back to water and then to ice. We say that water passes through *three states of matter:* solid, liquid, and gas, with changes of temperature. Similarly, if enough heat is passed into iron, it melts, and then, if sufficient heat is passed into the liquid iron, it becomes a vapor. Iron becomes liquid at 1530° C. and becomes a vapor at 2450° C. Passing heat into substances makes them liquids and gas; taking heat out of substances changes them from gases

301

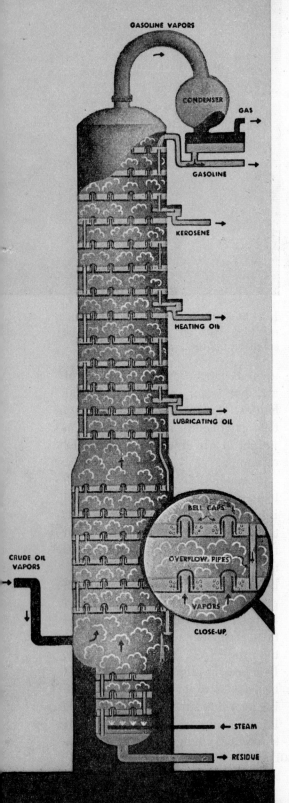

GASOLINE VAPORS

CONDENSER

GAS

GASOLINE

KEROSENE

HEATING OIL

LUBRICATING OIL

BELL CAPS

OVERFLOW PIPES

CRUDE OIL VAPORS

VAPORS

CLOSE-UP

STEAM

RESIDUE

to liquids and then to solids. Air becomes liquid at 192° below zero centigrade. Carbon dioxide becomes solid (dry ice) at 78.5° below zero centigrade.

Distillation. You learned in the study of water that the purest water is prepared by distillation. Water is heated until it boils away in vapor. The vapor is condensed again to water. As the water vapor passes away, solid matter is left behind. Pure water for the chemical laboratory and the drug store is prepared by distillation.

Suppose you had a bottle containing a mixture of liquids such as alcohol and water. How could you separate them? In industry, distillation is used to separate liquids that are mixed together or mixed with gases and solids. All liquids do not boil at the same temperature. Water boils at 212° F., but alcohol boils at 172° F. In the preparation of alcohol, molasses is fermented, and a mixture of water and alcohol is obtained. If this mixture is heated to 172° F., the alcohol boils away before the water. The alcohol vapor is then cooled and condensed.

Petroleum is a mixture as it is obtained from the earth. By distillation of the crude oil, various liquids are obtained. The crude oil is changed to vapor. In the tower in the

Here you see how crude oil is distilled at a large refinery, and how the various products of oil are obtained

Standard Oil Co. of N. J.

illustration at the left, the vapor cools as it rises. The various liquids condense, each at its own temperature, as the vapor approaches the cooler top of the cylinder. Thus gasoline, naphtha, benzine, kerosene, and lubricating oils, vaseline, and paraffin are separated.

Distillation is also used to break up solid materials, which are mixtures of several things. By destructive distillation of coal, that is, by heating the coal in retorts and collecting the gases which distil over, a long list of products is obtained. Among them are the gas which is burned in cities that have no natural gas, ammonia, naphthalene or tar camphor (the familiar moth balls and moth flakes), carbolic acid, creosote, and coal tar. Distillation of wood gives wood alcohol, acetone, acetic acid, and other products.

Other uses of evaporation. More important to us is evaporation over which we have only a partial control which must, however, be maintained. Failure to remember that control may lead to chills, pneumonia, and death. You know that the heat of the body leads to perspiration and causes evaporation of the perspiration. The evaporation of perspiration is nature's method of preventing us from getting so hot that we would sicken and die. The heat is taken up by the water as it evaporates, and losing heat, the body cools. But it must not cool too rapidly. When we are "overheated," it is most important to lose heat slowly.

At Great Salt Lake man takes advantage of evaporation to obtain quantities of salt from ponds into which water is led to evaporate

Pull on a sweater or coat or wrap a blanket around yourself, keep out of a draft, and cool off slowly. Control evaporation if you wish to keep well.

The scientist and the manufacturer have other uses for evaporation. Suppose you had a mixture of

Why would water power for industry be lacking if there were no evaporation in the air?

sand and sugar. Do you know any way to separate them? Very simple. Chemists and manufacturers constantly have such problems. This one is easily solved. Mix the sugar and sand in water. The sugar dissolves and the sand does not. Filter the mixture. The sugar solution flows through the filter, and the sand remains on the filter. Or you may simply let the water containing the sand and sugar stand. The sand settles to the bottom, and the water containing the dissolved sugar may be poured off. This sugar solution may then be heated and the water evaporated. Sugar remains behind.

Perhaps the greatest use of evaporation to us is nature's use in preparing rain. All the water that falls as rain comes from the surface of oceans, lakes, streams, the moist earth, and the plants and animals. Heat raises it in the air. Evaporation from the sea, the soil, and the plants takes heat just as it does when water is evaporated from the kettle on the kitchen stove. The water that is supplied to our crops, to the streams and lakes and wells, and, in turn, to our animals and ourselves, falls as rain. The water power from the waterfall and dam come from the rain falling to earth. First that water had to be raised up to the mountaintop, up to the level of the clouds. Heat raised it, the heat of the sun.

If there were no heat. Coal and oil come from the earth, and wood grows up from the soil. Our food, too, comes from the good earth. What energy makes them grow?

You know that coal is the remains of plants that grew long ages ago. Oil too seems definitely to be the remains of living things of ages long gone by. Our fuel thus was once alive. Like our food, it grew and died, taking its substance from the earth and returning the substance to the earth again. What made it grow? What makes our food grow? You know the answer.

The energy that sustains life upon the earth is the energy of the sun. You know that without the sunlight, plants cannot grow to make our food and fuel. When the short days of winter come and the cold air engulfs the plants, they cease to grow. Were the earth to wander away in space from the life-giving energy of the sun, all life would promptly cease. Water would cease to flow and become solid. The internal heat of the earth would gradually be radiated into outer space, and the earth would be a cold, dead ball of rock.

To Learn How Heat Begins and Travels

I. Read the section, "How do we get heat?"

1. EXPERIMENT No. 76. Set a large beaker of water on a tripod. Drop in a little fine sawdust. Heat one side of the bottom of the beaker. Watch the bits of sawdust. How do they move? Why? How is heat carried through the vessel of water? What is the name for this kind of heat transfer?

2. EXPERIMENT No. 77. Attach with candle grease or wax a number of tacks

along the under side of an iron bar. Support the bar and heat one end. Notice the order in which the tacks drop as the wax melts. Does any iron travel from the heated end of the iron bar to the far end? Does heat travel through the iron bar? What is the name for this kind of heat travel?

3. Experiment No. 78. Hold your hand near a hot iron or in the sunlight. Does anything travel and carry the heat from its source to your hand? What is the name for this mode of travel?

4. Read the section, "How heat travels."

5. Demonstrate with books and boys conduction and convection as suggested in the section. Think up a way of demonstrating radiation with the books.

6. Refer back to Experiments No. 11, 12, and 13, Chapter Fourteen, on the demonstrations that heat causes substances to expand and taking away heat causes them to contract.

7. Read section, "What heat does to substances."

8. Read the rest of the chapter.

II. Test yourself:

1. Name the usual sources of heat.

2. What makes our bodily heat?

3. Name three ways in which heat travels, and give an example of each.

4. What is the name for the process by which the sun's energy reaches the earth? How do you know that it cannot reach the earth by convection or conduction?

5. If you carried a bucket of hot water upstairs, would you say that the heat reached the second floor by conduction or convection?

6. What happens to the volume of solids, liquids, and gases when they take up heat? How can you show it?

7. What use is made of the expansion and contraction with change of temperature? What precaution is taken in construction because of this change?

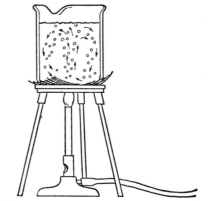

This experiment shows heat rising by convection

8. Mention some convectional movements in the house that are due to the change in volume with temperature. Mention some such movements on the surface of the earth.

9. What change in state does water undergo with change in temperature? What other substances undergo similar changes with change of temperature?

III. Think out these questions:

1. Heat develops in other ways than those mentioned in the chapter. Can you think of some other ways?

2. Do you know of other fuels than those mentioned in the chapter?

3. Are telephone wires between the poles tighter or looser in winter than in summer?

4. By what processes does the surplus heat get out of the automobile radiator?

5. Write down in a list all the uses you can think of that are made of the change of state from solid to liquid, to gas, and reverse.

IV. Vocabulary. Be careful of these scientific terms. You have read them all, but just what is the scientific meaning of each?

radiation	energy
evaporation	distillation
radiant	convection
conduction	

Chapter Forty-two

How We Use and Conserve Heat

Why we add heat to our food. Animals eat their food raw, but man has learned to cook. We know no race of men who did not cook, not even the cave men of the Old Stone Age. We know of no animal that has learned to make and use fire. It looks as though cooks made the man—and they may ruin him. We shall not learn in this book how to cook foods, but we shall study a little about the changes that cooking makes in the food.

In a potato the grains of starch, which are the food substances of the potato, grow in microscopic cells having walls made of a tough substance called *cellulose*. Paper is

The diet of Eskimos includes considerable greasy and fatty foods. Why?

Philip D. Gendreau, N. Y.

made of this cell-wall substance, cellulose. You know that you cannot digest paper. Neither can you digest the cell walls of a potato. Therefore, the digestive juices of your body have difficulty reaching the starch grains inside the cells. When the potato is cooked, the cell walls burst. The digestive juices can then reach the grains of starch and digest them. Therefore, cooking makes the potato much more digestible. In another way cooking aids. When starch is roasted, it is changed into a new substance called *dextrin*. Dextrin is slightly sweet and more digestible than starch. Baking, roasting, or toasting often makes food tastier and more digestible.

Meats, too, are made more digestible and tastier when cooked. The meat that we eat is usually the muscle of the animal. The muscle cells are bound together by thin sheets of tough tissue. Cooking softens and destroys tissues, and the digestive juices can then reach the cells more readily. At the same time the juices of the meats are freed and add to the flavor and appetizing odor of the meat.

There are several different ways of cooking. There is no one best way. The food, the facilities, and the family must determine the right method. In general, people who lead inactive, indoor lives would do well to avoid fried foods. In vigorous outdoor life in cold climates, the grease is valuable as fuel food. In indoor life, grease is difficult to digest. In general, tender meats are better roasted and tough meats may be made enjoyable by destroying the connective tissue by stewing. In boiling vegetables, a common error is cooking much too long. Long cooking makes many vegetables tough and tasteless, and destroys their vitamins. Good sweet corn cooked less than five minutes is delicious, while the same corn cooked fifteen minutes is hard and tasteless. New cabbage steamed ten minutes is tender and of delicious flavor, while the same cabbage boiled a half hour is like slippery leather.

In addition to making food more tasty and more digestible, both very necessary qualities of food, cooking also kills parasites that may be present. It is unsafe to eat meats that have not been thoroughly cooked. In spite of inspection by government agents, meats may contain minute worms coiled up inside tough little sacs. If these are not killed by cooking, they grow inside the person who eats the infected meat. Tapeworms may live in the human intestine, and more minute worms, called *trichina*, bore through the walls of the intestines and travel through the body until they come to rest in the muscles of the person who has eaten them. These worms are sufficiently widespread among our domestic animals to make it un-

Ewing Galloway, N. Y.

Heat is important in pasteurizing milk

safe to eat any meat that has not been well cooked.

You have studied in earlier pages the use of heat to destroy bacteria of decay and disease in milk and other foods. If you have forgotten, turn back to the pages on pasteurization and canning of foods.

Heating the home. You learned while studying the action of water that water comes up from the cellar to the bathroom or to the radiators because hot water is lighter than cold water, quart for quart. The hot water system of heating the home uses the same principle as that of the hot-water faucet in bathroom and kitchen. In a steam-heating system, steam is made in the boiler and passes up through the pipes to the radiators. There it condenses to water as it gives up its heat. The water then returns to the boiler. Hot-air systems use convectional

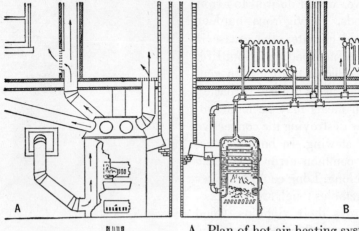

A. Plan of hot-air heating system
B. Plan of steam-heating system
C. Plan of hot-water heating system

S—SAFETY VALVE
E—EXPANSION TANK

currents of air instead of steam or water. The air is heated in chambers around the fire box and rises through air ducts, or large pipes, within the walls to the rooms where it escapes through registers. In pipeless heaters hot air rises directly into the room above the heater from air ducts around the fire box of the furnace.

Heat in industry. Much of the heat that runs our industry is used to run dynamos that generate electricity. The heat derived from burning coal or oil makes steam which drives the engines which, in turn, run the dynamos that generate electricity. Very often it is more convenient and economical to turn one kind of energy into another so that it may be transmitted about town or shut off when not wanted. The energy of moving machinery of a factory is often derived from the electrical energy brought by wires from the power plant. In the power plant, heat energy changes water to steam which generates energy of motion. In the dynamo, the energy of motion is changed to electric energy. We may carry the energy back a step further to the growing coal forest of long ago that took up the radiant energy of the sun and stored the substances of the earth in the growing plants. So the sun's energy appears again in the whirling machine or in the light above it.

Even the falling water that turns the dynamo in the hydroelectric plant owes its power to the radiant

Philip D. Gendreau, N. Y.

Heat is used in industry in a multitude of ways. Can you name some?

energy of the sun. Without the sun's energy received on earth, the water would be solid ice. Without the radiant energy, the water would not evaporate to fall as rain upon the hills and flow down again, turning the water turbines in the power plant on its way to the sea.

Conservation of heat. Have you noticed the coats of the cattle and horses in winter? Have you felt the fur of a rabbit, a squirrel, or other furry creature in the winter months? It is soft, thick, and fluffy. If you have worn a fur coat you know that fur is warm. In the Arctic nothing compares with fur, except feathers. Have you seen ducks swimming in icy water? Fur and feathers are the wild creatures' nonconductors of heat (substances which retard the passage of heat). They keep in the bodily heat generated

by the oxidation of food. Well-fed, the wild animals and birds seem not to mind winter cold.

Man must provide his own nonconductors to keep in his bodily heat. The best clothing for this purpose comes from animals. After fur, wool is the best nonconductor. The part-wool coat is easily distinguished from the all-wool coat on a cold day. Even in summer, wool garments are valuable at times. A day in a wet cotton bathing suit may be very uncomfortable and may be followed by a bad cold. Cotton, silk, and rayon are the goods to allow the bodily heat to pass out readily. Wool is the goods to retard its passage.

Our houses, too, have walls and roofs to reduce the conduction of heat outward in winter and inward in summer. Air spaces in walls are provided as a means of *insulation*

Nature gives the Eskimo dog in the Arctic a coat of warm insulating fur. Man insulates his home to retain the heat

(separation to prevent conduction). These air spaces should be "dead" spaces so that air cannot move around, and heat be transferred by convection. Insulating materials are sometimes inserted in the walls. These materials may be cork, minerals, fibers from sugar cane, and straw. These materials may be made into boards and built into the walls or they may be packed in loosely. The air spaces left between the particles and fibers help to prevent the conduction of heat. Country ice houses are made with double walls filled with sawdust. These keep out the heat of summer so well that the ice may last through the following autumn. The walls of refrigerators are insulated with cork, excelsior, or mineral wool to reduce the passage inward of outside heat. Vacuum bottles for keeping food hot or cold have double walls of glass. Air is pumped out of the space between the walls leaving a *vacuum* (emptiness). The space is then sealed. Heat passes very slowly through this vacuum, and the contents of the bottle remain warm.

To Learn How We Use and Conserve Heat

I. Study by experiment, observation, and reading.

1. EXPERIMENT No. 79. If you have a microscope, cut a thin slice of raw potato and examine under the microscope. Then cut a thin slice of a cooked potato and examine it. Notice the cell walls and the starch grains. Add a drop of iodine to each to see how quickly the iodine penetrates in each case. What happens to the cell walls in cooking?

2. Taste a raw potato and a cooked potato; a piece of raw beef and a piece of cooked beef.

3. Read the section, "Why we add heat to our food."

4. Refer back to Experiment No. 13, the movement of air (Chapter 14).

5. Read the sections, "Heating the home," and "Heat in industry."

6. Experiment No. 80. What kinds of clothing keep in the heat best? Wrap a test tube with one thickness of wool cloth, and a second test tube with cotton cloth of the same weight and color. Fill these and another unwrapped test tube with water at the boiling point. Put a laboratory thermometer in each. Take the temperatures at regular intervals of a few minutes. Record the readings and times in a table.

Conclusion: What is the effect of clothing on retention of bodily heat? Which kind of cloth retains the heat best?

7. Experiment No. 81. What substances are valuable for insulating a house? Similarly determine the rapidity of cooling of test tubes of hot water embedded in the same thickness of sawdust, ground cork, asbestos, crumpled newspaper, and other substances.

8. Experiment No. 82. Devise an experiment to learn what substances are valuable for insulating a refrigerator.

9. Read the section, "Conservation of heat."

II. Test yourself with the following questions:

1. Tell three ways in which food is improved by cooking.

2. In heating a house with a furnace, either of two different substances may be used to carry the heat from the furnace to the rooms. What are these two substances? (Think this out. It is not necessarily answered in the chapter.)

3. Why does hot water rise from cellar to hot-water faucet or to radiators?

4. Why does the hot air rise from the furnace to the rooms?

5. What can be done to keep the heat in the house?

6. What does nature do to keep heat in the bird's or animal's body?

7. What materials are best for clothing to retain the heat in the body?

III. Think out these questions or try them:

1. Try the taste of cabbage, carrots, and other vegetables cooked a few minutes and cooked a half hour or more. Season each in the same way. This experiment may be carried out in the laboratory or at home.

2. It is said that two layers of light underwear are warmer than one thick layer of the same weight as the two. Why?

3. Could a refrigerator without ice be used to keep vegetables from freezing in winter? Your reason?

4. Why was the log house of the backwoodsman often warmer than the frame house of the modern farmer in the same country?

IV. Vocabulary. These suggestions are all common words, but make sure that you know what they mean. Very often people use words without fully understanding them. Use care in spelling.

cellulose	nonconductors
convectional	conduction
transmitted	vacuum
conservation	insulation

These are all cold-blooded animals

Chapter Forty-three

Heat and Life

How nature heats and cools you. A cold day makes you step lively and a hot day slows you up. If you ever asked yourself why you step lively on a cold day, you probably answered yourself that you did it to keep warm. Of course that is the right answer. But if you just sat still on cold days, nature, your nature, might take a hand in the matter and set you moving in a way that you could not stop. You might start shivering. Shivering is nature's way of making you move when you are too stupid to move yourself. If you will not walk yourself warm, nature tries to shiver you warm.

Why does shivering make you warm? Or why does walking make you warm? Walking or shivering takes energy. A form of energy that the well-fed body can readily get is heat. You get heat inside the body, as outside, by burning things. In the body you burn foodstuff. You keep a lot of it stored away in the body just to burn when you need heat and action. A kind of sugar is stored in the muscles and in the liver. When you burn the supply in the muscles by making them work, the blood brings more from the liver. When living cells of the muscles burn up the liver sugar, you feel the heat. Another fuel stored in the body is oil or fat. Some people store large

These are all warm-blooded animals

quantities of it. Other people store very little. Always some is stored, even in "skinny" people. It is bad management to let the store of fat get too low, just as it is bad management to let the fuel in the cellar get too low. You may need it in a hurry when you cannot get it in a hurry. A little fat is an excellent thing.

You slow up on a hot day because nature does not want you to get too hot. You do not need to reason out with yourself that it is a hot day and that you should do nature a favor by going slowly. You just feel languid and not disposed to hurry around. Nature takes care of the matter. Of course, some people do hurry around on hot days, drive themselves to hard, continuous work, and they sometimes collapse with heat stroke. The temperature at which your cells work healthily and happily is 98.6° F. If the temperature rises to 99.6° F., you have a fever and probably feel a little sick. If it gets up to 100° F., you should be staying in bed; in fact, at 99.6° F. you had better be in bed if you do not want the temperature to run up and up. If the temperature goes up only two or three degrees, you are very sick. Nature slows you down by making you feel sick and like lying in bed.

While you are in health, nature has ways of keeping your temperature down. When you feel hot, your face is flushed. The blood is coming to the surface and brings the heat to the skin which, acting like the automobile radiator, passes off heat.

Your body is a much better radiator, however, because, as you learned earlier, nature uses the principle of evaporation to help keep down the temperature. The evaporating perspiration cools the skin. The body must be kept down to 98.6° F. if you are to be healthy.

If you have a dog, you will notice that he also acts as you do on a brisk, cool morning. He feels like racing and playing. On a hot day, he prefers to lie still. If you have driven a horse, you know how frisky a horse may be on a cool morning and how deliberate it may be on a hot day. On a still, hot day in the fields and woods, the wild animals also are lying low. On a cool, breezy day they are out and hunting or chasing about. So it is with squirrels, chipmunks, ground hogs, and birds.

Cold-blooded and warm-blooded animals. Certain kinds of animals, however, respond in a very different way to a fall in temperature. When a sudden cold snap drops down in autumn, you may find a snake sluggish and numb, unable to crawl out of your way. Frogs and toads also slow up with the cold. Cold numbs all the tribe of reptiles, frogs, and toads. We call them *cold-blooded animals*. Their temperature falls with the temperature of their surroundings. And they warm up and become active with their surroundings. Look out for the snake basking on a warm rock on a hot day. He is then as quick as lightning. All the cold-blooded animals speed

If your temperature goes up, the place for you is in bed. Fever is a warning

up with rising temperature and slow down and become sluggish with falling temperature.

You too would slow up with falling temperature, if your body temperature fell. You are one of the warm-blooded creatures whose body temperature remains the same throughout the year. When the temperature outside falls, nature stimulates your cells and they burn more food. You eat more. You are more active. You put on more clothes. So do squirrels, foxes, and other fur-bearers. Their body temperatures must be kept up. If the body temperature falls, they become sluggish, and unlike cold-blooded animals, then they die. Only warm-blooded animals that hibernate slow up in cold weather. Their temperature falls somewhat, but they cannot

freeze and live, as the cold-blooded animals can.

How hot and cold can animals be? Although the cold-blooded animals, like snakes and lizards, become very active, and perhaps "happy," on a hot day, there is a limit to the heat that they can stand. And the limit is not very high. Very few things can live if their body temperature rises to 120° F. That, you will notice, is well below the temperature of boiling water, 212° F. In the hot springs there are certain plants, algae, relatives of the seaweeds, that live at temperature about 120° F., and there are also certain little water insects and certain little crustaceans, little cousins of the crabs. But that is about all that can endure such heat, if the body temperature rises. Men can live, for a

314

time, at higher temperatures, but the body temperature does not rise. If it rose, they would promptly get sick, and if it rose much, men would die. A body temperature of 106° F. is very high for a sick man. Certain of the cold-blooded animals can live at higher body temperatures.

If you have seen what happens to a piece of meat when it is boiled, you have seen why an animal cannot stand a high temperature. The living material in its body just becomes hard, and does not work. The meat we eat is generally the muscle of the animal. When a muscle hardens like cooked meat, it can no longer contract and relax like a muscle.

Living substance is largely water. Your body is over half water. When the temperature falls to 32° F., water freezes. A muscle cannot work when the water in it is frozen. Glands, such as those that produce the digestive juices, secrete substances dissolved in water. They could not work if the water were frozen. So animals cannot be active if body temperature is at freezing.

How heat determines where to live. Living things are found only with a narrow range of temperature, between freezing and 120° F. That leaves some parts of the earth with small chance for living things. In the interior of the Antarctic Continent explorers found only ice and snow. The only things they found alive were certain microscopic things that were just resting when the temperature was low. In the interior of

Greenland, there is perpetual ice with no living things unless there are some to be found with the microscope. Under the ice at the North Pole, however, the Russian explorers who camped there on the sea ice reported things alive in the sea when they dug holes through the ice and dredged the sea below. Jellyfish and crablike creatures were alive under the ice. But that was below the ice where the water had not frozen.

On the rest of the earth, temperature governs the distribution of animals and plants. You know that the polar bear, the musk oxen, and the reindeer are creatures of the cold. The Arctic fox and the Arctic hare, like the Barren Ground caribou, migrate southward in the cold of winter, but move north again when the land warms in spring. The caribou and reindeer that stay in the north in winter dig away the snow with their hoofs to feed upon the crusty lichens called *reindeer moss*. There is a land in Canada known as the "Land of the Little Sticks" for here the trees grow only a few inches high. Farther south the trees rise steadily in height until the evergreen forests stretch across the continent.

You are familiar with the temperate climate. You may not know all its trees and smaller plants by name, but you know that there is a wealth of different kinds. A great variety of animals live on these plants, and other animals live on the plant eaters. They are different from the animals of the far North. The

Sparse vegetation in the Arctic Circle is evident in this picture taken in Alaska. Compare it with the tropical landscape opposite

difference is due to the heat in their surroundings.

Then you have at least seen pictures of the dense forest of great tall trees in the equatorial regions. You are familiar, at least in the zoo, the museum, or in pictures, with the very different sort of animals in these hot regions. Arctic, or even temperate-zone, animals are ruled out by their inability to prosper in intense heat.

If you go fishing, you know that in the water, also, temperature rules the activities of the water dwellers. Along the northern coast fishing is poor in winter. Fish move up from southern waters as the warm sun adds heat to the water. Lobsters come in from deep water offshore to their summer grounds where they may be caught. In the big lakes salmon and

trout are close to shore in the spring, but as the water warms, they retreat to the deep holes in the lakes. The fisherman who does not know the deep holes has small chance of taking these fish when the lakes have warmed up enough for you to enjoy going swimming.

Controlling the heat of the environment. Nature provides many creatures with good warm coats of fur or feathers that keep in the heat of the body, and she provides them with good appetites in winter to encourage them to keep up the supply of bodily fuel. But nature does not always provide enough food. Some animals lay up food for the bodily fires in winter. Many animals have learned to build some sort of shelter to shut out the wind and

Tropic vegetation is lush and plentiful. What accounts for the difference between this scene in the South Pacific and the one on the opposite page?

the rain. It may be only an improvement upon shelter that they find. The squirrel makes a warm bed of leaves. The fox finds holes among the rocks if he can, but may dig them out to suit himself.

Only one living creature has learned to add heat to his shelter by using fire. You can guess which one that is. The use of fire separates man from all the brute creation. With the elaborate shelters which man has created, he has made a new winter environment. A city person may travel about and spend the winter with remarkably little time in the winter environment that nature makes. Warm trains, cars, and automobiles may take him to his day's work, where he lives in summer heat. Warm conveyance takes him back home to a summer-heated dwelling. Again, warm vehicles may take him to a summer-warm theater where he may watch the tropic trees bow before tropic breezes and hear the calls of tropic birds and the pound of the surf on the coral reef.

How to Study Heat and Life

I. Study temperature and life by experiment and observation.

1. EXPERIMENT No. 83. With a thermometer take the temperature of members of your class. A clinical thermometer (doctor's thermometer) is most easily used, but a laboratory thermometer will do. Shake down the mercury in the clinical thermometer as you have seen the doctor do. Do not jar it against the table or it will break. Wash the bulb of the thermometer with alcohol to kill

any germs and then place it under the tongue for two or three minutes. After each use, before using on the next person, wash the bulb in alcohol. If you use a laboratory thermometer, read the thermometer before removing from the mouth.

2. Take the temperature while resting and then after exercise that has warmed you up well. What else has happened to your body in the exercise besides increasing your feeling of warmth?

3. Take bodily temperatures on cold days, on warm days, indoors and out.

4. EXPERIMENT No. 84. Take the temperature of a bird, a canary bird, a pigeon, or a chicken. Hold the thermometer under the wing against the body. Do you see any reason why a bird's temperature should be different from that of a human being?

5. EXPERIMENT No. 85. If you have a gentle dog, you might take his temperature.

6. You might assemble pictures to illustrate animal and plant life in the polar, temperate, and tropic climates.

7. On your hikes note down the kinds of plants that seem not to be greatly harmed by the winter and note the animals that are abroad. What kinds of plants have disappeared and what kinds of animals, including birds and smaller creatures?

II. Read the chapter.

III. Test yourself:

1. How does your body try to adjust itself to cold days without your taking thought?

2. How does your body adjust itself to hot days without your taking thought?

3. Tell how the automatic cooling system of your body works.

4. How do warm-blooded animals act on a cool day? How do cold-blooded animals act?

5. Why can living things not endure very high temperatures? What is the highest temperature of the body at which living things can be active?

6. What is the lowest temperature of the body at which living things can be active? Why can they not be active at lower bodily temperatures?

7. How do warm-blooded animals adjust themselves to the Arctic winter?

8. How do cold-blooded animals adjust themselves to cold seasons?

9. Write down a list of all the improvements upon nature that man makes to combat cold winters; to combat hot summers.

IV. Think these out or investigate:

1. Is man more successful in combatting extremely hot summers or extremely cold winters? Name some recent advances in adjusting conditions to meet the extreme seasons.

2. Name some of the ways in which man responds, just as the wild animals do, to the extreme heat and cold.

3. Certain cold-blooded animals live within the Arctic Circle; for example, mosquitoes, shellfish, and fish. Can you explain why they do not die out?

4. When bacteria of disease make a person sick, the temperature goes up. Does high temperature, when a person is sick with infectious disease, do any good?

V. Vocabulary. Just what is meant by the following?

cold-blooded   perpetual
warm-blooded

Were there any other words for your list?

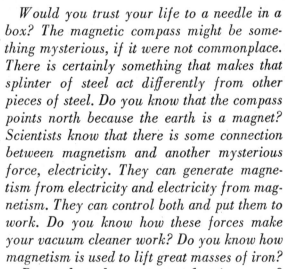

Unit Nine

Magnetism and Electrical Energy

Would you trust your life to a needle in a box? The magnetic compass might be something mysterious, if it were not commonplace. There is certainly something that makes that splinter of steel act differently from other pieces of steel. Do you know that the compass points north because the earth is a magnet? Scientists know that there is some connection between magnetism and another mysterious force, electricity. They can generate magnetism from electricity and electricity from magnetism. They can control both and put them to work. Do you know how these forces make your vacuum cleaner work? Do you know how magnetism is used to lift great masses of iron?

Do you know how to get an electric current? Do you know how to get heat from electricity? Do you know why a fuse is used to blow out and stop the current just when you want light? Do you know why the telegraph can send messages and the telephone and radio talk?

Do you know how the current makes the trolley car and electric locomotive go? Do you know what is behind the electric meter dial? Can you read the meter?

(1) *Ewing Galloway,* (2) (3) (4) *Philip D. Gendreau*

Chapter Forty-four

Magnetism

How magnets act. You have seen a compass and perhaps have guided your course with one. Do you know why it points where it does? As a student of science, you demand an explanation that uses "laws of science," without spirits or mystery. Let us try to find a scientific explanation.

A magnet that you may buy in a five-and-ten-cent store will help you to learn something about magnetism. You might find in the store a straight bar magnet or one that is bent like a horseshoe. The straight bar magnet will be better for our experiments. Try to pick up various things by touching them with the magnet—a dime, a penny, a nail, a pen, a needle. The magnet seems to pick up or attract only certain things. It picks up iron and steel, but has no apparent influence on a variety of other things. You will notice also that the needles cling to the ends of the magnet but not to the middle. If you get a nail hanging to the end of a magnet and then touch the nail to a second nail, the second nail hangs on to the first nail. A third nail may hang to the second. Each nail in turn

A magnet dipped in iron filings holds the filings at its ends

becomes a magnet as long as the first nail holds to the magnet. Detach the first nail from the magnet, and the whole string of nails falls apart. When a magnet touches iron or steel, the iron or steel becomes magnetized.

You can easily make a magnet of your knife blade or scissors. Stroke the blade several times with the magnet, always in the same direction, never in the reverse direction, and always with the same end of the magnet. Then touch the point of the blade to a needle.

The magnetic compass. You can make a compass. Select a long needle, preferably a steel knitting needle. Stroke it always in the same direction on the end of the magnet. Test it by touching another needle or iron filings. Then tie a thread to the middle of the needle and hang it up. If the needle is heavy enough to overcome the twist of the thread, it will point north and south like a compass needle. It is a compass.

Now bring an end of the magnet near the suspended needle or near the end of a compass needle. If the needle moves toward the end of the magnet, reverse the magnet and bring the other end toward the same end of the needle. The needle then moves away. If your magnet has an N stamped on one end, you will find this end repels the north end of

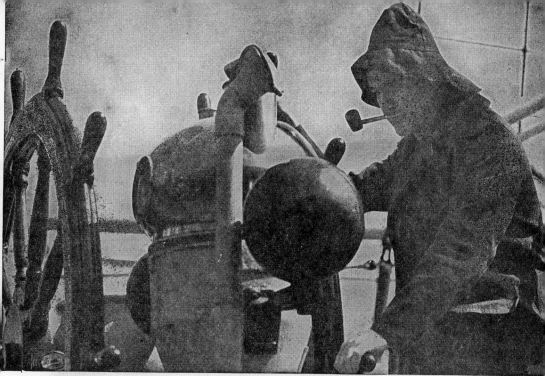

The mariner steers his ship by a compass, the principle of which is the same as the principle of your small pocket compass

your needle, but it attracts the south end of your needle. Instead of saying the *north end* we say the *north pole* of the magnet. Magnetize a second needle and suspend it so that it points north and south. Notice which end is the north pole of this magnet. Bring the north pole toward the north pole of your first suspended needle. You find a law of magnetic poles. Like poles repel each other and unlike poles attract.

Magnetic field. If you shake some iron filings on a pane of glass or a sheet of paper and hold the magnet below, you will see that glass or paper does not stop the magnetic force. If you tap the glass, the iron

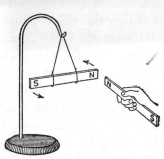

The north pole of the bar magnet repels the north pole of the suspended magnet

This boy is showing the lines of magnetic force

of the earth. The north magnetic pole lies several hundred miles away from the true north pole, north of Hudson Bay. Its location slowly changes. The compass points to that place. Therefore, on most parts of the earth the compass does not point to true north. Government surveys determine the position of the compass needle in various places.]

What will happen to the compass needle when the wire approaches it?

filings arrange themselves along curved lines from one pole of the magnet to the other. Evidently magnetism acts most strongly along certain lines. They are the lines of magnetic force. The area over which the magnet produces an effect is the magnetic field. If you take a very small compass and place it on a line of force indicated by the line of iron filings, you will find the compass needle points along the line. As you move the compass along the line, the needle continues to move with the line of force until it meets the pole of the magnet.

The earth is a huge magnet. The compass needle takes a position along a line of force. It points north because the lines of force lead to the north pole of the earth magnet. The earth is surrounded by a magnetic field just as the steel magnet is. The lines of magnetic force run from the north magnetic pole of the earth to the earth's south magnetic pole.

[The north pole of the earth magnet is not quite on the true north pole

Magnetism first cousin to electricity. Magnets as well as electricity are needed to run the trolley car, the vacuum sweeper, the electric refrigerator, the telephone, the telegraph, and the electric light. Magnetism and electricity are related to each other. You can show it by simple experiments. Attach two ends of a copper wire to a dry cell. Then bring the wire above a compass needle, pointing the wire in the same direction as the needle, that is, parallel to the needle, not crosswise to it. As the wire approaches the needle, you see the needle swing to right or left. If you turn the wire around so that it is again parallel but with its ends in the opposite direction, the needle swings across to the other side. A change in the electric current makes the needle move. If you disconnect the wire from the battery, the needle again moves back and points north. If you touch the wire to the terminal post of the cell, the needle swings away again. As the current changes, the magnetic field around it changes.

Electromagnets. Now make an electromagnet, the kind of magnet

Ewing Galloway, N. Y.

Many times stronger than the electromagnet that you made, this giant industrial magnet can lift tons of iron. Yet its principle is exactly the same as that of your small magnet which can lift only a few nails

that can pick up a ton of iron, as shown above. Take a soft iron nail, any kind of nail, and by touching it to another nail see that it has no magnetism or so little that you cannot notice it. Now wrap several turns of wire such as is used on electric bells around the nail. Connect the ends of the wire to terminals of a dry cell. Then bring the nail to the compass or to some iron filings or small nails. You find the nail has become a magnet. Disconnect the wire from the cell, and the magnetism is gone. The nail and coil of wire form an electromagnet. The great electromagnet that picks up tons of iron differs from our little nail and wire only by its great size and the strength of the current.

Try wrapping the wire ten times around the nail or soft iron core, and then touch it to a pile of very small nails. Then wrap the wire twenty times around the core, and touch it to the pile of nails. You find that it picks up more nails. Try your

How does the number of turns of wire affect the strength of the magnet?

twenty-coil magnet connected with one dry cell and then connected with two dry cells as on page 323. You find that it again can pick up more nails. Now answer these questions: What effect on the magnetism is produced by increasing the size of the coil? What effect has increasing the strength of the current?

Electromagnets are very common. The trolley car and the dynamos that generate the current for the trolley line and for your house and for industry use electromagnets. Small electromagnets are widely used.

Every electric motor uses electromagnets. When you hear the electric refrigerator start up, the electromagnets get to work. The vacuum sweeper uses them. When you step on the starter of your automobile, electromagnets are used in turning the machinery. The generator in your car that charges the battery uses other electromagnets. The electric bell, the telegraph, and the telephone use them. Before we can study these instruments we must first study something more about electricity.

How to Learn about Magnets

I. Read the chapter.

II. Directions for the following experiments are given in the chapter:

1. EXPERIMENT No. 86. What substances are attracted by a magnet?

2. EXPERIMENT No. 87. How may a knife blade or scissors blade be magnetized?

3. EXPERIMENT No. 88. How can you make a compass?

4. EXPERIMENT No. 89. What is the law of magnetic poles?

5. EXPERIMENT No. 90. How can you show the magnetic field?

6. EXPERIMENT No. 91. How does an electric current affect a magnet?

7. EXPERIMENT No. 92. How can you make an electromagnet?

III. Test yourself:

1. How can you tell whether a piece of steel is magnetized?

2. How can you make a magnet out of a piece of steel?

3. How can you learn which is the north pole of a magnet?

4. How can you make a compass?

5. What is the law of attraction and repulsion of magnetic poles? How can you prove it?

6. Do paper, glass, and brass stop magnetic influence? How can you show that your answer is correct?

7. How can you show the magnetic field?

8. How can you show that there is some relation between magnetism and electricity?

9. How can you make an electromagnet?

10. Tell two ways by which you can increase the strength of an electromagnet.

IV. Think out these questions:

1. What would happen to the compass if you carried it beside a mountain in which there was a huge deposit of iron ore?

2. Suppose a ship took on a load of iron. What might happen to the compass? This is corrected by fastening pieces of iron close to the compass in the correct positions. How do you suppose the correct positions are found? Why does this correct the compass reading? What advantage has an electromagnet?

V. Vocabulary. Have you added new words to your list?

Chapter Forty-five

The Electric Current

How to get electricity. You can get electricity by combing your hair with a rubber comb. Did you ever hear the comb snap and crackle when you combed your hair on a cold, dry morning? You can also get electricity by rubbing a rubber rod on a piece of fur or a glass rod on silk. That kind of electricity is not very useful. You cannot put it to work. We need an electric current.

You can get electricity from dry cells to light a flashlight or to ring a doorbell. A dry cell is a zinc can, filled with a damp paste made of certain chemical substances: ammonium chloride, powdered carbon, zinc chloride, and manganese dioxide. In the center of the can is a rod of carbon. Attached to the zinc and to the carbon rod are binding posts for connecting wires. The chemical substances in the cell undergo changes which result in an electric current when wires are properly connected. The zinc is gradually eaten away and the battery "wears out."

The battery of an automobile is a storage battery. We send a current into the battery when it is charged, and then draw a current out. In the battery are lead plates in a solution of sulfuric acid. When an electric current is sent into the battery, the lead absorbs oxygen from the water and sulfuric acid and becomes a red substance, lead peroxide. When the current is led out, the red lead peroxide changes back to gray lead. In the change from one chemical substance to another, electricity is given up.

The great supply of electricity which lights our cities, runs cars and locomotives, and supplies our factories comes from dynamos.

For experiments at home or in the laboratory you can make a simple electric cell. You need a tumbler,

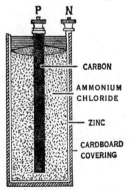

A dry cell. *P* is the positive post; *N* is the negative post.

CARBON

AMMONIUM CHLORIDE

ZINC

CARDBOARD COVERING

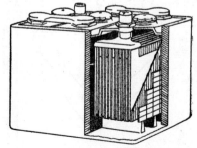

A storage battery

Ewing Galloway, N. Y.

Why are two poles necessary on a trackless trolley bus?

strip of zinc, a strip of copper, and some sulfuric acid. Make a solution of one part of acid to ten parts of water and always pour the acid into the water. Never pour the water into the acid, for the acid may be blown into your face. Arrange the cell as on page 329. The electricity comes from the action of the chemical substances, zinc, copper, and sulfuric acid. Chemical energy is changed into electrical energy.

An electric circuit. Electricity will not work unless it can go somewhere and come back again. To get a current there must be a circuit. If you attach one end of a wire to the binding post of a dry cell and the other end of the wire to an electric bell, you will find that the bell does not ring. If another wire is added from the bell to the other binding post of the cell, the bell rings. The current makes a circuit from the cell, through the bell, and back to the cell. If you put in the circuit a switch, such as an electric button, you can complete the circuit when you want the bell to ring and break the circuit when you want it to stop. Similarly a light switch completes the circuit when you want light and breaks the circuit to shut off the light.

Conductors and insulators. Electric currents do not flow through all kinds of substances. There are conductors through which the current flows and nonconductors through which it does not flow. Most metals are conductors, but some are

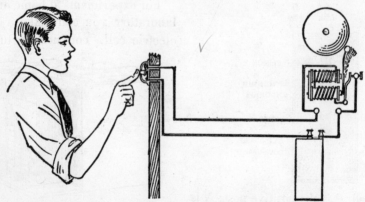

This diagram shows how an electric current is made and broken

better conductors than others. Copper is one of the best. Therefore, electric wires are usually of copper. Aluminum is a good conductor but not so good as copper. Aluminum, however, is much cheaper and therefore is sometimes used in electric wires in place of copper. Rubber, silk, wool, and resins, are nonconductors. They are used to cover electric wires to insulate them. Insulators on electric wire poles and supporting the wires as they enter our houses are porcelain or glass.

Heat and light from electricity. What makes the light in the electric bulb? In an oil lamp and in a candle something burns to make the light, but nothing burns in the electric bulb. If you heat iron red hot, it gives out light. An electric current heats metals as it flows through them. The greater their resistance to the flow, the hotter they get. If you connect up three dry cells as shown on page 330 and then connect the end cells with a piece of iron wire, the iron wire gets warm. If you use instead a piece of copper wire, it heats little or not at all. Iron offers more resistance than copper. If you use a very fine copper wire, it warms more than a heavier wire. The small wire offers more resistance than the large wire and so it gets warmer.

In an electric heater, toaster, or an electric iron, the current passes through a wire or ribbon made of nichrome, an alloy or mixture of iron, chromium, and nickel. This

Black Star, N. Y.

Insulators on a transformer tower

metal has considerable resistance and becomes hot. You can see the wires glow in the electric toaster.

In the electric bulb a fine wire of the metal, tungsten, is used. When the current flows, the wire becomes very hot and glows, giving us the light. If air were left in the bulb, the metal would burn. Therefore, the air is pumped out or replaced by nitrogen gas or by argon gas which will not allow burning.

Why does an electric iron become hot?

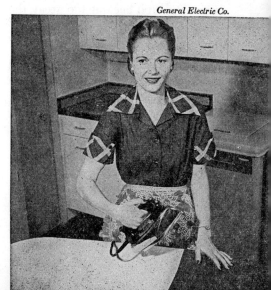

General Electric Co.

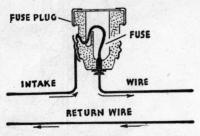

How does a fuse work?

What the fuse is for. You have heard of a short circuit blowing a fuse. Sometimes as someone is moving a lamp cord, the lights go out. "Fuse blown." The fuse is a piece of wire made of a mixture of metals, chiefly of lead, that melts easily when heated. This fuse wire is inclosed within a cartridge or fuse plug and is inserted in the fuse box, often in the cellar. The fuse fills a gap in the circuit. The electric current entering the house must flow through this fuse wire. If too much current flows in, the fuse wire melts and thus shuts off the current. The more current that flows through a wire the hotter the wire becomes. If there were no way to shut off the current when it became too great, the wires in the walls might become hot enough to set the house afire.

A short circuit may make the wires hot. The insulation is rubbed off a lamp cord, perhaps under a rug where it is walked upon. The bare wires may touch each other or some other object that conducts away the electricity very rapidly. With less resistance, more current flows through the wire. The increased current heats the wires and may heat them enough to set fire to woodwork or rug. To prevent such a flow of current the fuse is inserted and melts as the current rises.

After having a fuse blow time after time, a person may become impatient and put in a fuse that will not melt until a higher temperature is reached. Thus a 15 ampere fuse may be replaced by a 20 ampere fuse. This replacement is exactly the wrong thing to do. The fuse blows to protect the house. The right thing to do is to find the cause of the increased current. It is generally due to a defect in the appliances that have been connected or to a defect in the wiring. A bare wire touches something and allows the current to flow away more easily than through the wires. When the defect is found and corrected, the proper fuse will carry the current. The most dangerous thing to do is to replace the fuse with a penny, for the current may become dangerous without warning.

How to Learn about the Electric Current

I. Study electricity by experiment and observation.

1. EXPERIMENT No. 93. How can you get electricity?

Tear up a piece of paper into small bits and lay them on the table. Touch a rubber rod to the paper. Does anything happen? Rub the rubber rod briskly with fur and again touch the paper. Does anything happen now?

Touch a glass rod to the pieces of paper and then rub it briskly with silk and touch it again to the paper. Is there any change in the behavior?

Suspend a second rubber rod so that it swings freely. Bring the end of the first rod near it. Does anything happen?

Rub both rods briskly with the fur. Again bring the first rod toward the suspended rod. What happens? Bring the fur close to the suspended rod. What happens? Rub the glass rod briskly with the silk and bring the glass toward the suspended rubber rod. What happens? Bring the silk close to the suspended rubber rod. What happens?

Conclusions: Think over what you did and saw, and write down a series of statements.

2. Get an old dry cell. Take it to pieces and identify the parts described in the text.

3. If you can get an old automobile battery, open it at the top, lift out the plates, and identify the parts as described in the text. Be careful not to get the acid on your hands, for it will burn; or on your clothes, for it will burn holes in them.

4. EXPERIMENT No. 94. How to make a simple electric cell.

In a tumbler make a solution of one part sulfuric acid to ten parts water. Caution: Pour the acid into the water. Do not pour the water into the acid, or the acid may be blown into your face. Connect the wire to the zinc and to the copper. Lay a compass on the table. Lower the zinc and copper into the acid. Bring the wire over the compass. Do you see any evidence of electric current? You will remember that you learned in the last chapter that electricity affects the magnetic compass. If the strength of the solution is right, the cell will ring a bell. Often due to impurities in the zinc, the current fails. If mercury is rubbed on the zinc, the current will again flow.

5. EXPERIMENT No. 95. What is an electric circuit?

How do the charged rods act when brought together?

Caution: Do not connect the binding post on the zinc cover of a dry cell with the carbon in the center, for that will short circuit the cell and ruin it. Connect a wire to either pole of the cell and to a bell. Does the bell ring? Now connect the other wire to the other pole of the cell and to the other post of the bell. Does the bell ring? Disconnect it immediately. Now unscrew an electric button to see how it works. Then connect one wire from the zinc to the one post of the button. Connect a second wire from the other post of the button to the post of the bell. Connect a third wire from the second post of the bell to the carbon. Push the button. Does the bell ring? Is there a continuous circuit from the cell and back to the cell?

Remove one wire from the button. Attach the wire to a glass rod and the

A homemade electric cell

How electricity heats metals

glass rod to the button so that the current would need to flow through the glass rod. Does the bell ring? What sort of substance is glass? Try a rubber rod; a stick of wood; the lead of a pencil sharpened at both ends so that you can attach wire to the lead.

6. EXPERIMENT No. 96. When does an electric current produce heat? Connect up the three cells as shown in the picture. Be careful. If you connect them wrong you will short circuit the cell and discharge it. Connect two wires from the cells to a bare copper wire of the same diameter. Touch the bare copper wire. Does it warm up? Remove this bare piece and put in turn a copper wire of heavier size, a finer wire, and an iron wire. Which warms up? Put in the nichrome wire. What is the effect?

Conclusions: What kinds of wires create resistance enough to heat up?

7. Examine an electric toaster or heater to see what warms up when connected to the house current.

8. If you have a clear electric bulb, look in to see what heats up enough to give light. Gently detach a frosted bulb to find what is inside that heats up.

9. Examine a fuse.

II. Read the chapter.

III. Test yourself:

1. How can you generate electricity very easily?

2. How can you easily get a current of electricity?

3. What is in a dry cell such as is used as a battery for a flashlight?

4. What is in an automobile battery? Why is it called a *storage battery?*

5. What generates the supply of electricity for cities and for country?

6. If you took a wire and connected a dry cell with an electric bell, would the bell ring? Why?

7. To make sure that current does not flow out of the wire into the side of your house where the wire is fastened, what would you do?

8. Name some nonconductors. What is the best substance to carry the current?

9. What makes the light in an electric bulb?

10. Why is a filament of copper wire not used inside an electric bulb? Of what metal is the filament made?

11. Why do the wires become hot in an electric toaster? Would a copper wire do instead of nichrome in the toaster? Your reason.

12. Fuses sometimes blow out and leave you in the dark. "Why do they use them?" What is a fuse?

13. How may a short circuit occur in a lamp cord? Why is it dangerous? What should you do about it?

IV. Think these out:

1. Is electricity rare or common in nature?

2. Why does a fuse blow out in an automobile? What might happen if no fuse were used?

3. Why do you sometimes get a shock when you touch an electric wire, yet the repairmen take hold of the live trolley wires? Do not touch a live trolley wire that you see repairmen handling. You may be killed instantly.

V. Vocabulary. What new words did you find?

circuit   insulators   conductors

Chapter Forty-six

Messages by Electric Current

The electric bell. How often does your electric bell get "out of order"? It usually is not hard to fix. The bell is a simple application of the electromagnet. When you press the button, an electric current flows through the spring *armature* to the electromagnets. They become magnetized and draw the armature down to strike the bell. But as soon as the armature is drawn down, the electric circuit is broken and no current flows, the electromagnet loses its magnetism, and the armature springs back to its original position. There it closes the circuit, the current flows, the magnets again draw the armature, and again the bell is struck. This is repeated about four times a second and gives the continuous ringing of the bell. A buzzer works the same way except that it has no bell. The armature with the spring working with the electromagnet forms an automatic circuit breaker. If the current was not broken when the clapper struck the bell, it would be held down and would not strike again. It would then be necessary to push the bell button for each stroke of the bell. Such a bell could be used for tapping out a message somewhat as with a telegraph.

How the telegraph sends messages. You can easily make a telegraph instrument as soon as you understand the principle. It is simply the principle of the electromagnet. Arrange a coil around a soft iron core as in the picture on page 332. Connect one wire with a dry cell. Hold the other end of the wire in your right hand. In your left hand hold a light bar of soft iron or a long iron nail close to the end of the core of the electromagnet as shown. Now touch the wire to the post of the dry cell. You feel the bar drawn down to the core. Stop the current by lifting the wire from the post of the cell, and the bar comes up again. That is the principle of the telegraph. In the telegraph instrument the current is turned on and off by a switch called the *key*. When the current is turned on by pressing the key, the bar called the *armature* is pulled down sharply and makes a click. When the current

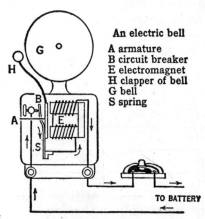

An electric bell

A armature
B circuit breaker
E electromagnet
H clapper of bell
G bell
S spring

TO BATTERY

How the telegraph works

series of dot-and-dash combinations. The table below shows the dot-and-dash combinations of the letters of the alphabet. In the latest teletype instrument the operator does not work a key up and down, but types the message on a keyboard like that of a typewriter. Electrical impulses are sent out over the wire. At the receiving end, a typing machine types the message again on gummed strips which are pasted on the message blank.

In 1832 Samuel F. B. Morse's instrument clicked out over the wire between Washington and Baltimore the message, "What hath God wrought?" Now "electric brains" at message centers sort out thousands of messages and direct each to its proper destination at the command of a symbol at the opening of the message. Hundreds of messages speed over the same wire at the same instant. They are carried by waves of electricity similar to radio waves. Radio beams carry even more messages at once, up to two thousand.

is turned off, the armature is pulled up by a spring and strikes a metal stop, making another click. The time between these clicks forms the dots and dashes of the code.

The language of the telegraph. When the armature goes down and up quickly, click-click, it is a dot. When it is held down for an instant, click—click, it is a dash. The language of the telegraph is a

Why the telephone talks. The fellow on the other end of the tele-

A	·—	H	····	O	———	V	···—
B	—···	I	··	P	·——·	W	·——
C	—·—·	J	·———	Q	——·—	X	—··—
D	—··	K	—·—	R	·—·	Y	—·——
E	·	L	·—··	S	···	Z	——··
F	··—·	M	——	T	—		
G	——·	N	—·	U	··—		

The Morse continental code

phone does not really hear your voice. You talk to the telephone and the telephone talks to the other fellow. When you talk you set the air vibrating or shaking. The transmitter of the telephone into which you talk has a metal disc which is set vibrating by the vibrating air. Behind the metal disc is a little box filled with grains of carbon. The front end of the box is a carbon disc which is attached to the metal disc. The rear of the box is another carbon disc. Electric wires are connected to the two carbon ends of the box, and a current is sent through. When you talk and make the front end of the box vibrate, the grains of carbon inside the box are set vibrating, first packing close together and then spreading apart slightly. When the carbon grains are packed together, more current flows through the box and out the wire in the rear. When the carbon grains spread out,

Electric "brains" sort out thousands of messages at receiving centers

their resistance to the current is increased, and not so much current flows through the wire and out of the rear of the carbon box. The wire from the rear of the box is the line to the receiver which your friend is holding to his ear. The current over this line varies with your speaking.

The air vibrations set up by the voice cause the diaphragm *b* to vibrate. This causes similar vibrations in the plate *e*, and varies the distance between it and the stationary plate *d*. Plates *e* and *d* are each connected to one wire of an electric current at *f, f*, and the intensity of the current through the circuit is varied as conduction of the current is increased or lessened by the compression of the carbon granules (shown by dots) between the stationary and moving plates *e* and *d*. In the receiver the current acts upon an electromagnet **E, E**, which pulls the diaphragm **D** and so sets up vibrations similar to those made by the voice in the transmitter

333

Bell Telephone Co.

The telephone switchboard seems a maze of confusing wires. Now connections on most local calls are made automatically by dials .

In the receiver is a metal disc and behind it a horseshoe magnet. Around the poles of the magnet are coils of wire. When the current goes over the wire from the transmitter into which you are talking, it varies in strength. When the current is increased, the magnet becomes stronger and draws the metal disc of the receiver toward it. When the current weakens, the magnet weakens, and the metal disc moves forward again. Thus the vibrating disc of your friend's receiver keeps time to the vibrating disc of your transmitter. The vibrating disc of the receiver makes the air vibrate, and your friend hears.

This is the telephone in simple form. You can rig up such a telephone with dry cells and talk to your friend next door. In a great telephone system there are many complications added. Various pieces of apparatus make connections either by an operator or automatically. For long distances the current must be increased, and additional apparatus is used to produce a current that will carry through. In very long distances the message must be repeated in stations along the route, repeated not by human voice but by electrical appliances. One cable can now transmit 240 separate conversations in both directions at the same time, gathering currents from 240 different telephones on one end and sorting them out to the right 240 telephones on the other end. It can carry 2880 telegrams. The same line can carry telephone and telegraph messages at the same time.

Electric messages without wires. You learned that waves of energy are constantly speeding through space. These waves are light—ultraviolet, infrared, and other waves. Some of these waves come to us from the sun and others seem to come from the far reaches of space. Still others start on earth. When the Indian lighted a signal fire on a hill to send a message to another Indian on a distant hill, he sent out light waves. Scientists have learned to send out other waves. You will recall that the waves differ in wave length. They also differ in the number of vibrations a second, that is, in their frequency. Electrical devices are used to produce waves of

334

different lengths and frequency. These devices are exceedingly complex, but the general principle of the wave messages is easy to understand.

You have probably seen an electric spark jump. When electric sparks jump across a gap, they send out electric waves speeding through the air. Indeed, they do not need the air but would speed through space. These waves will make sparks jump gaps in a distant station. The jumping sparks can be made to spell out a message in a code of dots and dashes just as the clicks of a telegraph instrument do. This is the general principle of the wireless message first sent across the ocean by Marconi. This method is not now used.

In the speaking radio, a speaker talks into an instrument called the *microphone* which is like a very delicate telephone transmitter. The vibrations of the speaker's vocal cords set up vibrations in the air. The air vibrations cause vibrations in a plate in the microphone which, in turn, modify electric currents. These varying currents are used to modify a

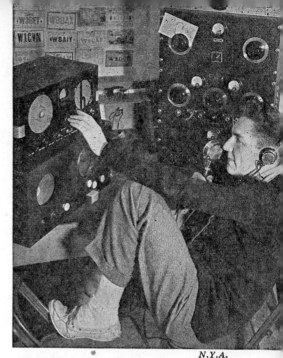

N.Y.A.

This "radio ham" is operating his own small radio station by which he may talk to friends all over the world

powerful current which sends electric waves out from the *antennae,* wires extending high in the air. The electric waves speeding through the air strike the aerial of your radio. They cause varying currents in your radio system. These varying currents cause vibrations in the disc of the loud speaker, and the vibrating disc, in turn, causes vibrations of the air, and you hear.

How to Learn about Messages by Electric Current

I. Read the chapter.

II. Study the telephone and the telegraph by experiment and observation.

1. Get an electric bell that you can take apart. Read through the section on the bell and find the parts.

2. Perform the experiment (EXPERIMENT No. 97) described in the section, "How the telegraph sends messages."

3. If you can get a telephone receiver and transmitter, unscrew the parts as you read the section on the telephone and find the parts described. If you cannot get the instruments, locate the parts in the diagrams which are shown on page 325.

4. EXPERIMENT No. 98. Make a telegraph instrument as indicated in the

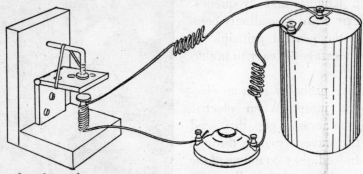

A homemade telegraph

diagram. With the code before you, send a message to a friend.

5. EXPERIMENT No. 99. With the telephone transmitter and receiver and a set of dry cells, rig up a line to the next room or to the next house. The diagram shows how.

III. Test yourself with the following questions:

1. Why does the clapper strike the electric bell? Why is the ringing continuous?

2. Why does the telegraph instrument click?

3. How does your voice alter the electric current in the telephone? How does the current start vibrations of the air at the receiving end of the telephone line?

IV. Think out the answers to these questions:

1. In what way are the telephone and telegraph alike in principle? Does the electric bell use the same principle?

2. Many telephone lines have only one wire. You learned that the electric current must make a circuit to do its work. How do the one-wire telephones work?

3. Work out a plan by which either of two buttons may ring the same electric bell. Then demonstrate it.

V. Vocabulary. What did you find new?

transmitter   vibrating   disc

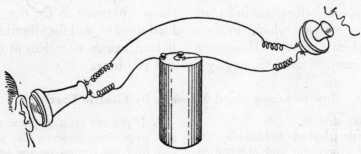

A homemade telephone

Chapter Forty-seven

The Current at Heavy Work

Generating electricity for city and country. You found that electricity produced magnetism. Magnetism also produces electricity. If you send a current into a wire coil around a core of iron, magnetism is produced in the iron. If you spin a coil of wire between the poles of a magnet, a current flows through the wire. You must rotate the magnet so that it cuts across the lines of magnetic force.

This is the principle of the *dynamo* or generator that produces the current that lights our cities and turns our machinery, and of the generator that produces the current in the automobile. The figure shows another detail of the dynamo. The current generated in the coil is led away by two pieces of carbon called *brushes* which touch the rings to which the coil wire is connected.

The current flows first in one direction and then in the opposite direction. A 60-cycle dynamo reverses its direction 60 times a second. This produces an *alternating current* (a.c.). This is the current generally used in lighting houses and running machinery. It will not do for some work, however. It will not charge a storage battery for an automobile. It will not do for electroplating or electrotyping. In these operations *direct current* (d.c.) is

needed. Alternating current is changed to direct current by an attachment called a *commutator*.

The great dynamos are built on the same principle as the simple apparatus in the diagrams below. Instead of a simple magnet several large electromagnets are used. They are called the *field magnets*. Several coils made up of many turns of wire form the moving part or *armature*, turned by steam or water power.

What makes the trolley car go. When the armature of a dynamo is turned, current flows out of the wires. Suppose now the armature is not turning, and a current from another source is sent through the wire. Immediately the armature begins to turn. That is what happens in an electric motor. We send

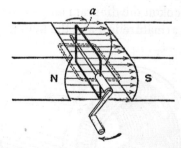

A simple dynamo. *a* is the armature.

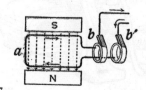

bb are the brushes of this simple dynamo

Philip D. Gendreau, N. Y.

Assembling an electric motor. It is simply a dynamo in reverse. This motor, in principle, consists merely of the simple machine shown in the drawings below

in a current and the armature turns. In the dynamo we turn the armature and get current. In the *motor* we send in a current and get motion of the armature. A motor is just a dynamo with the forces working the other way around.

Look at the diagram on page 339. The armature is *a* and the field magnet is *b*. A current is sent into the armature. The iron core becomes an electromagnet. Look at position A. The south pole of the armature (electromagnet) and the north pole of the field magnet attract each other. By the time the two poles come together, a device reverses the current in the armature or electromagnet

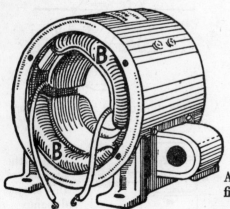

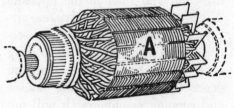

A dynamo taken apart. *BB* are the field coils. *A* is the armature

338

The trolley (1) is run by electric motors. Current is fed from powerhouses where dynamos are located. In this case it is picked up from a third rail, visible between the other two. The Diesel-electric locomotive (2) generates its own current from an engine burning Diesel oil

and the south pole of the armature becomes a north pole. The two north poles repel each other as in position B. Therefore, the armature keeps on turning. This is the principle of the electric motor wherever you find it used, in the automobile, in the electric refrigerator, in the vacuum sweeper, electric fan.

General Electric Co.

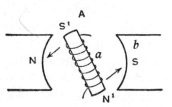

Principle of the motor

Ewing Galloway, N. Y.

A bolt of lightning may contain millions of volts

To run a trolley-car line both dynamos and electric motors are needed. The dynamos are located in the power house. The dynamos for the cities of Buffalo, Rochester, and Syracuse are at Niagara Falls, 160 miles from Syracuse. The motors that turn the wheels of the cars are in the cars.

How electricity is measured. You have heard of *volts*, and you know that they have something to do with electricity. In a hazy sort of way you probably know that a volt is a measure of electricity. Perhaps you have heard of *amperes* and *kilowatts*, and you know that they also measure electricity. Now let us see what these words mean.

One stream of water may flow with more force than another stream.

So it is with electric currents. One current has more force than another. The force is measured in *volts*. A dry cell may give a current of 1.5 volts. If you touch the two binding posts of the cell, you will hardly feel the current. It cannot force its way through your fingers. The battery of an automobile may have a force of six volts. That can force its way through your fingers and give you a tingling kick in the knuckles. The house current has generally a force of 110 volts. People have been killed with a house current. Do not touch an electrical appliance when you are standing in the bathtub. The water increases the conductivity, and the current of 110 volts may easily cause death. The Southern California Edison Company's power plant high in the Sierras sends a current of 220,000 volts 240 miles across the desert. A flash of lightning may have several million volts.

Currents of water do not flow at the same rate; nor do currents of electricity. The rate of flow is measured in *amperes*. Watch the ammeter (ampere-measurer) on the dashboard of your automobile to see how the flow of current varies as you speed and slow, and as you turn on the lights. The resistance to the current is measured in *ohms*. Iron has more resistance than copper as you can easily demonstrate (Experiment No. 96). Nichrome has so much resistance that it gets hot and glows in the toaster. The

340

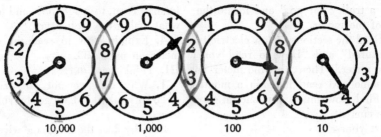

The dials of an electric meter

fine wire of tungsten in the electric bulb has so much resistance that it gives out enough light for a person to read by.

If you increase the resistance, a smaller current flows. If you increase the force (electromotive force), a larger current flows. You can calculate the flow (amperes) from the force (volts) and resistance (ohms). Flow (amperes) equals force (volts) divided by resistance (ohms), $C = \dfrac{V}{O}$. This statement was discovered by the German scientist George Simon Ohm, for whom the ohm is named. The statement is called *Ohm's Law*. The other two units of electricity are also named for scientists, the volt for the Italian scientist, Alessandro Volta, and the ampere for the French scientist, André Marie Ampére.

The measure of electrical power is the watt or kilowatt (1000 watts).

If you use a kilowatt for one hour, the company charges you for a kilowatt hour.

How to read your electric meter. The electric meter contains a small motor through which a portion of the current passes. The motor turns the dials that you see on the front of the meter, as in the picture below. In reading, simply write down the reading of each dial in order. Thus (look at the dials in the figure) starting at the left, 3174 kilowatt hours. Read your meter today and again a month from now. The difference in readings shows the consumption in kilowatt hours. Find on your last electric bill the rate the company charges. If it is ten cents a kilowatt hour, your bill is easily calculated.

How to Learn about the Current at Heavy Work

I. Study electric currents by experiment and reading.

1. Experiment No. 100. Arrange a coil of wire, a horseshoe magnet, and a compass as shown on page 334. Rotate the coil while the long wire is held above the compass. Is the compass deflected? What does that indicate? Read the section on "Generating electricity."

2. Read the section on dynamos on page 329.

3. Experiment No. 101. Get a model or toy motor or one from a household electric appliance. Connect the toy motor with dry cells. Connect the heavier motor through a switch to the house current. When you close the switch, what happens? Read the section, "What makes a trolley car go," and locate the parts of the motor.

4. Read the sections, "How electricity is measured" and "How to read your electric meter." Then read the meter in your home and read it again a month later. Find how much you should pay for the current.

II. Test yourself:

1. How can you generate electricity from a magnet? What use is made of this?

2. Look at the picture below and explain the dynamo.

3. To run a trolley car, vacuum sweeper, fan, or electric refrigerator, what two electric machines must be in the system? Where does the power come from? Turn to page 331 and explain what makes the motor turn.

4. Explain how to read the electric meter on page 333.

III. Think these out:

1. Why can we not put frictional electricity (the kind we get by rubbing) to work?

2. Why does the nichrome wire in the electric toaster glow, but the wires leading to it do not get warm?

3. How many watts are marked on the electric bulbs you use? How many on the toaster and other appliances?

IV. Vocabulary. Suggestions:

alternating	ampere
dynamo	ohm
volt	kilowatt

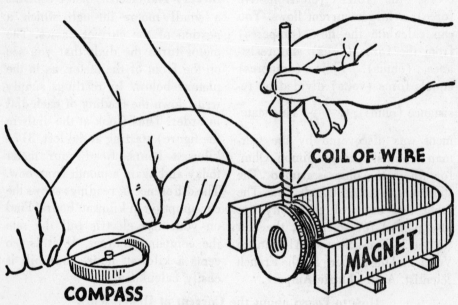

COIL OF WIRE

MAGNET

COMPASS

Apparatus for Experiment No. 100

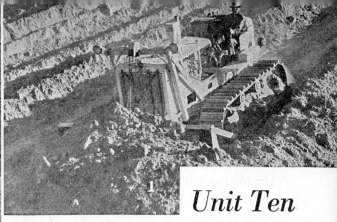

Unit Ten

Making Work Easier

Without means of reducing labor we would live like animals, and the world would support fewer people. Man learned to reduce his labor perhaps about as soon as he learned to labor. When he swung a club on the head of a bear, he had learned to work more effectively and more easily than if he attacked the bear with his hands. He could hardly kill a bear or mammoth with his bare hands, yet we know that early man killed many such animals, for we find the bones that he split open. When the Egyptians built the pyramids, they used inclined planes and rollers to move the great stones. They thus greatly reduced the labor of raising the great blocks of stone one above the other. Since these days of long ago we have continued to find ways of reducing labor and in consequence have performed feats of labor that the ancients could never have performed. We are still finding ways of reducing labor about the shop and about the house. As a result working men now demand six hours of work a day when fifty years ago twelve, fourteen, and more hours a day were common. In this chapter we shall see some of the basic ideas behind the machines that make work easy so that we can do more work with less effort and so find time for other things than drudgery to keep alive.

(1) (5) *Philip D. Gendreau,* (2) (3) (4) *Ewing Galloway*

Chapter Forty-eight

How Matter Is Peculiar

On taking up space. If another fellow got into the line at the ticket window or the lunch counter ahead of you, you would either need to push him out or wait until he moved out. You could not both occupy the same spot. If you had a glass brimful of lemonade and dropped in a big piece of ice, some of the lemonade would flow out of the glass on to the tablecloth. This is a peculiarity of things—they take up space. Two things cannot take up the same space, as you have found if you and your friend when skating ever tried to put your heads in the same place at the same time. An object, matter, or stuff takes up space.

On having weight. You are very well aware of another quality of matter. It weighs something. That is what made both heads hurt when you and your friend tried to make them occupy the same space at the same time. If you had tried to put your head into the space occupied by the same quantity of air, it would not have hurt. Your head would have pushed the air aside be-

Two objects cannot occupy the same space at the same time. The drivers of these automobiles found out this fact when they collided

Courtesy Philadelphia Police

cause your head weighs somewhat more than an equal volume of air. But the air weighs something. Try picking up an empty automobile tire and one that is pumped hard with air. You will find that air has considerable weight. You know that water has weight if you have carried a bucketful. So all things have weight. All matter has weight and occupies space.

What is weight? Weight is something that makes the piano unpleasant to bump your head into. It is something that makes a bucket of water unpleasant to carry up four flights of stairs, or a hundred yards from a well. Weight makes things hard to pick up.

If you hold up a block of wood and let go of it, it goes down. Why does it not go up? It will go up if you hold it under water and let go of it. It floats, but why? Will a piece of granite float? Yes, if you let go of it in a basin of mercury. Why does the rock float?

Whether a thing falls or rises when you let go of it depends upon where you let go of it. You find that water weighs more than wood, quart for quart. You find that mercury weighs more than rock, quart for quart. You find that water weighs more than oil, quart for quart. Pour some olive oil in a tumbler and pour some water on top of it and find what happens. The heavier thing pushes the lighter thing up. The lighter thing goes up because the heavier thing goes down.

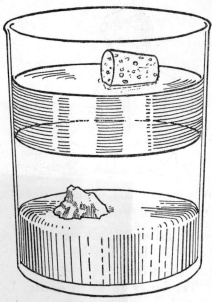

A stone will float on mercury, water will float on mercury, oil will float on water, and cork will float on oil

Wood weighs more than air, quart for quart. Therefore wood pushes air aside and falls.

Things go down because the earth pulls them down. The earth pulls some things harder than it pulls others. The weight of a body is due to the pull of the earth, or the attraction of gravity. The weight is a measure of the earth's attraction for that body.

The earth pulls the mercury more strongly than it pulls the granite. Therefore, the granite is pushed up by the mercury. The attraction of the earth for water is greater than its attraction for wood; therefore, the water pushes up the wood. The attraction of gravity for water is greater than for air; therefore, when you pour water from a tumbler, the

Why does the coin not move when the card is snapped?

water falls. We say an object is heavy if the attraction of gravity for it is great.

Tendency to keep going. Let us review an idea we developed in studying the revolution of the planets, for the same laws of science govern planets and baseballs. Did you ever slide forward when dad jammed on the brakes to avoid hitting another car? Or did you nearly tumble over when the trolley stopped suddenly or swung around a curve? Do you know why it is hard to start a barrel rolling or why it is necessary to start the

What makes the coal leave the shovel?

car in low gear? Do you know why it hurts when the sidewalk stops your head? Do you know why the speeding car smashes up when it hits the pole? All for the same reason. It is another of those peculiarities or characteristics of matter.

You can snap a card from under a coin without moving the coin. A trickster can jerk a tablecloth from under a pile of dishes without a smash, but you had better use the card with the coin.

A barrel cannot move itself, and if you start it rolling, it cannot stop itself. So it is with a car. It sounds sensible enough to say that if you place an object somewhere it will stay there provided nothing moves it. It may not sound so sensible to say that if you start a thing moving, it will keep on moving if nothing stops it. Yet if you stop a baseball with your head, it hurts because the ball tends to keep on moving. The reason that a driver must step hard on the brakes of the speeding car, is because the car tends to keep on moving. If the brakes do not hold and stop it, the car hits a pole. It is smashed because the car tends to keep on moving. The passenger on the front seat is thrown through the windshield because he tends to keep on moving when the windshield stops.

We have a name for this tendency. We call it *inertia*. We say that a body at rest stays at rest and a body in motion stays in motion in the same direction because of inertia, unless changed by outside force.

Inertia helps your big brother—or your mother—to shake the dirt out of a rug. The rug is jerked back while the dirt keeps going. Inertia helps send the coal out of the shovel into the furnace. When you tie a stone to a string and whirl it around your head (out-of-doors), inertia keeps the stone going around and the string pulled out straight. Inertia sends the mud flying off a spinning wheel and water off the turning grindstone. [This particular exhibition of inertia is called *centrifugal force*, meaning "the force that flies from the center."]

The pendulum. Now for another experiment. A great scientist performed this experiment and discovered laws of science. It is so simple that few people would study it. Get a yard of string, a stone or weight of two or three ounces, and a support to hang the weight from. Peg it up as shown at right. Draw the weight aside and let it go. There is a pendulum. You raised the weight and gravity pulled it down. Inertia carries it past its lowest point. Gravity stops it and pulls it back. Inertia keeps the pendulum swinging.

It is not very exciting to most people to watch a pendulum, but three hundred years ago, the great Italian scientist Galileo (1564–1642), then eighteen years old, watched the chandelier swinging gently, as a pendulum, in the cathedral at Pisa. He timed its swings by

Try this experiment with a phonograph and bits of paper to demonstrate centrifugal force

counting his pulse, for watches were few and chiefly curiosities in those days. He found that its swings took equal time. That suggested using a pendulum for keeping time. In later experiments with pendulums he worked out the laws of their swinging. He found that the time it takes a pendulum to swing does not depend upon the weight of the pendulum, nor upon the distance it swings (unless that distance is very great), but it does depend upon the length of the pendulum. The longer the pendulum, the slower it swings. With his laws Galileo could calculate how long to make a pendulum

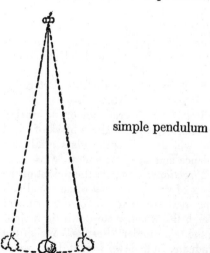

simple pendulum

so that it would swing in one second. [Note that not Galileo but Huygens later applied the pendulum to the clock.]

Properties of matter. We have learned three peculiar qualities or, as the scientist says, properties, of matter. (1) Matter occupies space; (2) it can be weighed; (3) it has inertia. These properties have a great deal to do with how matter behaves, and when we do work with matter, they may make the work hard. We shall see next how to handle these properties to make work easier.

What matter is. Now having learned some things that matter does and what it is like, we are ready to say what matter is. Matter is anything that occupies space and has weight. Anything that meets those two qualifications is matter and anything that does not meet them is not matter. Can electricity be weighed and does it take up space? No. Therefore, it is not matter. Does air take up space and does it have weight? Yes. Therefore, it is matter. If you wish a common word to use in place of matter, you might say *stuff, material,* or *substance.*

To Learn How Matter Is Peculiar

I. Study matter by experiment and observation.

1. EXPERIMENT No. 102. Fill a glass brimful of water. Gently lower a stone into it. What happens? Why?

2. Does the air weigh anything? Can you prove it?

3. Which weighs more, water or oil? Prove it by EXPERIMENT No. 103. Plan the experiment and carry it out.

4. What then would happen if you poured water on the top of oil? Prove your answer by experiment. Plan your experiment carefully and call it EXPERIMENT No. 104.

5. Why does wood float? Determine by EXPERIMENT No. 105.

Materials: A graduate or measuring glass, preferably metric; a block of wood that will drop into the glass graduate; balance and weights; water.

Directions: Compare the weight of the block of wood with that of an equal volume of water in the following manner: Weigh the wood. Note down the weight in the table under "Results." Weigh the graduate. Note down weight. Pour water

into graduate until it comes to a mark about halfway up the glass. Note down the volume. Drop the block of wood into the graduate of water. Push it under the water with a wire. Then read the volume again. Note it down. The increase of volume is the volume of wood. Note down the volume of the wood. Now determine the weight of the volume of water. Dump out the water and wood. Pour in a volume of water equal to the volume of wood. Weigh. You can now find the weight of water of the same volume as the wood. Which is heavier, wood or water?

Results:

Weight of wood	_____
Weight of graduate	_____
Volume of water	_____
Volume of water after submersion of wood	_____
Volume of wood	_____
Weight of water of same volume as wood	_____

Conclusion: Why does wood float?

6. Does wood have weight? Does water? Does air?

7. EXPERIMENT No. 106. Place a small card projecting over the edge of the table. Lay a coin on top of the card. With your finger snap the card. Does the card sail away? Does the coin? Why or why not?

8. EXPERIMENT No. 107. Set up a pendulum as in the figure on page 339. What determines how fast a pendulum swings? Make a guess. Then try out your guess by experiment. Think out the experiment; try it; then write a report in the usual form.

II. Read the chapter.

III. Test yourself:

1. Does air take up space? How can you show by experiment that your answer is correct?

2. Does air weigh anything? Prove it by experiment.

3. Why does one thing weigh more than another? Why is it heavier?

4. Why do things fall when you let them go? Could you let go of any object where it would not fall? Tell about it. Why does it then not fall? What is weight?

5. Why are you thrown forward when the brakes are applied on a moving car? You learned in an early chapter of some things that keep on moving, age after age, because nothing stops them. What

are they? What do we call that tendency to keep on going?

6. Mention several ways in which that tendency is useful to us in everyday life.

7. Mention some ways in which that tendency is a disadvantage.

8. What is a pendulum? How does the pendulum show gravity? inertia? On what does the time it takes a pendulum to swing depend?

9. Mention three "properties of matter."

IV. Think these out:

1. Can you mention "anything" that does not weigh anything? This is a hard question, but think a while.

2. Do you know anything that does not fall in air? The reasons.

3. What makes things go? If things tend to stay still when they are still, what makes things go in the world? That is another hard and interesting question. Try it.

4. Which of the "properties of matter" that you have just learned make work hard? Which help to make work easy? Do not be surprised if you get contradictory answers.

V. Vocabulary. Ask your teacher whether you should learn those terms enclosed in brackets [ ] or parentheses ( ) in the text.

matter   weight   inertia   properties

Chapter Forty-nine

Why Work Is Hard

What is work? You have some idea, but you probably cannot tell exactly what work is. Science could never have developed the automobile, the airplane, the telephone, and the radio unless scientists could tell exactly what they meant. Among the ideas that scientists have had to define is the idea of work.

Now let us get the idea. Put a pint of water in a vessel and raise it exactly one foot. Now raise the pint of water two feet. You did twice as much work in the second case as in the first case. Now put two pints of water in the same vessel and raise it two feet. You did twice as much work in the third case as in the second. Place the vessel of water on the table. No work is done while the vessel rests on the table.

Now let us try again. If you lift the table, you do work. If the table is screwed to the floor, and you try to lift it, do you do work? Get a good hold and lift hard. Do you do work? No, says the scientist, not if you exert yourself until the perspiration comes through the back of your shirt. You do not work until the thing is moved. If you move a

Inertia makes it hard work to push a stalled automobile. Once these men start the car rolling, will their work be easier?

matchstick, you do work. If you do not move the table, you do no work. It matters not how much you try to do work. You must move something or you do not work. Work is done when a force moves a body through a distance.

Why work is hard. It makes a big difference to you whether you move a pint of water or a five-gallon can of water. Weight is one thing that makes work hard. Again, if a five-gallon can of water is standing on the sidewalk and you push it out of the way, it takes some effort. If the five-gallon can of water is standing in a small wagon, it takes much less effort to move it. If a heavily loaded wagon is standing on the sidewalk, it may take considerable effort to start it moving, but once under way, it may take less effort to keep it going. Perhaps you have helped to push a stalled automobile. It takes considerable push to get it started, but it moves along with much less effort after you get it rolling.

You know all these things, but let us try to see why they are so. Why is it harder to slide the five-gallon can of water along than to push it in a wagon? Why is it harder to pick up a five-gallon can of water than a pint of water?

You know that the earth is pulling the five gallons of water with considerably more force than it is pulling the pint of water. You must overcome the weight, or attraction, **of gravity** to do the work. An ob-

This fellow is working hard. **How might he make his work easier?**

ject at rest tends to stay at rest. Therefore, it is hard to move the standing automobile. An object in motion tends to keep going. Therefore, it is easier to keep the car moving, but harder to stop it. You must overcome inertia to do work.

Now why is it easier to move the wagon with the five-gallon can of

What slows you down when you slide for base?

water than to slide the five gallons of water? If you set the brakes on the wagon, it would be harder to pull. If the axles and hub bearings were rusty, it would be harder to move than if they were polished and oiled. The difficulty is due to rubbing, or *friction*. The wheels and the oil reduce friction.

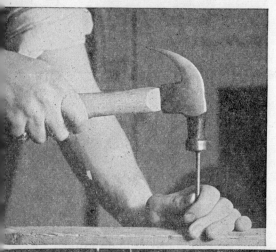

So we may conclude that work is hard because matter weighs something, because it has inertia, and because of friction.

What causes friction. If you rub together two planed boards and then two rough-sawn boards, you find that the planed boards slide over each other very easily but the rough boards offer much resistance. That resistance is friction. The friction is produced by irregularities on the surface of the boards. Even the planed boards have fine irregularities, but you will need to study the surface with a lens or magnifier to see the finer roughness. Polished iron is so smooth that the naked eye does not see the irregularities, and two such pieces of iron slide over each other easily. If the iron is

What keeps a nail from pulling out and the rope on the tug from slipping?

Philip D. Gendreau   *Ewing Galloway*

This woman fell on an icy street because of lack of friction. Can you name other circumstances where friction would prove helpful?

rough-cast, the two pieces slide with more difficulty. Even the polished iron offers some resistance due to friction, but the surface needs to be magnified to show the roughness to the eye. Rusty iron is covered with rough particles, and rusty bearings make hard pulling on the wagon or roller skates. If the rust is polished away and then the bearings flooded with oil, friction is much reduced. The oil fills the minute depressions, and the two pieces slide or float over each other.

Why friction is bad. Friction makes work harder when you drag something along. Friction also develops heat. Perhaps you have seen a person driving a car with the brake on and smoke coming from the rear where the brake bands have been set afire. If you have had

the experience of sliding down a rope, letting the rope run through your hands, you know that you may have the skin burned off your hands and rubbed away in a short distance. Friction also wears out your shoe leather as it wears out the brakes of a car, and it is remarkable how fast it wears out the seat of a small boy's pants when he has found a long board to slide down.

When we want friction. Sometimes you want friction. You would have a sorry time walking down the street if there were no friction between your soles and the sidewalk. At times nature reduces the friction by spreading a coating of ice over the sidewalks and streets. Then people, automobiles, and horses have little control over their actions. The highway department

353

spreads cinders on the road to increase the friction. The motorman on the trolley car turns sand on the track to increase the friction. The automobile could not run without the friction of the tires with the street. The brakes would not stop the car without friction. We need friction in our machinery, but we must have it under control. We need friction in many other places. Nails, for example, would be useless if it were not for the friction of the nails with the wood. Knots in string, clamps, scouring powders, all owe their usefulness to friction.

To Learn Why Work Is Hard

I. Study friction by experiment, reading, and thought.

1. Read the section, "What is work?" Perform the experiments described. Experiment No. 108. Write the report.

2. Experiment No. 109. What makes it hard to pull a load?

Drive a tack in near the end of a board; attach a short string to it, and the string to a spring balance. (1) Draw the board along the table by pulling the spring balance. A force of how many pounds is required to pull the board along the table? _____ (2) Put a weight on the board, and again pull. Result: A force of how many pounds is required to pull the board? _____ (3) Put three pencils under the board with the weight and pull. Result: A force of how many pounds is required to pull the board? _____

3. Read the section, "Why work is hard."

4. Did you ever slide on the ice? Did you ever try to walk on the ice? Why was it easy to slide and hard to walk on the ice?

Read the section, "When we want friction."

II. Test yourself:

1. How can you show what the scientist means by *work?*

2. Which is doing more work, an ant carrying a crumb of bread or a horse pulling at a wagon that will not move?

3. Why is work hard? Use illustrations to make clear what you mean, or demonstrate by experiment.

4. When do we want to increase friction? When do we want to reduce friction?

III. Think these out:

1. Does the foundation of a building do any work? Does a boy idly drumming on the desk?

2. Besides weight, inertia, and friction, is there anything else that makes work hard?

3. You found that friction is sometimes a good thing. Are weight and inertia ever valuable?

IV. Vocabulary. Watch scientific meanings:

work　　　　　　　　　friction

Apparatus for Experiment No. 109

Chapter Fifty

Making Machines Do the Work

Making things slide more easily. Try pushing a heavy box along the floor and then put a small handful of marbles under it and try it again. Try placing some pencils under it. The marbles are ball bearings acting like the steel ball bearings in the wheels of an automobile. The pencils act like the roller bearings used in heavy machinery. A rolling object has less friction than a sliding object. Perhaps you have tried ball-bearing roller skates and compared them to the old-style rollers in which the inside of the roller is the bearing. Wheels, roller bearings, ball bearings, and oil are means of reducing friction and so make work easier.

How to put a rug under the piano. Do not try to lift the piano. Women have hurt themselves that way and so have men. Get a rod or bar or narrow board, say six feet long. Put one end under the piano and a block under the bar. Then just put a little of your weight on the long end of the bar and up goes the piano.

The bar is a *lever* and the block is the *fulcrum.* Call the distance along the bar, from the fulcrum to the piano, the *load arm* or *resistance arm.* Call the distance from the fulcrum to the end you bear down on, the *power arm* or *effort arm.* If you want an easy job, make the resistance arm short and the effort arm long. Then you move the effort arm a long distance and move the

A lever to reduce labor

Each oar is a lever to increase speed

Philip D. Gendreau, N. Y.

How does a ball bearing reduce friction?

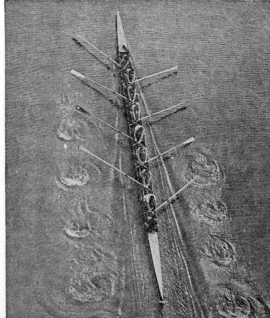

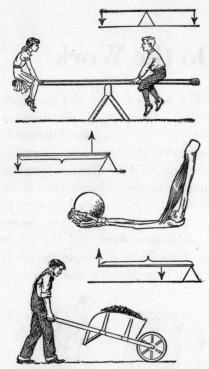

Kinds of levers. Read the text and then think out what is the fulcrum, the effort arm, and the resistance arm in each case

resistance arm a short distance. In the oar of a boat, the resistance arm is long and the effort arm short. The resistance arm moves a greater distance than the effort arm. Such an effort arm is harder to move than a long effort arm but gives increased speed. The lever enables you to do work easier or faster depending on the relative lengths of the effort arm and resistance arm. A lever is a simple machine, a device for doing work.

A law of the lever. When you perform Experiment No. 110, you discover a law of the lever. (Look at the picture in Experiment 110 on page 351.) The ruler is balanced on the pencil when the fulcrum is six inches from each end. If you place a two-ounce weight at one end and a one-ounce weight at the other, you must place the fulcrum four inches from the two-ounce weight to secure a balance. Try it. Then notice $2 \times 4 = 1 \times 8$. The effort multiplied by the length of the effort arm equals the resistance multiplied by the length of the resistance arm. Notice also, if you pull down the two-ounce weight till it touches the table, it moves one-fourth inch while the one-ounce weight moves one-half inch. $2 \times \frac{1}{4} = 1 \times \frac{1}{2}$. The effort multiplied by the distance it moves equals the resistance multiplied by the distance it moves.

How to put a barrel on a truck. The long way up a hill is the easier way. Long stairs are easier to go up than short steep stairs rising to the same height. When a truckman wants to put a barrel on the truck, he rolls it up an inclined plane. He rolls the barrel a longer

How does the incline plane help?

distance if the plane is long, but it is easier to roll it. He does the same amount of work when he puts the barrel on the truck whether the inclined plane is long or short. It is easier to move the load over the longer distance. The less the angle of the inclined plane, the longer the distance and the less the effort required. If you had to put a 400-pound barrel into a truck four feet high, you would do it over an inclined plane ten feet long by using an effort of 160 pounds. As in the law of the lever, resistance times distance equals effort times distance. $400 \times 4 = 160 \times 10$.

The inclined plane is another simple machine which enables us to work more easily. A wedge is an inclined plane used in a slightly different way to make work easier. Perhaps you have seen a wedge used to split a log or to raise a post.

If an inclined plane is wrapped around a post, it becomes a screw. The closer together are the grooves in a screw, the more gentle is the inclined plane, and the easier it is to turn. Screw jacks are used to lift weights, such as automobiles, or to exert pressure, as in a vise.

Pulleys. When you hoist a sail on a yacht, you use pulleys. The hayfork that fills the haymow is raised by a pulley. The pulley is another simple machine to make work easier. It is easier to pull down on the rope than to lift the weight directly upward in Figure A. If you use two pulleys as in Figure B, you can raise a hundred-pound weight with a fifty-pound pull, but you will need to pull two feet of rope for every foot you raise the weight. As

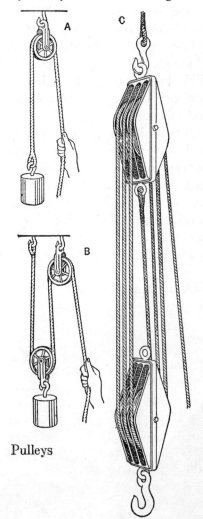

Pulleys

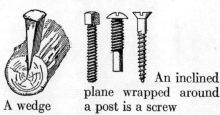

A wedge   An inclined plane wrapped around a post is a screw

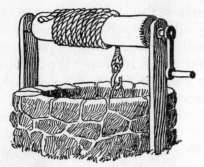

A windlass

in the lever, effort multiplied by the distance it moves equals the resistance multiplied by the distance it moves. $50 \times 2 = 100 \times 1$. With this law of the lever in mind, you can easily calculate distance and effort.

If you increase the number of pulleys, you can lift heavier weights, but you will need to pull more rope. In Figure C you will need to pull six feet of rope through the pulleys to raise the weight one foot, but you can raise 600 pounds by a 100-pound pull. $100 \times 6 = 600 \times 1$.

The wheel and axle. The steering wheel of an automobile enables you to turn the front wheels with ease. If you have looked into the pilot house of a steamboat, you have noticed that the steering wheel is very large. The larger the wheel, the easier it is to steer. The ship's capstan raises a heavy anchor with ease because of the long bars which the sailors use to turn it. Effort, load, and distances follow the same law as in the lever. Look at the picture of a windlass. When its handle makes one turn, it moves through a circle six feet around and the bucket rises one foot up the well. An effort of ten pounds raises a bucket of water weighing sixty pounds.

Complex machines. The things for making work easier that you have just studied—lever, inclined plane, pulley, wheel, and axle—are simple machines. The machinery of an automobile or airplane or other complicated machinery is only a

Look at these pictures carefully and see whether you can tell what simple

Philip D. Gendreau, N. Y.　　　　　　　　*Ewing Galloway, N. Y.*

series of simple machines. Their complexity is due to the great number and combinations of simple machines. Look at the sewing machine, the typewriter, or the parts of an automobile and figure out the simple machines which you have just studied. Machines may be used to multiply force and so make work easier, increase speed, change the direction in which a force is applied, or make work more accurate.

How to Learn about Making Machines Do Work

I. Investigate simple machines.

1. Refer back to Experiment No. 109 in the last chapter. What made the work easier? Instead of pencils try a few marbles, ball bearings, or lead shot. The pencils represent what kind of bearings? The balls represent what kind of bearings? Plan an experiment that will show another way of making sliding easier.

weight; a triangular block about one-half inch high.

Directions and results: (1) Tie a string around the four-ounce weight, and attach the spring balance. Raise the weight. Result: How many ounces of effort did it require? (How much does the spring balance show it took to lift the load?) (2) Balance the ruler on

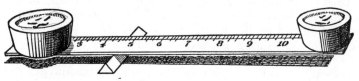

Apparatus for Experiment No. 110

2. EXPERIMENT No. 110.

Question: How can you reduce the labor of raising an object?

Materials: A four-ounce weight; a spring balance; a ruler; a two-ounce

the sharp edge of the block. Call the ruler the lever and the block the fulcrum. Place the four-ounce weight on one end of the ruler and the two-ounce weight on the other. Push the ruler

machines and what combinations of simple machines are shown in each

along until the two-ounce weight raises the four-ounce weight. How many ounces of effort raised the four-ounce load when using the lever?

Conclusion: Tell one way in which a load may be raised more easily than by lifting it directly?

3. Read the sections, "How to put a rug under the piano" and "A law of the lever."

4. Experiment No. 111. Learn, by experiment, an easy way to put a barrel on a truck. Get a toy car, a board two or three feet long, a pile of books, and a spring balance. Put a string around the toy car and lift it with the spring balance. What is the reading of the spring balance? Then lay the board slanting from the table to the top of the pile of books forming an inclined plane. Draw the car on its wheels up the inclined plane, pulling on the spring balance. What is the reading of the balance?

Conclusion: Which is the easier way to raise the weight, to lift it straight up or to draw it a longer distance up the inclined plane?

5. Read the section, "How to put a barrel on a truck."

6. Experiment No. 112. How to make work easier with pulleys. Get a single and two double pulleys, a spring balance, a pound weight, and a cord. Lift the pound with the spring balance. How much effort does the scale show? Rig up a pulley as in A, page 349. How much effort? Rig the pulley as in B. How much effort? Rig two double pulleys. How much effort?

Conclusion: Which is the easier way of A over a straight lift? of B? of two double pulleys?

7. Read the rest of the chapter.

II. Test yourself:

1. What is an easier way to get a heavy box across the floor than sliding it across? Why is it easier?

2. Tell three ways that are easier than lifting a heavy object straight up.

3. How can you arrange a lever to enable you to do work more easily? How can you arrange it to enable you to do work more quickly?

4. What is the law of the lever that you have learned?

5. Do you do less work in raising an object with a lever than in lifting it straight up?

6. Why is it easier to roll a barrel up an inclined plane than to lift it straight up?

7. What do you gain by using one pulley? What do you gain by using two?

8. Here is a trick question. Suppose there was a windlass over a well thirty feet deep. The handle of the windlass moved through six feet while the bucket rose one foot. How much less work would you do in raising a twenty-five-pound bucket of water by windlass than by raising it directly, hand over hand?

III. Think these out:

1. What kind of simple machine is a doorknob? a fish pole? a claw hammer? a nail?

2. What kind of simple machine is used to open a wooden packing case when it arrives at the store? to hoe the garden? to sweep the floor? to raise the window? to fasten the window?

3. What kind of simple machine is most common around the house?

4. Is it easier to move heavy things with a long lever or with a short lever?

5. Do you get more energy out of a machine than you put in?

6. Can you find a lever in your body? Are there any other simple machines in your body?

IV. Vocabulary.

lever	inclined
effort	pulley
fulcrum	plane
resistance	windlass

Unit Eleven

The Changing Earth

You have read of the Roman towns of Pompeii and Herculaneum destroyed by Mount Vesuvius, or more recently of the island of Martinique destroyed by Mount Pelee. You have heard of earthquakes and tidal waves that have destroyed lives, cities, and country. You have read of hurricanes that have torn up trees and washed away dwellings and even land.

Kill Devil Hill on the coast of North Carolina, from which the Wright brothers flew their airplane in the flight that began the aircraft industry, has moved almost a quarter of a mile since the memorable day when the first successful flight was made. This coast is loose sand, and the winds constantly move it about, overwhelming woods, villages, and farms. Cape Hatteras lighthouse farther south, once well back from the water, is now in danger of being undermined by the sea. Currents constantly shift the sands and change the beach. Inland, small lakes and ponds have filled up in recent years. Gullies eat into hillsides. Rain water and creeks carry soil and rocks down the valleys. Stream beds are filling with mud and gravel. Dredges constantly dig debris out of harbors and river channels. Rain and frost gnaw away the land. The earth changes.

(1) (4) *Ewing Galloway*, (2) (5) *Black Star*,
(3) *Philip D. Gendreau*, (6) *S.C.S.*

6

Chapter Fifty-one

How Hills Wear Out

What is mud? After a rain you have seen the muddy water running in a river or brook or you have seen it lying in puddles. After a flood along a creek or river you perhaps have seen mud in a great sheet covering the meadow. People who have gone through the experience of being flooded out of their homes have found the floors covered with a layer of mud when they returned. Along the flat river valleys, or bottoms—or *flood plains*, as the scientists say—the bottom of the valley is built up level with mud of one flood after another. The rich lands along the Mississippi are such mud-built flood plains. On the smaller rivers of the Mississippi system similar flat fields of mud have produced great yields of corn since the days of the early settlers. On many of these "bottoms" the farmers use no fertilizer and grow corn year after year on the same land. Every year or two, the river overflows its banks and spreads a new layer of fertile mud over the field at the end of winter. The yearly overflow of the Nile kept Egypt's fields fertile through the centuries. Where does the river get its mud?

If you rub some of the mud between your fingers, it is soft and slippery. If you take just a little bit of mud, it may seem just a trifle

How may the productivity of the farmland along this river be improved when the flood waters recede?

gritty. If you examine the coarser mud with a lens, you may find something that looks like tiny particles of rocks. If it is very fine mud, you will need a microscope to see the particles. Some of these bits of mud particles are like miniature rocks with their corners knocked off. Some particles are clear and glassy. Some are dark and shining. Some are just dull. If you examine mud from many places, you may be surprised at the great variety of particles that make up mud. And you find that there are a good many varieties of mud. Mud is not just mud, but there are kinds of mud. The kind of mud depends upon where the mud came from originally and what has happened to it.

Where mud comes from. Now let us call to mind certain facts that we have seen with our own eyes

about mud. After a rain we have seen muddy water running down a terraced lawn where the children have been running up and down and worn off the grass. The little stream of fallen rain water that comes tumbling down the dirt path is muddy. It runs out on the cement walk, leaving a coating of slippery mud. As the mud did not fall from the clouds with the rain, it must have come from the lawn where the grass was worn away. Again, along a concrete road at the foot of a sloping cornfield or a field that is freshly plowed, the rain carries out a small deluge of mud. Through a road cut it may carry out a big deluge of mud and rocks and spread it on the concrete road. Mud comes with rain from bare earth.

Now let us go into the field again and look around and ask some

Mud in rivers and streams comes from fields like this where rain has washed away the soil

S.C.S.

1

2

3

questions of nature. We will take a hike along a stream where we have found mud. If we .can get into a hilly country or at least a country where there are rocks, it will be more interesting in our study of where mud comes from. Let us look in the bottom of the brook bed. If it is a rocky region, we shall find, no doubt, some loose rocks there. If the brook goes tumbling along down a slope, we shall probably find at the bottom of the slope a more level place. There the brook water is in less hurry. If we go down into the bottom of the little brook valley and poke around in the water and at the water's edge, we may find some more about how the water handles mud and coarser stuff. At the foot of the rapids on the steep slope, we shall probably find loose stones. A little farther along we may find gravel, and still farther along where the water flows more slowly, sand and then mud.

Let us look at the current again as it comes down the slope. It is almost a waterfall on the steepest part. It is going fast at the foot of the slope. Then it slackens speed. Out on the level it moves along quite leisurely. The rocks, gravel stones, sand, and mud seem to be assorted according to the speed of the current. The loose rocks lie

What happens to stones, sand, and mud in each of these three streams? On the facing page are shown the effects of moving water on rock

(1) Ewing Galloway, (2) (3) Black Star

where the speed was first reduced at the foot of the slope. Then gravel comes promptly afterwards, and the sand a little farther along the level. Finally, where the water was moving along slowly, is the mud.

If you wade out in your bare feet, you may examine the deposit more closely, and learn a few more facts. As you wade among the loose rocks at the foot of the slope, they tumble easily and slide over one another. Watch your toes; they may have the skin rubbed off by the tumbling rocks. You can see on the rocks spots where they have rolled and slid and rubbed off the moss and slime that collects under water. As you turn downstream, the gravel stones tumble over your toes when you dislodge them.

Some questions and answers. Why did the rocks and big stones settle first in the brook? Apparently it was because of a slowing of the water. Why did the gravel settle next? It contains the next biggest stones. Why the sand following? Its particles are next in order of weight. Why did the mud settle last of all? It contains the finest and lightest particles.

Now some more questions. What happens to those rocks as they tumble down the slope when the brook is in flood? What happens to the

Potholes (1) (3) are caused by the whirlpool action of water using a smaller stone as grindstone. (2) Stones rubbed round against each other

U.S.D.A.

gravel stones as they tumble along? They rub and grind away their surface and the surface of the rock bed, just as they grind away the moss on their surface and the skin off your toes. A grindstone grinds away the blade of a knife the same way. Perhaps you have had the experience of sharpening your pocketknife on a grindstone and have been a little surprised, and perhaps a little more annoyed, to find that you had ground away a big part of your blade. So nature grinds away the rocks. Finer and ever finer they are ground until at last they float along after each rain as mud in the water.

The traveling hills. A hundred million brooks tumble down a hundred million hills. Each brook is tumbling rocks and gnawing away the rocks of its bed. Each rain brings into the brook mud and sand from the brook banks and from the fields along its course. Here and there a great downpour of a thunderstorm or the rapid flood when the snow melts under a warm spring rain brings in a torrent of mud and gravel from a bare field. Rain after rain, a hundred million rains fall upon the hills. A hundred million snows melt in the warm spring rains. What will they do to the hills?

Examine a cliff. You may find the rocks perfectly dry as far as you can see or you may find water oozing out of the joints. If you visit a cliff after a rain, the rocks are wet, and rain water is probably oozing out of the cracks. If you visit it in winter, you may find ice in the cracks and icicles hanging from the cracks. You might try an experiment with freezing if you have never performed it. Fill a bottle brimful of water and cork it tightly. Pack it in salt and ice or freeze it in the electric refrigerator.

How might you account for the broken stones at the bottom of this cliff?

Ewing Galloway, N. Y.

You will see the bottle burst, as water pipes and automobile radiators sometimes burst when the water freezes. When water turns to ice, it expands. When winter comes, water in the cracks of the rocks turns to ice and expands. Expanding, the water forces apart the pieces of rock. When the ice melts, the loosened pieces of rock come tumbling down. Bumping into projecting points of rock, more rocks are broken and tumble down.

You learned in your study of water that water is a good solvent. It dissolves many things. As water seeps through the rocks and through the soil, it finds many minerals that will dissolve. The great limestone caves have been dissolved out by the water seeping through until it often dissolves away a passage big enough to allow it to flow as a stream. Your earlier experiments in evaporating water showed that ordinary water contains dissolved materials. When water contains carbon dioxide from the plants growing in the soil, it forms a weak acid and dissolves away many minerals very easily. Limestone, for instance, dissolves readily in water containing carbon dioxide.

We may find some of the rocks covered with those crusty little plants called *lichens*. Some hardy lichens live attached to the surface of the rocks, like paint. Mosses may be growing in the crevices and perhaps some grass or even blackberry bushes or young trees. All these plants are breathing out carbon dioxide through their roots, and the carbon dioxide dissolves in the soil water to form an acid. The acid dissolves away minerals from the cliff.

Rain, frost, plants, animals on a million cliffs, and boys on some thousand cliffs, quarrymen and miners on others, are all digging

How do conditions such as this crumble away rocks, cliffs, and hills?

Philip D. Gendreau, N. Y.

away rock and tumbling them down. The boys, the quarrymen, and the miners have not been at the work more than a few thousand years, but animals and plants, rain and frost have been at it for millions of years. What is the end of it all? Millions of years of sun and rain and frost, of plants growing, and of animals tramping and digging will have some effect on the hills.

Let us look at some of the fragments of rock at the foot of the cliff. Do you remember the stones that we found in the brook bed? Take some of each kind back to school, some from the brook bed and some from the base of the cliff. Lay the small stones from the two places sides by side. Can you tell them apart? Very easily. As the water rolled the stones along downhill in the bottom of the stream, it ground off the edges until rounded pebbles were formed. Round pebbles mean that water has been tumbling the stones about. The stones from the bottom of the cliff are angular and sharp. When you come upon gravel and pebbles in your hikes through the country, you can tell something about the past history of the stones.

Land erosion. Hike through the bottom of a valley where a stream is tumbling along. What has the stream done to the valley and the hills? Hike up to the top of the hill and look over the country. Why are the valleys there? Why are the high hilltops about the same level?

You have seen the muddy rain water flowing down and digging gullies in the bare hillside. It is not hard to realize that the rain water dug the gully. You have seen the rocks and stones tumbled by the brook. Is it hard to realize that the brook has ground down the valley in which it flows? If you have seen a canyon or a gorge of a river, you may realize that the river ground out that gorge aided by the frost, the rain, and the plants and animals that attacked the cliffs at its sides. When you stand on a hilltop and look over the countryside picking out the valleys of rivers and creeks, you may realize that all those valleys were dug away by rain, frost, plants, and animals. The word meaning wearing away is *erosion*.

In the lands where the sand and dust blow over the bare rocks, there is also nature's sand blast eroding the rocks. Perhaps you have felt the sting of sand in the face and have seen your companion's face turn scarlet on the hike through the wind-blown sand and felt your own face burn like fire. In the dry country, wind-blown sand is an important agent in wearing away the rocky face. There is no vegetation to hold the sand to the earth. Every wind that blows does its bit at gradually grinding away the solid, exposed rocks.

It is not hard to realize that glaciers grind away the surface of the earth. Millions of tons of ice pushing forward over the ground force before the glacier the soil and loose rock. They cut down to the hard rock surface. Great pieces of rock buried in the bottom of the glacier dig out grooves in the rock surface. The scientist, and you also as a student of science, may recognize the glacial grooves when they are visible. If you live in a part of the country that was covered by the great glacier of the last Great Ice Age, you may find such smoothed and grooved rock surface. Valleys have been carved out which the observant scientist can distinguish by their shape from the water-cut valleys of rivers.

What is the end of all the erosion of soil and rock? It is slow, but it is certain. The mountaintops are tumbling gradually

Philip D. Gendreau, N. Y.

Wind carves stone, too. Fine grains of sand carried by wind have blasted this graceful arch

down. The hilltops are moving slowly down into the valleys. Down the valleys restless nature slowly

Can you see how the river has carved its way through the land in a deep canyon?

Ewing Galloway, N.Y.

U.S.D.A.

Glacier scratches on piece of stone

slow, certainly change. From a study of the rocks, scientists tell us that the low Appalachian Mountains are the remains of high land that once was there. The hills that stretch down the eastern country, east of the Appalachian Mountains, are the remains of the Older Appalachian Mountains, once as high as the modern Rocky Mountains, mountains in ages before the present Appalachians were born. Mountains must change. Nature wears them away and the country becomes lowland, and that great leveling of the high places of the earth is by common forces that we can study on our hikes through the country.

moves the ground-up rock and soil. The unnumbered rivulets and brooks, the creeks and rivers are moving the mountains and hills slowly but certainly away. The land surface is changing under the slow but ceaseless forces. Change, though

How to Study about How the Hills Wear Out

I. Read the chapter.

II. The best way to study the erosion of the land is to go out in the fields and along the streams and study it in the field. If you cannot go now, make the journey by photographs. Have clearly in mind what you want to see supported by evidence, and then search pictures for evidence. In books and magazines and newspapers you may find pictures that furnish evidence for the erosion process described in the chapter. Another way to make the picture journeys is to attempt to explain the cause of the hills, valleys, cliffs, meadows, and other features that you see in the pictures. Make sure that you find the evidence for any statement that you make in explaining the features.

1. Search for flood plains along brooks, creeks, and rivers. If you have a camera, take some pictures to show

the class your discovery. How can you tell that the flood features that you find are made of mud from the stream?

2. Search for mud plains at other places and try to account for them.

3. Examine some mud by allowing it to dry thoroughly and then spreading it on a piece of paper. Study it with a lens or with a microscope if you have one. Draw sketches of the particles as you see them magnified.

4. Search for the evidence that mud is carried out of a plowed field or bare slope by the fallen rain.

5. If you have not done so, perform the experiment of mixing gravel, sand, and mud in a fruit jar. Fill the jar almost full of water and shake up thoroughly. Then set it on the table and allow the water to stand until the water is clear. In what order did the particles settle in the jar? Why did they settle in that order?

6. Study the distribution of coarse stones, gravel, sand, and mud in a

370

brook. Account for the deposits that you find.

7. What evidence do you find that a stream wears away solid rock? What effect has this wearing process on the loose stones in the brook bottom?

8. Study a cliff as suggested. Is the rock jointed or without joints? Are the rocks all dry or wet? If you visit the cliff in winter, look for ice in the crevices. Look for lichens, mosses, and other small plants. What effect do they seem to have upon the cliff? Compare the rocks at the foot of the cliff with those in the bottom of the brook. How do you account for the shapes? If the cliff is topped with a layer of soil and plants, study the penetration of the roots. Could the roots of plants have any effect upon the rock?

9. Stand on a hilltop overlooking a valley. Can you account for the existence of the valley? How did it get there?

III. Test yourself:

1. Name some places where mud is found. How did it get there?

2. How does mud differ from sand and gravel? How is each made in nature?

3. What effect does a stream flowing downhill have upon its bed? What are the "tools" with which a stream does its work?

4. Are cliffs permanent features of the landscape? What forces of nature are constantly acting upon them?

5. What forces of nature make river gorges?

6. How does an old river valley differ in appearance from a young valley?

7. What effect have glaciers on the surface of a country?

8. What effect upon the highlands will result from the operations of all these forces? If there were no contrary forces of nature, what would be the end of all their work?

IV. Think these out:

1. What human activities are influenced by the processes described in this chapter?

2. Does man try to combat any of these processes? How?

3. Would you expect erosion of the hills to go on faster in dry land or in moist climate?

4. What factors of the climate along the Gulf States would tend to wear out the hills rapidly? What features in the northern Rockies?

V. Vocabulary. Did you find any new words?

These old Pennsylvanian hills, part of the eastern Appalachians, were once high mountains. What has worn them down?

Ewing Galloway, N. Y.

Chapter Fifty-two

Where the Hills Go

Where water drops its load. Rain is wearing away the hills and carrying away the land. Where does the water carry the land?

You have seen, no doubt, a fan-shaped spread of sand and mud where the water runs out from a steep field. Where the water flows down from the mountains, there is often a very large fan-shaped mass of gravel, sand, and mud. These deposits are called *alluvial fans*. (*Alluvial* means "left by running water.") Such alluvial fans are found along the sides of the Rocky Mountains and along the Sierras. You can see small ones on your hikes in almost any country. Where the mountains are high and the rains are heavy, the washed-out material may fill in a large part of a valley

floor. At some places at the eastern foot of the Rocky Mountains the alluvial fans extend out for a hundred miles over the Great Plains. In the valley of California they extend out from both the Coast Range and the Sierras. Much of the coastal plain along the eastern United States was formed in this way from the streams that flowed down the slopes of the ancient Appalachians.

Why a stream changes its curves. If you have hiked along a stream, you have noticed the bends that sometimes make you walk in the direction opposite that which you were following a little while before. Currents cut in the bank on one side and leave shallows on the other side. The deeper outer side of the curve continues to cut in and

This alluvial fan was formed by sediment-laden water pouring down the hillside. The water then dropped its load on the more level ground at the foot of the hill

U. S. Geo. Survey

the shallow inside curve is gradually deserted by the stream. Thus the curves and bends grow continually bigger. In great flood plains, like those of the lower Mississippi, the curves may cut through on the bends, and the river straighten itself, leaving an oxbow lake.

Thus the flood plains in the lower courses of rivers are slowly but continually changing. They are being built constantly higher and broader through the years. The curves are continually growing bigger until they cut through and the river straightens itself. Then the curving begins again. And with each high water, some of the material which has been deposited is picked up again and carried on downstream. Slowly the mud that has started from the hills at the headwaters of the river makes its way downward, stopping time after time when the river slackens, only to be picked up once more and carried farther.

When a river builds a delta.
When a river enters a lake or the sea, or when a brook enters a pond, its speed is checked very quickly. Its carrying power is quickly lost. Then it drops much of its load at the entrance to the lake or sea. This forms a delta. You can find many little deltas on your hikes, if you hike with your eyes as well as your feet. You often see deltas where a brook or creek enters a slower and larger stream. A great river like the Mississippi or the Nile, carrying a vast quantity of material, builds a great delta. These deltas are constantly growing bigger. The Colorado River, flowing into the Gulf of California, built a great delta that has added many square miles to the land. If you will look on a map of Italy, near the head of the Adriatic Sea, about twenty miles south of Venice and fourteen miles in from the sea, you will see the town of Adria. It was once a port on the sea.

Can you trace the original course of this river before it straightened itself out and left an ox-bow lake?

Harold M. Lambert, Phila.

This boulder is being carried along slowly but surely by a glacier

The Po River built a delta and moved the sea fourteen miles away. The Rhone River in France built a delta fifteen miles in fifteen centuries.

Where a glacier drops its load. If you live in any part of the

This is a terminal moraine—gravel and debris that has been dumped by a glacier when it melted

country once covered by the glacier of the last Ice Age, it is fun to hike over the country looking for the material left by the glaciers. The rocks that the glacier picked or pushed along were left when the ice melted. It is not difficult to recognize such material. There is a mixture of sand, gravel, boulders, clay all jumbled together. Water, as you learned, does not leave material mixed in that way. Water sorts the material, leaving heavy material first and the lightest material last. Glacial material is not so sorted.

Hills of loose material are common in the northern, glaciated part of the United States and Canada. At the ends of the glaciers the material is heaped in an embankment. This embankment is called a *terminal moraine*. The terminal moraine of glaciers coming down a mountain valley is left as an embankment across the valley. The terminal moraine of the continental glacier of the Ice Age is in many places a long hill stretching across the country. When glacial material is left in a valley, it often forms a dam across the valley, and the streams that enter the valley form lakes behind the dams. If you look at maps of the northern tier of United States and of Canada, you will see great numbers of lakes, small and large. These are glacial lakes formed in valleys dammed by material left by the melting of glaciers. The great glacier changed the face of the country by digging and carrying away material and by dropping it in new places.

Wind-built soil. If you have not experienced the dust storms, you probably have seen a swirl of dust travel through the air. A choking cloud of dust sometimes rides on the squall before the thunderstorm. The dust may fall again. From dry lands like the flood plains of much of the Mississippi and from the sagebrush plains, winds pick up the dust and carry it along. During the great drought of recent years, the dust from the drought-parched lands beyond the Mississippi fell on the Atlantic seaboard. Suppose that drought had gone on for a few centuries. For many centuries the sagebrush lands have yielded dust to the hurrying winds. Where does it fall?

In Kansas and Nebraska there are beds of a peculiar soil thirty feet thick that is believed to have been brought there by the winds. This soil is called *loess* (pronounced lō′ĕs). At many other parts of the Mississippi valley as far east as Indiana, there are smaller deposits of this soil. In Germany and in China and other parts of Asia are more beds. Some of the beds in China are hundreds of feet thick. Winds are constantly at work changing the country by digging away the dry land and depositing the soil in other places.

The journey's end. Eventually the water that flows down the rivers reaches the sea, except where a river

S.C.S.

Such dust storms as this have carried away the good soil from many farms.

flows into a salt lake without an outlet. In the sea, water must deposit that load that it carries. Just as in the little pool of the brook, when the stream slackens, it drops

This is the suction arm of a great dredge used to dig out the sediment which rivers have deposited in harbors

Philip D. Gendreau, N. Y.

first its heavier materials, farther along its lighter grade. Fine mud is laid down last. This material that settles in the water is called *sediment* from a Latin word which means "to settle." Along the coasts of all continents, the material that once made their hills and plateaus is gradually being spread out below the adjacent sea. Even the mighty mountains with their solid rocks are gradually torn grain from grain, reduced to sand and mud, and laid level beneath the sea. The sea is the grave of the land.

The waters bring with them not only mud but dissolved material as well. The constituents of the rock that are soluble must in the end be dissolved. We have seen how carbon dioxide in the water forms an acid and helps it to dissolve minerals. Other acid substances also

To build, man makes mortar. How is it similar to the mortar nature uses?

are obtained from the decay of plant materials and add to the solvent power of the soil water. The water finally carries a very considerable load of dissolved material to the sea. If all the dissolved material were deposited on the ocean floor, it would make a layer 175 feet deep over the entire ocean bed. That is more than one fifth of all the land above sea level. The water leaves the sea only by evaporation, and when it evaporates, the dissolved minerals are left in the sea. So, like the part of the continent that was floated and rolled along by the rivers, the part that was dissolved eventually reaches the sea.

As it was in the beginning. We have not reached the end of our story. You have probably seen mortar or concrete made and laid. Lime is mixed with sand and water, and then the pasty mass is allowed to dry. Mortar holds bricks together. Some of the mortar used by the ancient Romans is still holding stone walls. Concrete roads are hard as natural rock, indeed much harder than some rocks. Man is imitating nature in making this artificial stone. Water saturating the beds of sand and mud below the sea contains natural cements, among them lime compounds. It contains also iron which forms compounds that act as cement. You know that the mechanic can weld sheets of steel together so that they form one piece. So nature uses iron, but by a rather different method arrives at the same

Here are layers of sandstone. How does the existence of this stone show that this land was once under the water?

end of fastening together separate particles of sand. As the sediment piles up more and more sand or mud or limy skeletons, the weight grows. If you have carried a bag of sand, you know it is heavy. The great weight of the overlying sediment helps to make the cementing mass of sand hard. So layers of rock are formed. Such rock formed from the sediment is called *sedimentary* rock.

So the story goes on through the uncounted ages. Rock is torn to pieces by the rain, forest, and other agencies, carried away by running water, dropped in the seas to spread out upon the sea bottom. Lime, iron, and other substances, aided by the weight of the overlying sediment, cement the particles of sand, mud, and limy skeletons and shells into rock. From rock to gravel, sand, and mud and back to rock again.

How to Learn Where the Hills Go

I. Read the chapter.

II. You will enjoy studying this chapter most in the field, and learn it best there. If you cannot go to the field, make the most of pictures.

1. Search for small alluvial fans where the rain water washes down a grade. If you can visit a mountain region, try to locate large alluvial fans like those in the pictures. If they are covered with woods, they are not easily distinguished, but if you view them from a height, they are often very plain. You can work them out with a little study where a stream or rainwash comes down a hill or mountainside. Make a map of the alluvial fan to show the class and, if you have a camera, take pictures.

2. Experiment in a brook or river to learn how large stones may be rolled along at different velocities of current and where materials come to rest.

3. Try an experiment with a board and a bucket of water in which you stirred gravel, sand, and mud, to learn where each is deposited. Notice the speed of the water as it runs down the board and then as it moves over the ground. What has the speed to do with the deposit of sediment?

4. Search for flood plains along a brook. Map or photograph them to show the class. Compare them with maps and photos of large flood plains.

5. Study the bends in a brook or creek. Compare the inside curve with the outside curve. Which has the deeper water? the steeper bank? What will happen to each side of the curve if the current continues in its present course?

6. Search for ponds with brooks entering. Study the kind of material brought in by the brook. Estimate how much of the pond has been filled by sediment. Search for ponds being filled by plants growing in from the sides. Look for land that is evidently ponds that have been filled in either by sediment or by plant growth.

7. Unless you live in a glaciated country, you will need to use pictures and maps to study what glaciers do to a country when they melt. If you compare a large-scale map of portions of Canada and the northern states with the states farther south, you will see the lakes due to the glacier. Pictures of the northern vacation land have many views of glacial lakes. If you live in the glaciated area, you may have lots of fun finding the deposits of glacial drift. They are very common. Again a camera helps in reporting to the class what you have seen.

8. From the bottoms of ponds and lakes you can dredge up, even with a long stick, materials which resemble some of those in the sea. Get some and study them with a lens. What makes up the sediment? Where do you suppose it came from? Dry some thoroughly and again study it with the lens. Take a supply to school to allow your class to study. See if the sediment varies in different parts of the pond. Can you offer a reason?

9. Have you ever found deposits of shells on dry land? How do you account for them?

III. Test yourself:

1. What evidence have you seen in pictures or in the field that running water carries away rock and soil from hills and mountains?

2. Why does water lay down the deposits called *alluvial fans?*

3. How does a river carry cobblestones? When does it leave them?

4. When does a stream carry its heaviest load? Why?

5. When does a stream lay down its load? Why?

6. How do flood plains arise? Why is the land frequently swampy and wet back from a stream but dry right at the bank?

7. What makes a stream change its course?

8. In what way are streams enemies of lakes?

9. How can you tell glacial deposits from water deposits?

10. How do glaciers form lakes? What sort of evidence would support your answer?

11. How is it supposed that loess soils were formed?

12. What eventually happens to materials carried by a river?

13. What processes help to change sediment into rock?

IV. Think these out:

1. What is the lower limit below which rain and streams cannot cut the land surface?

2. What is the lower limit of wind action?

3. What produced Death Valley, 276 feet below the level of the sea?

4. Erosion has been going on for ages. Why are there any continents left above the sea?

V. Vocabulary.

alluvial	glaciated
terminal	sediment
glacial	moraine
loess	constituents

Chapter Fifty-three

The Unsteady Land

Land rises and falls. If you found a great bed of sea shells on a mountain a mile or more above the sea, you would have very good evidence that that land was once under the sea. Beds of sea shells and coral are found over half a mile above the sea on the west coast of South America. Sea beaches now above the level of the sea are found on the coast of California and in eastern North America. Rocks in the Baltic Sea that at one time were dangerous rocks just under water are now well above the water. On the island of Crete in the Mediterranean Sea are found the remains of ancient docks now nearly thirty feet above the sea.

There is much other evidence to show that land has risen from below the sea. Limestone and sandstone rocks that were the lime and sand that once settled in the sea bottom are now mountains high above the sea. These rocks are two miles high in the Rocky Mountains. That land was once sea bottom. All the central part of the United States, where now are the great corn and wheat lands, was sea bottom at one time.

In other parts of the earth the land has sunk. Sometimes at very low tide along the coast of New Jersey, North Carolina, and on southward, stumps of trees are exposed below usual tide level. On the coasts of Greenland the stone houses that were used by the ancient Norsemen are now under water. On the southern end of Scandinavia, there are remains of streets now under water. The bays along our eastern seacoast and the fiords of Norway are valleys of rivers that have been flooded by the sea when the land sank.

The solid ground beneath our feet is changing. It is slowly sinking along the coast of southeastern United States. It is rising on our west coast. Southern Scandinavia is sinking at the rate of about two and a half feet a century. London is now sixty or seventy feet lower than the land was during the late Stone Age. It is sinking at the rate of nine inches a century. In volcanic regions like the Mediterranean, the land has gone down and up in historic times. The land around the Great Lakes is playing seesaw. It is tilting up on the Canadian side, and the harbors are getting shallower. It is tilting down on the United States side, and the harbors there are getting deeper.

Folded rocks. You may, on your hikes or picture journeys, see rocks in layers as in the pictures on pages 377 and 381. Such rock is called *stratified* rock, meaning rock arranged in layers. Sand and mud and lime are laid down in such

379

Ewing Galloway, N. Y.

At one time land such as this in the middle west was sea bottom. Now it is fertile farmland

layers beneath the sea and become rock. They are formed of the sediment that settles in the sea. Therefore, they are also called *sedimentary* rock. The sand becomes sandstone, the mud becomes shale, and the lime becomes limestone. If they are above water, it is evidence that the land has risen from the sea.

In this Norwegian fiord the sea has filled a sunken valley

Ewing Galloway, N. Y.

Very often in hilly or mountainous country, you will come upon stratified rock that is no longer in horizontal layers. The layers may be tilted or standing on end as in the picture on the opposite page. Sometimes you see them actually in folds. Sand, mud, and lime could never be laid down in that position under the sea. After the rocks had formed, they must have been tilted and folded.

How mountains are made. Folded and tilted strata are found in the mountains. They indicate that the land was lifted into gigantic folds, as if the crust of the earth had wrinkled. The huge folds formed the mountains. In the Appalachians these huge folds of rock are very easily seen. As soon as the rock layers begin to rise, the rain, frost, and streams begin their work of tearing them to pieces and level-

These rocks were tilted into their present position after they had been laid in horizontal strata or layers

ing them to the ground. In the history of the Appalachian Mountains, folded layers of rock formed the mountains and then, in the course of ages, they were worn down almost to a plain. Then again they were lifted up, but this time without much additional folding. Again the rain and streams attacked them and carved out valleys in the softer rocks. The hard layers of rock stand out as mountains. This is the condition of the Appalachians today. As we see them, the mountains are the result of folding and erosion.

The Adirondack Mountains in New York State and the Sierra Nevadas in California are mountains of somewhat different type. The stratified rock occurs on the sides of these groups of mountains. The heart of the mountains is not stratified rock but granite. The granite was formed by molten rock cool-

ing below the surface of the earth. The molten material came in under the stratified rocks. [It is called, therefore, *intrusive* rock.] Originally the stratified rock covered the whole mass of the intrusive rock. Erosion, however, has dug away all the stratified rock from above the granite hearts of these mountains.

The Appalachians were folded and lifted, but erosion wore them down

This granite heart of a mountain was originally molten rock, thrust up from the earth's interior

Here we meet granite mountains, bordered by folded and tilted rock.

Very often in the folding of layers of rock, the rock breaks across the layers. The two sides may then slip one upon another. This movement produces a *fault*. You can easily see faults if you hike through a rocky country, as along a stream that has cut away a hill exposing the layers of rock. The fault may slip only a very small fraction of an inch at any one time, or the slipping might be constantly but exceedingly slow. The slipping of a fault produces an *earthquake*. In the course of ages, upward slipping may cause the rise of a mountain. In the Great Basin, block mountains have been formed by faulting. In other mountains faulting usually occurs along with folding.

Volcanoes also have produced mountains. Mount Vesuvius is still building, and so is Mount Lassen in California. Mounts Hood, Rainier, Shasta, and other famous peaks in our West are dead volcanoes or, perhaps, only sleeping volcanoes. Many other famous and beautiful mountains are volcanic cones. Fujiyama, of which the Japanese never tire, is a typical volcanic cone. The highest mountains of America and of Africa are volcanic.

What a volcano is. A volcano is an opening in the surface of the earth through which hot rock comes forth. If the hot rock is liquid, it may flow out as streams of lava. Sometimes the hot rock is blown to small pieces and falls as ash and dust. As the material comes out from the volcano, it builds up a cone. If the eruption is chiefly lava, the lava may spread out and flow some distance before it hardens and forms a broad, flat cone. The volcanoes of the Hawaiian Islands are of this type. If the material is ash or cinder, a high steep cone is built. In the center of the cone on the top is an opening, the crater. In active volcanoes a part or all of the crater may contain bubbling lava, and explosions of gases may throw masses of hot lava into the air. Poisonous fumes and steam may rise from the crater.

One of the most destructive volcanic eruptions of recent times was that of Mount Pelée on the little island of Martinque, one of the

West Indies. In two minutes a great cloud swept down from the volcano to the city of St. Pierre, five miles distant, demolished the city, and destroyed almost every one of its 30,000 inhabitants. Two other eruptions had been known, in 1762 and 1851. Then the volcano slept until the latter part of April, 1902. At that time the volcano gave indications of an eruption. Steam, fumes, and ashes were thrown 1300 feet in the air. The poisonous vapors killed horses in the streets of St. Pierre. On May fifth, mud which had accumulated in the crater broke out and flowed down the valley killing a number of people. There were earthquakes, and the cables leading to the island were broken. Explosions like the report of artillery were heard as far as 300 miles away. On May eighth came the black cloud that overwhelmed the city. Buildings and trees were thrown down and then took fire, either from the hot gases or from the hot ashes. A few minutes later came a flood of rain, mud, and stones. The temperature of the cloud of steam, sulphurous vapor, and dust was 1400° to 1500° F. Other eruptions followed throughout the summer. In some of these eruptions clouds of steam and ashes were thrown to a height of six or seven miles.

The eruptions of the Hawaiian volcanoes are much safer to look upon. Indeed, the inhabitants go out to watch the streams of lava. There are clouds but no ashes and so little

How was the volcano of Vesuvius built up?

noise that only people in the neighborhood would know of it. The flows of lava built the volcano. Mauna Loa, the highest of the Hawaiian volcanoes, is 14,000 feet above the sea, and it rises from the sea bottom, 16,000 feet deep; that is a total height of over five miles built up from the sea bottom. Four volcanic cones make up the island of Hawaii. The whole group of islands have been built up from the sea bottom by the flow of lava. Many other groups of islands in the Pacific are similarly the tops of volcanoes that rise from the bottom of the sea.

Lava flows from fissures. Sometimes instead of coming out of the earth through a great hole, lava comes up through a great crack or fissure. In an earlier age great flows of lava occurred from fissures in eastern Oregon and Washington.

Layer after layer of lava was poured out until it formed a great plateau over 200,000 square miles in extent. Hills and mountains were buried by these successive lava flows. At one place 1500 feet of this lava lies above the top of an old mountain peak. The Snake River has cut a canyon through the lava plateau in some places 4000 feet deep. On other parts of the West and in other countries, such as in India and in Iceland, are great plateaus built of lava. In 1783 such an eruption from fissure occurred in Iceland.

In many places molten rock forced its way between layers of sedimentary rock and slowly hardened far below the surface of the ground. The Palisades of the Hudson are the edge of such an intrusive sheet of lava. The famous Giant's Causeway on the north coast of Ireland is a similar sheet, in which the columns of hardened lava are of hexagonal form.

The cause of mountains and volcanoes. We cannot learn by experiment and direct observation the cause of the rise and sinking of land or the cause of volcanoes. There are many things in science, and especially in the science of the earth, that we cannot learn directly. Then the scientist gathers evidence from all possible sources and thinks out a theory, or supposed explanation, of the facts. Very often different scientists present different theories to explain the same set of facts. When new facts are learned, one or another of the theories often is given up because it no longer fits the facts. Often an entirely new theory is presented as new facts are assembled.

So to account for the rise of mountains and volcanoes, there have

The crater of Kilauea in Hawaii is safe to watch in spite of steam and eruptions

Ewing Galloway, N. Y.

been several different theories at different times. It has been calculated that the temperature of the center of the earth is over 5000° F., and the pressure 47,000,000 pounds to the square inch. According to one theory, as the surface rocks slip or shift, the interior hot rock may find a way to the surface. The explosive eruptions of volcanoes has been attributed to steam pressure when water reaches hot rocks. Heating by radium rays has been suggested as a cause of disturbance. The readjustment of uneven balance as the rocks are eroded from one area and the sediment piled up in another may account for some changes. A

folding up of layers of rock as the crust settled down to fill spaces from which the hot, plastic rock had oozed out might account for the folded mountains. An older theory attributed the folding to the wrinkling of the layers as the earth cooled.

You need not try to remember all these theories. A few years hence they may all be discarded as new facts are found and mathematical scientists make further calculations. Scientists expect theories to change. They must either be proved true by experiment and observation, or they later will be found unsatisfactory and will be altered or abandoned.

How to Study about the Unsteady Land

I. Read the chapter.
II. One of the best ways to have fun on a hike is to hunt evidence of the change in the earth's surface. By this time you probably can

recognize sandstone, shale, and limestone. Locate them in the country that you visit and decide what they tell you of the past history of that land. Maps and

The Snake River has cut a canyon through a lava plateau in Oregon and Idaho

Black Star, N. Y.

pictures will serve for parts of the country that you cannot visit.

1. Search for sea shells, including fossil shells, imbedded in rocks. In certain parts of the country, fossils of sea animals are very abundant. Can you find evidence of ancient beaches?

2. Visit coasts, look over the harbors, and decide whether the land has risen or sunk. If you cannot visit the coasts, maps and pictures may tell you much of the past history of the coast. Study maps of the coast lines of the eastern and of the western coasts of North America, and the coast of Norway. What is the condition of the coast line, and how do you account for it?

3. Look for stratified rock in cliffs, rock ledges, railroad and road cuts, and along creeks. Pictures often show the stratified rock. Folded rocks and faults are common in hilly and mountainous regions.

4. Study pictures of mountain peaks. Try to decide whether a peak is granite or stratified rock. Try to account for its altitude and its jagged or rounded condition. Try to pick out the old volcanoes from their pictures.

5. Study a map of the Pacific. Note islands on the coast of Alaska and the tiny islands over the South Pacific. Can you account for each group?

6. Study the map of the West Indies and pictures of the islands, especially of the smaller islands. Can you decide why the islands are there? Note the chain of smaller islands from Puerto Rico to Trinidad. Most of these islands are similar to Martinique. What would that seem to indicate about the earth's crust below the sea on the curved line marked by these islands?

7. Look over the maps of the various sections of the earth and locate the vol-

canoes. Do you find that their location follows a more or less definite plan? Can you suggest any reason?

III. Test yourself by answering the following questions:

1. What evidence indicates that certain lands have risen above the sea? Mention some lands that have risen.

2. What evidence indicates that certain lands have sunk? Mention some lands that have sunk.

3. Mention two ways in which mountains arise. Mention mountains of each type.

4. What did you discover in general about the location of volcanoes? What does this indicate?

5. What two general types of volcanoes occur? Mention some volcanoes of each kind. What causes the greatest destruction in volcanic eruptions?

6. Name some mountains in the United States that are extinct volcanoes.

7. In addition to eruption from volcanoes, mention two other ways in which molten rock has built land surfaces. Mention land that has been built up in each way.

IV. Think these out:

1. Examine the map of the west coast of South America. Does that coast seem to be a rising or a sinking coast? Your reasons? Compare it with the coast of British Columbia and Alaska.

2. How has the rising of land in earlier ages affected man? What use has man made of sunken coasts?

3. There are no such active fissures today as those from which made the great lava plateau of eastern Washington. Does that indicate anything about the changing earth?

V. Vocabulary.

stratified	fault
sedimentary	fissure

Chapter Fifty-four

The Changing Ocean Shore

The force of waves. On a visit to the seashore, if you take a little time off from bathing and doing nothing in particular, you have a great opportunity to see the forces of nature changing the face of the earth. In some places the changes are as rapid as those of man on the land and shore line at the summer resort. Indeed, one night's storm may undo years of man's work, and it may bring changes in the face of nature, closing an inlet, opening another, building a bar or digging one away. Generally, however, as in the interior of the country, the great changes that are wrought in the surface of the earth are exceedingly slow. They are slow, but, like the wearing away of the hills, the wearing and building of the shore line at the ocean front is as relentless and inevitable as death.

If you have been hit in the middle of the back by a breaker, you know that breakers have force. On the coast of England it was determined that the force of the waves in summertime was over 600 pounds to the square foot. When 600 pounds hits you between the shoulders, it is not much wonder that it knocks you heels over head. And when a storm wave hits a boat, it may crush it like an eggshell. The winter waves on the English

coast had a force of over 2000 pounds to the square foot, and in winter storms often there are waves with a force of three tons to the square foot. A block of rock weighing eight tons lying twenty feet above the sea was moved seventy-three feet. It is little wonder that waves wreck the summer resorts when the storm winds get behind them.

The work of waves. Dashing waves with a force of 600 pounds to the square foot can roll rocks along. Did you ever feel the sand dragged over your feet as the gentle current ran back down the beach after the breaker ran up the beach? On beaches with good-sized pebbles, you can hear them roll after each wave as water runs back, dragging the pebbles with it. On cobblestone beaches, there may be quite a roar as the waves run back. With each incoming wave, the sand, pebbles, and cobblestones are flung up again on the beach, only to be again dragged down. It is little wonder that they are round stones. The corners are worn round by the ocean's ceaseless grinding mills. Granite blocks dumped in the sea to protect a lighthouse on the coast of New England were worn round in one winter. Square blocks of rock tumbling into the sea from a cliff, are

The tremendous force of waves eats
continually at the rocks

worn to round cobbles, cobbles are
worn to pebbles, pebbles are worn
to sand, and sand worn to mud. It
is only a question of time, and in
some sections, like the stormy, rock-
bound coasts, it takes remarkably
little time to grind square blocks
to pebbles.

These stones have been worn round by
the continuous action of waves rolling
up the beach

When waves with a force of 600
pounds to the square foot roll those
stones against a cliff, or with a force
of three tons to the square foot in a
winter storm fling them against the
cliff, even the cliff feels it. The
rolling stones grind away the solid
rock. The base of the cliff is gnawed
back by the waves and their teeth,
the pebbles and cobblestones. A
cliff is easily gnawed back into the
hill. The water itself has an astound-
ing force when it is confined, as in
the cracks and joints of the rock.
The force of 600 pounds to three
tons concentrated in a crack in the
rock is like a terrific hydraulic
press that forces apart the great
blocks of rock. Caves are sometimes
worn in the seaward face of a cliff.
The waves rush into these sea caves
and, when the water is high, fill and
pound the sides and tops of the
cave. Often holes are worn through
the roofs of caves and water spouts
upward. These form the "blow-
holes" or "spouting horns."

Waves, aided by the rocks they
roll around, are steadily grinding
away the land. They are leveling
off an area, and the sea is advancing into this area over the land.
This wave-cut is shallow water. The
waves do not act very deeply below
the surface. They cannot reach very
high up on a hill or cliff, but by con-
centrating their effective work at the
base of the cliff, they undermine the
rock above. Huge masses come tumbling down. These big boulders are
attacked by the dashing waves with

grinding rock and pebbles and gradually worn away. New boulders tumble down and in turn are worn to pebbles and sand. The wave-cut terrace or level area is steadily broadened. This cliff moves back farther into the land. On the island of Nantucket off the south coast of Cape Cod, the sea cliff has moved back six feet in a single year. On the English coast, land where villages and farms stood a hundred years ago has tumbled into the sea.

On an irregular coast line, with projecting headlands and receding bays, it is the headlands that suffer most under the attack of the waves. They are slowly cut back. The shore line thus is made more regular by the cutting off of the points projecting into the sea.

How currents build land. The distribution of the material cut out and ground down by the waves leads to the building up of the bottom in other places. The wave-cut terrace is extended seaward by a terrace built up of the loose material. When a shore current carries the sand out from the headland and across a bay, the current meets the deeper, stiller waters of the bay. It loses speed and drops the load of sand. Gradually a bar is built across the entrance to the bay. When the bar has been built up so far that the waves strike it, more changes occur. The waves toss the sand until it appears above the water as a sand spit. The sand spit grows to be a beach. If the bay is small with no large

Philip D. Gendreau, N. Y.

"A spouting horn." Waves force their way through an opening in the rocks

stream entering from the land, the beach may be built across the bay and a lake or lagoon formed behind the beach. Here again the waves are straightening the shore line, but this time by building.

Such wave-built beaches are found both on rocky and on sandy

Many a lighthouse has found itself in a precarious position when the sea ate away the rock beneath it

Ewing Galloway, N. Y.

These brush fences were built at Cape Hatteras to slow the shifting sands of the beach

shores. On the rocky shores, they are found at the heads of bays or in smaller coves. On the sandy shores of the eastern and southern states from Long Island to Texas, the beaches form long narrow islands outside of bays, or sounds. The tide and the river water run between the islands in narrow inlets. If you examine maps of these States, you will find narrow islands and inlets along the coast. With the exception of the largest rivers, streams entering bays or sounds discharge their waters behind the beaches rather than directly into the sea.

The changing sand beach. The beaches and bars are constantly subject to change. Sometimes in a storm great sections of a sandy beach may be carried away by the waves and shore currents. Sand may be drifted across and fill an inlet, and the waves wash out another which is quickly

widened and deepened by the tidal currents. Even in mild weather these beaches slowly change. Currents dig away sand in one place and deposit it in another. The site of some summer resorts on the Atlantic coast have gone to sea. At other places the beach has moved out a mile or more into the sea since the resort was founded during the last century.

Changing bay to land. The lagoons behind the sandy beach islands very often become rapidly shallow. Silt brought in by the streams is spread out in these bays and sounds. Coarse marsh grasses and other plants grow in the shallow water. They help to make the water still, and mud settles more easily. The dead salt-marsh grasses and their tangle of roots build up a sod. One can walk over this sod. It continues to grow up until it is above the level of the high tides.

How is a coral island built up in the middle of the sea? This is a small one in the South Pacific

Then it has become a green, grassy plain, and with a little farther sifting in of soil and the growth of other kinds of plants, becomes part of the land. Here nature is forcing back the sea and adding to the continents.

How animals help to build land. In the warmer waters of the earth, the tiny coral animals are adding to the land surface of the earth. These little animals grow only where the water is clear, warm, and shallow. They live attached to the bottom, either to rocks or to the dead skeletons of other coral. They live only where the sea water brings them abundant food, for they cannot go in search of their food. Along the tropical coasts, the reef-building corals live in all the oceans. There they form barrier reefs along the shore with lagoons behind, next to the land. Waves break off pieces of the coral and grind them up as the waves grind rocks. Waves toss up the pieces of coral and the coral sand on to the reef, and it rises gradually above the water. Meanwhile the coral animals on the outer edge of the reef continue to grow outward toward the food-bearing currents of salt water uncontaminated by fresh water. Gradually the reef moves outward. The lagoon may continue to grow shallower. Eventually more land surface may be created.

How to Study the Changing Ocean Shore

I. The most interesting way to study the changing ocean shore is to prowl along the shore. If you live a thousand miles from an ocean shore, you can study some of the processes in pictures and more in lakes, ponds, and some even in brooks. Get into the field whenever you can to study the forces of earth that change the earth.

391

1. Look for the evidence that waves and currents have some effect in moving earth materials. You can find this evidence wherever water runs on land.

2. Look for evidence that rapidly moving water has more force than gently moving water.

3. Look for evidence that water actually destroys solid rock.

4. Look for evidence that cobblestones, pebbles, and sand act as the tools of running water in grinding away solid rock.

5. Look for evidence that water carries away material to some distance.

6. Look for evidence that water builds up land above the water surface.

7. In the stiller waters look for plants that are aiding other forces in building up the land surface.

8. If you live along the warmer seashores, you may see the coral on the reefs. Do you find any other animals in the cooler oceans laying down hard substances that aid in the building of land?

In reporting to the class what you have seen, try to bring some of the evidence: material that has been worn by the water; sketches you have made; little sketch maps you have made; pictures you have taken. State the conclusions you draw from study of the evidence. Distinguish clearly the actual observation and your conclusions.

9. With a little homemade apparatus you can study and illustrate some of the processes discussed in the chapter. Take a large pan or a tub. Make shores with sand and fine soil. Gently pour in water to cover partly the lower shores that you have built. Note how the rising water changes the shore line. Compare with the rising and sinking of land and its effect on the shore lines. Make waves, not too vigorous, that wash up on the shore. How do they affect the steeper shore lines and the more gentle shores? Make waves that wash directly on the

shore and others that come in diagonally. Some tiny colored glass beads scattered at the water's edge will enable you to follow more easily the movement of sand by the waves and currents. You can also use colored beads in a pond or lake to study the transportation of sand by water. After you have read the chapter, see how many of the processes you can reproduce in this simple apparatus.

Shake some bits of red brick vigorously in a corked jar of water. Note what happens to the water and to the bits of brick. What process of nature does this illustrate?

II. Read the chapter.

III. Test yourself with the following:

1. How can it be shown that waves have force? How much force?

2. On what does the force of the waves depend?

3. What work does the force of the waves do?

4. How can it be shown that waves wear away cliffs? What land form replaces the cliff?

5. What enables the waves to dig away the cliffs?

6. What becomes of the material that waves dig from the cliff?

7. How far can the water carry the material that it has dug away?

8. How do plants and animals aid the water in its work of changing the surface of the earth?

9. How will an irregular coast line with many headlands be changed by the action of waves and currents?

IV. Think these out or investigate:

1. How do the processes of nature discussed in this chapter affect man?

2. How are other creatures affected by the natural process changing the seashores and lake shores?

3. Can man control any of these processes for his own benefit? How?

V. Vocabulary. Did you find any new words for your list?

Chapter Fifty-five

The Changing Climate

How the scientist knows. Is the climate changing? Even if we make allowance for what grandpop has forgotten when he tells us about the big snows they had when he was a boy, there may be something in his stories. The climate is not the same as it was at certain times in the past. Good crops were grown on land that later was called the Dust Bowl, where a good rain has not fallen for so long a time that the soil has blown away and the worthless subsoil is exposed. In the Southwest where the Pueblo Indians live, there are remains of Indian towns in regions where it is now too dry to grow the corn which was the chief food of these Indians. In Central Asia there are remains of irrigation works where now there is no water to be found for irrigation.

The movement of glaciers also tells us something about climate over long periods. When the snow falls and piles up in the mountains, it gradually changes into ice. Glaciers move slowly down the mountain ravines and valleys. When it reaches the lower, warmer lands, the ice gradually melts. If there is a long series of snowy years, the ice gradually grows and finally the glacier pushes farther down the valley. If there is little snow during a series of years, the glacier slowly

melts back at its lower end in the valley. Therefore, the advance of glaciers down their valleys or their retreat up the valleys show changes of climate. Just such changes can be found in modern glaciers, indicating that climates slowly change.

Scientists have studied the changes in climate in many ways which you might never guess. Would you guess that by digging mud out of a bog they could tell about the climate hundreds and even thousands of years ago? They can tell what kinds of trees grew around the bog in very ancient days, and the trees tell the kind of climate. Spruce tells of cold, damp climate, oak trees tell of warmer climates. The scientists find in the bogs layers of the pollen of the trees, grasses, and other plants that grew around these bogs. From the study of the pollen they can tell the changes of climate of the land during several thousands of years. They find that in the northern United States there were periods when the climate was colder than today and other periods when the climate was mild.

In still another way scientists have been studying the climate of centuries long ago. You know that tree trunks that are cut across, show growth rings in the wood. In a year when there is plenty of rain, the tree makes good growth and a wide ring of wood is made in the trunk. In years of little rain, the rings of growth are narrow. Therefore, by studying the rings in tree trunks, the story of the climate is read. The big trees of California tell the history of rains and drought since the days of Ancient Greece. The story told by the trees is one of wetter climate for a time and then drier climate.

By these studies it has been learned that the climate changes through the ages. For a series of years the climate is colder and rainier. Then for a series of years, it becomes drier. These changes are not haphazard but seem to be regular. The weather every twenty-three years seems to repeat itself. We should expect the weather twenty-three years hence to be the kind of weather that we are having now, but in the years midway between there would be a different sort of weather.

Great changes in climate. You have heard of the great Ice Age. Then a great glacier covered the northern part of the United States and Canada. Later the climate

(1) The dust bowl was the result of man's own misuse of the soil as well as a cycle of changing climate. (2) Why were the homes of the cliff dwellers in the southwest abandoned?

(1) S.C.S.   (2) Ewing Galloway

warmed, and the ice disappeared some twenty thousand or more years ago. No glaciers now exist in the United States east of the Rockies.

If we go back in the history of the earth to still more ancient days, there must have been still greater changes of climate. You know that coal is the remains of forests. In the ice-covered Antarctic continent, a continent still in the ice age, coal has been found. No tree grows on the Antarctic continent today. There must have been a warmer time for the south pole region. Remains of maple and other temperate climate trees have been found in Greenland. There nowadays willows a few

How do giant redwoods (2) tell scientists of climate many years ago? Antarctic mountains (1) contain coal. Why is this proof of a warm climate there in the past?

(1) Ewing Galloway (2) Underwood & Underwood

inches high are the big trees. That land, too, has seen warmer times.

Will the Ice Age come back? When the ice covered a half of North America and a large part of Europe and Asia, the land was a very different land from that of today. Ice covered all but the tops of some of the mountains. Many mountains were completely covered. The ice was a mile or more in thickness. It has been estimated that the last of this great ice cap melted away from the continent of Europe

Arctic seas were once warm. Can you think of a reason why this was so

and Asia only about ten or fifteen thousand years ago. That is very recent times in the history of the earth. And all of the ice is not gone yet. The interior of Greenland still is covered by a remnant of the great continental glacier. The Antarctic continent also contains a continental glacier. We are still in the Ice Age.

This country was once covered by a glacier. Why do boulders tell the story?

Only a part of the earth has emerged from the Ice Age.

At a very much earlier time, there was another ice age. That was about the end of the period that the scientists call the *Carboniferous*. It might have been two or three hundred million years ago. It does not matter much about an odd million or two of years when talking in such figures. Different scientists arrive at different estimates because they calculate from different facts. Years are so short in the history of the earth that usually they are not mentioned. The fact remains that there was a great ice age at a far earlier time than the last ice age. It was somewhere in the neighborhood of 250 million years ago.

Now we will go back another 250 million years. Then also there was an ice age. That is a very long time ago, 500 million years ago. Many things have happened to the surface of the earth since those days. The important thing for us at this moment is that there was an ice age somewhere about that time. Even before that time, about another 250 million years earlier was another ice age, 750 million years ago. The scratches in the rock and the glacial deposits show it. Here then are the records in the rocks of four great ice ages. And they occurred about 250 million years apart. It seems that about every quarter of a billion years, the earth has an ice age. When we speak of *The Ice Age*, we mean the last one. Nowadays when scientists have learned about the earlier ice ages, they speak of this last one as the *Pleistocene glaciation*, but you need not remember that term. Just remember that it is the last ice age that is meant usually, and that the ice melted away from the mainland of North America about 20,000 years ago.

Warm periods. Usually the earth seems to have enjoyed warmer climate. For thousands of years at a time there was no ice on earth except sometimes a little winter ice that melted in spring. You could have sailed over the Arctic Ocean where now no ship can force its way through the thick ice that lasts the year around. You would have been glad to sit down in the shade of Greenland forests where now the land lies under glacial period ice. In the Antarctic continent also you could have enjoyed a land where you would have needed no heavier clothing than a sweater occasionally. You might have seen green, fertile valleys, valleys that now lie beneath a vast and thick covering of ice, land that no man has ever seen because of its glacial covering. The warm periods, warmer than our present time, seem to have been the usual climate of the earth.

During the warm periods of the earth, there were periods of deserts. Vast deserts stretched over land that is now green with the vegetation brought by the rainfall through the year. Much of the interior of the continents at those times was like

The desert where petrified trees are now found once flourished with forests

the vast deserts of Central Asia or the Sahara. The rocks tell the scientist about the deserts. Red desert sandstone tell the tale. That kind of rock is formed from the drifting waste of the desert. Great areas of good land now show by their red sandstones that there once were deserts. These deserts have occurred at

Can you see where the glacier dumped its load as it retreated?

intervals in the earth's history. The desert rocks are deposits of the warm period and mark great stretches of continents that lay under the drying sun.

So let us answer the question, "Will the Ice Age come back?" Our first answer is that the Ice Age has not gone yet. The earth has not yet returned to its usual warm climate. It will be many, many thousands of years before the present Ice Age closes. Not until Greenland and the Antarctic continent are free of ice and the warm Arctic and Antarctic waters wash their shores, will the Ice Age be gone from the earth. But even then, it may return, after about a quarter of a billion years.

Why the climate changes. Scientists of the weather bureaus of various countries and of the universities are studying the cause of the change of weather and of climate. If a cause can be found, the forecasts of weather will be much more accurate than at present. If the weather for the next dozen years could be predicted, the destruction of farms of the dry belt and the destitution of the farmers might be prevented. If one could know beforehand that a drought year was coming, the fields could be left in grass instead of being plowed. The loss of the topsoil could be reduced or prevented. When a long series of dry years was about to start, the farmers and stockmen could be moved to better lands. Scientists are studying long range weather fore-

casting, and learning much about the coming of dry and wet periods.

One place to look for the cause of weather is on the sun. And something has been found there associated with our weather. Observatories in the deserts of Africa, Asia, and America have measured the sunshine day by day. By a study of the record of the floods on the Nile, the periods of rainfall at the headwaters of the Nile can be learned. A study of the fluctuations of African Lake Victoria lying under the equator tells us about the rainfall of equatorial regions. Increased rainfall at the equator and in the equatorial regions occurs at periods of eleven years. At eleven-year periods, also, the northern storms of our latitude shift farther south. On the sun at eleven-year intervals the number of sunspots increases. There are great disturbances on the face of the sun. We know that when there are such disturbances on the sun, there are electromagnetic disturbances on the earth. The aurora is unusually brilliant. The radio does not work well. Telegraph messages often cannot go through long distances for hours at a time. Apparently disturbances on the sun have considerable effect on the earth. Periods of greatest sunspot disturbances are periods of increased equatorial rainfall and of increased storminess away from the equator.

In regions nearer the poles, the weather does not show well the periods of the sunspots. In place of

(1) *Black Star,* (2)(3) *Ewing Galloway*

Scientists have found that at eleven-year intervals there are periods of an increase in sunspots (1), unusually brilliant aurora (3), and increased storminess (2) in regions of the earth away from the equator

eleven-year periods, the periods of increased severity of weather seem to come every thirty-five years. What makes these thirty-five-year periods is not very well understood. It seems to have something to do with the conditions of the polar seas.

The great variations in climate that bring the ice ages and the warm, dry periods seem to have nothing to do with the sunspots and perhaps not with the sun directly. These periods that come and go over thousands or millions of years seem to be associated with the surface of the land. At several periods in the past history of the earth, as it is told by the rocks, there have been times when there were great disturbances in the surface of the earth. Mountains arose. Then there were times when mountains were slowly worn down with no new mountains arising. The glacial periods followed the periods of mountain-making.

Mountains seem to be rather unusual features in the history of the earth. Usually the land surface has had few mountains or none at all. Then the earth became uneasy. The rocks were folded up in mountain ridges, volcanoes poured forth lava, and more lava flowed out from great fissures. At these uneasy periods mountains often rose to great heights. At the same time there were great elevations of broad stretches of land from the sea. Much that is now under the ocean waters was once land. At one time a great area of land stretched across from Europe to Iceland, then to Greenland

and the continent of North America. At another time, land stretched across from Siberia to Alaska. At still other times, other parts of what is now ocean were land. It must not be supposed, however, that at those times the present lands of the earth were also all above the ocean waves. At various times much of the present land was under the sea.

During the lowland periods the continents were small because much of our present land area was below the sea. You would not recognize the map of North America during the Great Coal Age. Most of the continent was in the east and north. The west was just a group of big islands. The central part of the country was a shallow sea. The warm waters of the tropical ocean washed up through what is now the United States and into the Arctic Ocean. Similarly, in Europe there was a sea covering much that is now land. The warm waters of the Indian Ocean could reach the Arctic. Coal forests grew in lowlands along the coast. At times the sea returned, covering the sunken land and laying sand and limestone deposits over the coal.

The climates of continents and oceans. You may go to the seashore to keep cool in summer, and you could also go there to keep warm in winter. The difference between summer and winter temperature in Seattle is 30° F. In North Dakota in the same latitude the yearly range of temperature is 73° F.

At the mouth of the St. Lawrence in the same latitude it is 50° F. The summers are hotter in the interior of the continent and the winters are colder. The coldest part of the earth is not the north pole, but the interior of Siberia. At this "cold pole" in Siberia the winter temperature may be 76° F. below zero while the temperature above the frozen Arctic Ocean is 30° to 50° F. below zero. The difference between summer and winter temperature at the Siberian cold pole is 120° F. while on the coast of Norway in the same latitude the range is 20° F. Continental climates are more severe than oceanic climates.

In the lowland periods of the earth's history there was little continental climate, for the continents were small. Furthermore, currents from the warm waters of the tropic oceans could flow north and south to reach the polar seas. There were no such great differences of ocean temperatures as exist today between the polar oceans and the equatorial oceans. The ocean waters did not freeze in the polar regions. The Arctic Ocean was free of ice the year round. The freedom from ice would influence the Arctic shores. Forests grew and have left their remains as coal. In the Antarctic continent the winter also was free of ice. Warm winds from the ocean brought growing conditions to the continent that is now covered with ice. Coal forests lived there, and their remains today are beds of coal.

U. S. Forest Service

The high Rockies cause a difference in climate on their western and eastern sides. These forests grow on the moist western slopes. Below is seen the **arid** land that lies to the east where rainfall is practically nonexistent

When the periods of mountain-making and land elevation arrived, great continents like those we see today arose from the sea. Continental climates were established. If the land rose much above its present altitude in North America, more snow would fall in Canada during the winter than could melt in summer. Then the glaciers would be slowly formed again. In the periods of land elevation, more snow fell than the summer sun could melt.

At the same time the warm currents that formerly flowed northward from the Gulf across North America and from the Indian Ocean across Europe until their waters mingled with the Arctic waters, were shut off by the land. The Arctic Ocean froze over. Then the cold Arctic winds added to the continental conditions of the great land masses. Ice formed until great continental glaciers moved down from the higher land and the north.

U. S. Reclamation Service

When mountains rise across the direction of the prevailing winds, they produce other effects in addition to the lower temperature due to their great height. When the mountains rose along the western part of North America like a great wall running north and south, they stood across the path of the winds from the western ocean. The strong winds had to climb the mountains. As they went up, they were chilled. When air is cooled, it can hold less water vapor. The winds lost the water vapor they had gathered over the Pacific Ocean. West of the mountains there was abundant rainfall. As the winds came down the eastern side of the mountains, they had little vapor to make rain in the interior of the continent. Deserts developed. The warmth of the western ocean was also shut out from the interior. Thus the trend of mountains north and south had important influence on the development of continental climate with its cold winters.

We do not know what caused the ice ages. It cannot be doubted that the increase in the size of the continents, the increase in the general height of the land surfaces and the rising of high mountain ranges, and the shutting off of the warm tropical ocean currents from the polar seas were important causes. Some scientists seem to think they are sufficient to account for the ice ages. It then remains to be found what causes the periods of continental elevation and mountain-making. Other causes of the ice ages also have been presented by scientists. One explanation was the shifting of the north pole so that the Arctic ice covered a different part of the earth. Another suggestion is that the sun gives less heat at some periods than at others. Each of the suggested explanations has met with difficulties. We can only conclude that we have not yet learned the whole cause, but that we have at least learned some very important contributing causes.

How to Study about the Changing Climate

I. Study the earth's changes of climate.

1. What evidence can you gather to show that the winters and the summers are not the same now as they have been? Ask older people and try to get the dates and, if possible, the temperatures and definite measure of the snow- or rainfall.

Consult the weather reports for the last fifty years, if you can find in the library a book which summarizes them.

2. In the field, search for evidence of the last ice age and for fossils of plants and animals of different climates. In some parts of the country such evidence of changed climate is easily found. If you cannot go afield at present, study pictures, noting those which show evidence clearly.

3. If you have a microscope or a good magnifying glass, study different kinds of pollen. Search the flowers of trees, grass, and weeds for it. Can you learn to distinguish certain pollens? Examine especially the pollen of spruce and pine in contrast to that of grass and weeds. Do you see how pollen preserved in the ground might tell something of the past climate of the region?

4. Examine the cut end of a log or branch. Are the rings of the growth all equally wide? How can you account for the difference, if any? Do you find a series of wide rings and a series of narrow rings? What does that indicate about the climate?

5. If there is a botanic garden in your city, search it for the types of trees and other plants that grow in hot climates and in cold climates. If there is a museum of natural history, search for fossils of hot climates and cold-climate plants and animals, and note where they were collected. Do you gather any evidence of changed climates? If you cannot visit gardens and museums, search for pictures, noting always the regions where the pictures were taken, and on the basis of the photographic evidence, draw your own conclusions.

6. Go into the library and look in books on geology for maps of the continents in earlier geological times. How have the continents changed? Do you suppose that the change of land and sea could produce any change in climate? Note the pictures of the plants and animals of those times. Do they show any evidence that the climate was different? It is interesting also to read how long ago each period was, although the actual number of years estimated may be very unreliable.

II. Read the chapter.

III. Test yourself:

1. Write down in a list the various ways in which scientists search for evidence of the kinds of climate in ages long past.

2. How are scientists studying our present changes of climate?

3. What evidence is there of ice ages in the past history of the earth?

4. What evidence is there that much of the earth's surface had once much warmer climate than at present?

5. What is the evidence for dry climates?

6. Is there any evidence to show that the changes in climate come at regular intervals or that they are irregular?

7. Is the earth at present in a hot age, cold age, or an age of temperate climate?

8. Why would it be advantageous to predict the weather for several years in advance? Is there any evidence that such prediction may some day be made? How are scientists today studying the question?

9. What suggestions have been made as to possible causes of short-period changes in climate?

10. What are some suggestions of the causes of ice ages and warm periods of the earth? Which are the more usual conditions of the earth's climate?

11. Explain how the land and sea distribution could affect the climate?

IV. Think these out or investigate these questions:

1. Suppose that the mountains of North America were lowered, and a new system arose extending east and west. How would the climate be affected?

2. Suppose the Alps were lowered and mountains extending north and south arose along the western coast of Europe. How would the climate be affected?

3. How would life in your part of the country be affected if the land were lowered 1000 feet? if it were raised 1000 feet?

4. Is it good reasoning to say that because the remains of elephants are found in Siberia, it was hot there when the elephants were alive?

V. Vocabulary. Did you find any new words?

Chapter Fifty-six

Earth's Changing Life

How we know. You have seen pictures of the dinosaurs. They are common in newspapers and magazines. Perhaps you have seen them in the movies. The animals themselves were once common, running and waddling about over land, swamp, and water where the automobiles and speed boats now skim along. The great race of dinosaurs is gone. Long after them, other great beasts wandered about the land that we call our own. You have heard of mammoth and mastodon. They passed with the Great Ice Age. Saber-toothed tigers and other great cats bigger than lions passed away. There were many other animals, large and small, that have only scientific names. They are gone. Plants, too, have changed. If you go outdoors and away from city streets, the commonest living things that you see are grass or trees. There was a time when there was no grass on the earth, and an earlier time when there were no trees. The forests of the great coal age were made of trees very different from the trees of today. Races of plants and animals come, and they go, to be seen no more as living things.

How we know what lived millions of years ago. Did you ever lose an overshoe in the mud? The mud holds on to some things. Perhaps you have seen an automobile stuck in the mud. It sometimes takes a great deal of power to get it out. Many bogs are just sticky, half-liquid mud, too thick to swim through and too soft to walk through. When an animal gets stuck in such a bog, it stays there. Men, too, have stayed there. From a bog in Europe a few years ago a human body, clothed in the garb of the seventh century, was dug up.

In some spots, for example in our west, there are found great masses of remains of animals that lived long ago. Apparently the animals had gathered at these spots. Perhaps here were water holes in a dry land. The water lay on the top of deep mud. The thirsty animals wandered into the mud and were caught in the sticky stuff, unable to tear themselves away. They sank below the surface of the mud or quicksand and were buried. Time passed, the water drained away, and the bog was covered over by drifting sands of a drier climate. Mud and sand changed to shale and sandstone. The flesh of the animals was gone, but the hard parts, each tiny particle replaced by mineral from the water, changed to stone. Along the seashore, great colonies of shellfish have been buried by drifting sand and mud. Their lives were smothered out, their shells were replaced by stone in the form of the shells. In the great coal forest, leaves, seeds, and trunks fell into the mud and were preserved. All the remains of such plants and animals are known as *fossils*. By the fossils we know the life that has passed away. They are nature's pictures of by-gone life.

The age of the old life. The first rocks that have clearly preserved animal fossils have a great variety of animals. These rocks were formed beneath the sea in the period that is called the *Cambrian*. (You need not remember the name, but we shall need to use it to tell what period we are talking about.) From the great variety of animals in these rocks, scientists decide that there must have been an abundance of animals still earlier, of which we have found no trace so far. The Cambrian are very ancient rocks, at least 500,000,000 years old, perhaps older. Even when those rocks were being formed from the sand washed in from still older rocks, the seas were well populated with animals and with seaweeds. Here are some of the kinds of animals: There were sponges, jellyfish, corals, starfish, worms, animals somewhat like oysters and clams, and others somewhat like lobsters.

Now onward again in history for a few more million years and we pause for a glimpse of the coal forests. This is the great Coal Age

This fossil leaf is millions of years old

(the *Carboniferous*). The land is now covered with plants, but not our present plants. You may know the little club moss that is sometimes used in Christmas decorations. Now it grows only a few inches high. In the Coal Age similar plants were trees. There were no flowers and no grass. There were abundant animals—of a kind—scorpions, centipedes, cockroaches, dragonflies. Some of these insects would have been worth seeing on the wing. There were dragonflies with a two-foot spread of wing. There were no butterflies, bees, or flies—and no mosquitoes.

Through the land of the coal forest wandered some backboned animals, vertebrates. If you have hiked about the country and looked in brooks and springs, you have seen the newts, or salamanders. They are little lizard-shaped creatures with

405

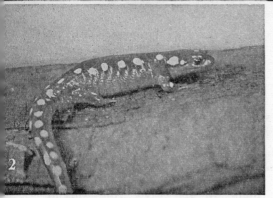

(1) *Philip D. Gendreau,* (2) *Hugh Spencer*

Dinosaurs such as the one above (1) roamed the earth long ago. The tiny salamander (2) or "spring lizard" is hardly fearsome today. Coal Age "spring lizards" were twenty feet long

plants were on the land. The continents were shaped and arranged differently. A new age had come to the earth.

The middle life of the earth. Now we will pause for a look at life in the age of dinosaurs. There were little dinosaurs no bigger than rats. There were little dinosaurs running about on their hind legs like chickens. Big dinosaurs were plodding around, eating plants and some eating other dinosaurs. Some of these big fellows were bigger than our elephants. The Thunder Lizard (Brontosaurus) was seventy feet long and weighed several tons. This great creature was probably harmless, unless it happened to step on another animal. Its food was the juicy plants of the swamps. Another great fellow, the Tyrant Liz-

smooth skin like a frog's instead of scales like a lizard or snake. Boys sometimes call them "spring lizards." In the Coal Age some "spring lizards" were twenty feet long.

At the close of the Coal Age, the earth went through an ice age. The coal forests disappeared. Many kinds of animals on the land and in the sea disappeared, never to come again. After the climate returned again to milder conditions, earth was a different place. The period of the old life had passed away. (It is called the *Paleozoic era,* which means "old life era.") **New** races of animals and new

The scorpion (1) was one of the first land animals. The skeleton of the prehistoric dinosaur (2) was one of the largest ever found by man. Can you imagine what it must have looked like?

ard, was forty feet long, and towered aloft on his hind legs, grasping and devouring other dinosaurs. Other dinosaurs swam like porpoises in the sea. Still others flew like great bats. In this age, too, birds appeared on earth. This is the Middle Age of the earth. (The scientist calls it the *Mesozoic*, which means the "middle life." You need not remember the name.)

The coal of our western states was forest in the earth's Middle Age. There were forests over much of the land that is now too dry for trees. At the latter end of the Middle Age the trees were our modern trees, while at the beginning the trees would have seemed very strange to us. Flowers blossomed upon the earth at the end of this period, but there were none at the beginning of the Age. The earth was becoming more modern.

The period of Recent Life. Again the earth became uneasy. Mountains arose. Volcanic activity such as the earth has never known since marked the unsteady condition. The mild climate of the Middle Age gradually faded and the seasons became more severe until the last great Ice Age held the earth in its grip. With the change in the continents and the seas, with the changed climate and the mountain-making, came a change in life. The dinosaurs passed from the earth. Their relatives today are alligators

A family of the Stone Age in front of their cave. At left is such a tool as they might have used

and crocodiles, lizards and turtles. And then a new era came, the era of Recent Life (*Cenozoic*). New animals arose. They were not reptiles like the dinosaurs, but were modern animals, the mammals. They are the common larger animals that we have about us from mice to elephants. They, unlike other animals, feed their young on milk. Milk-giving animals are the modern animals of the earth. Others are relics of the past. At first these milk-giving animals were not very much like our modern kinds. Some grew to an immense size and in bulk resembled our elephants and rhinoceroses, but some were bigger. Gradually, as time rolled on, the great modern families developed. Their bones turned to fossils which tell us the history. The cat family and the dog family, the bears, the great group of hoofed animals, the gnawing animals from mice to squirrels and beavers, the elephants, and the bats appeared. And, among the others, came the monkeys and apes.

Buried by accident in the gravels of the rivers of the interglacial periods of the last Ice Age, were found the oldest pieces of human skeleton. They were just pieces—a part of the skull, a few teeth, and a bone of the leg. Very different remains were found in countries as far apart as Java and England. We know very little about these early men, only what we can guess from a few bones. Later, as the great ice sheet was withdrawing from Europe, dead men were buried in caves. Of these men we know much more, for with the buried men were found weapons and tools. In the caves were found the bones of animals that they ate and the remains of their fire. They were the cave men, the men of the Old Stone Age. They made weapons and tools of chipped stones and they clad themselves in skins of animals they had killed.

Men have changed. Other races of men have followed the men of the old Stone Age. Men learned to make better implements of stone and to polish them. They learned to raise crops and domesticate animals, to spin thread, and to weave cloth. They learned to build boats and wagons. They cleared land of forest and built irrigation works. They built towns and cities. They learned to control the materials and forces of nature.

With the discovery of iron and steel, their power grew immensely. Not only the material, but the energy of nature was brought under control. The force of wind, of falling water, of heat, of steam, brought great changes in the world of men and, therefore, in the world of nature around about. Steam and the inventions that came with it brought the Industrial Revolution that you study about in your history. Later came the conquest of electricity and of the energy of light and other rays. Each of these great conquests of energy has brought further conquest of the materials of earth.

Man has come far since the Stone Age. He has learned to control the forces of nature through science. This great modern dam, controlling the flow of water and providing electric current, symbolizes what he can achieve

Tennessee Valley Authority

Through all the change the old problem remains, how to get along with nature, living and nonliving. We have tried to fit our lives to new forces unknown to the men of the Old Stone Age, unknown to the settlers of America, unknown to the men who fought each other in the war between the States, unknown only a few years ago. Scarcely do we seem to have found a way of fitting into nature and fitting to one another's lives, when new discoveries and new control of the materials and forces of nature upset our relations and lead to new difficulties with one another. We are learning to control the materials and forces of nature more rapidly than we are learning to control ourselves. We fit into nature more easily than we fit into the lives of other men. Wars and strife within the nations are greater and more terrible than in the past. We are conquering nonliving nature. We are conquering slowly the nature of living things. Shall we conquer the forces of our own nature and fit our lives one to another in peace and helpfulness in this changing world? We have faith that we can help one another, and by doing so bring peace both in our relations between nations and our relations within the nation.

How to Study the Earth's Changing Life

I. Read the chapter.

II. Study fossils.

1. Study an imitation of the making of a fossil. Get some plaster of Paris at the hardware store. It is used as patching plaster for walls. Make a paper tray by folding paper. Mix the plaster of Paris with water until it is a rather thick paste. Pour it in the paper tray. In the wet plaster lay a leaf. Grease a nut well and place it deep in the plaster. Set aside to harden until the next day. Then remove the paper and the leaf. You will see the impression of the leaf in the plaster. Many fossils are such impressions. If you inserted the nut in the plaster, saw the plaster across with an old saw. Remove the nut. Now fill the cavity left by the nut with a plaster that you have colored with paint. Again let dry. Many fossils are of this nature, mud filling in a cavity in rock left when a shell, animal, or plant was removed.

2. Hunt up pictures of fossils. Group them together in the order in which they lived on earth. If you are good at drawing and painting, make a series of large drawings or paintings to show animals that passed from the earth in early ages.

3. Hunt for fossils on your hikes. Search the coal bin. If the coal is well cleaned, you will probably find few fossils. If you can visit a coal mine, you may get many fossils of the coal age.

III. Test yourself with the following questions:

1. How are fossils made? Does the process still go on? Have you ever seen any step in the making of a future fossil?

2. Did you ever see a dinosaur in the flesh? Did any other man? How do we know that they ever lived?

3. How did the old life differ from modern life? Do you know of any animal or plant now living that is very similar to animals of the age of the old life?

4. What were the most abundant animals of the middle age of life?

5. What kind of animals marks the age of recent life?

Index

411